ARCHES, CONTINUOUS FRAMES, COLUMNS, AND CONDUITS

DEPARTMENT OF AGRICULTURE

U SOIL CONSERVATION SERVICE S

UNIVERSITY OF ILLINOIS PRESS, URBANA, 1963

ARCHES, |←————————————→|

CONTINUOUS FRAMES,

COLUMNS, |←————————————→|

AND CONDUITS |←————→|

Selected papers of Hardy Cross |←→|

With an introduction by Nathan M. Newmark

CONTENTS

INTRODUCTION

Hardy Cross came to the University of Illinois in 1921 at the age of 36, and spent here the most productive sixteen years of his life. His writings during this period, the most important of which are reprinted in this volume, have influenced structural engineering in America perhaps more than those of any other man. His "moment distribution" is universally known, his "column analogy" is still widely used, his method of analysis of flow in a network of conduits, though in another area of engineering, has been no less valuable.

With the advent of the high-speed digital computer, much of Cross's work has become less directly useful. Nevertheless, his skill as an engineer, and the power and beauty of his concepts, are still important and worthy of serious study. Hence this effort to bring together his most important papers, to make his works available at first hand to the many structural engineers who know moment distribution and his other methods only as filtered through textbooks written by authors with much less engineering skill and judgment.

The papers selected for this volume were chosen to present the most important and the most useful of Cross's works. These papers may be combined into several groups as follows:

(a) Papers dealing with the description of the method of moment distribution.[1, 2, 3]*

(b) Papers dealing with the problem of structural design as contrasted with analysis.[4, 5, 6]

(c) Papers dealing with particular design problems for specific structures.[7, 8]

(d) A paper dealing with the "Column Analogy" method of determining constants for use in moment distribution.

---

* The numbers refer to the numbering of the papers in the Table of Contents.

(e) A paper describing a new way of looking at the principle of virtual work.

(f) A paper on the analysis of flow in conduits or conductors.

The papers on moment distribution describe the procedure better than any description that has been given in textbooks since Cross's original development. The reader, whether he is interested in analysis or design, will find it most useful and profitable to refer to the original description of the method in order to learn some of the aspects of it that are not usually taught in classrooms or included in standard texts. The basis of the method, as a procedure leading toward design, rather than as an analytical tool, is indicated in Cross's reasoning and in his choice of procedures for the various aspects of the method. A better understanding of structural analysis and design will be attained from careful study of these papers.

Although the paper in ASCE Transactions (1) is very brief, it is most complete and thorough. Because of limitations in space in this volume, the many pages of discussion of Cross's paper are not reproduced. However, his closing discussion is given because it presents several new concepts that are not available elsewhere, including an unusual and simple method for dealing with moment distribution in tall building frames, and a method for handling the moment distribution analysis of arches on elastic piers.

The group of papers pertaining to the distinction between analysis and design is of the utmost interest to structural designers because of the implications of the control that the designer has over the final structure in his choice of a preliminary structure to analyze when he starts the design procedure. This is a matter that is still not well understood by many engineers in practice, and it is worthy of serious attention. This group of papers, the least understood of Cross's works, in the future will probably be considered the most important.

The papers on design of reinforced concrete columns and on the dependability of the theory of concrete arches are good examples of Cross's mastery of the physical details of a problem in spite of the apparent obscurity of the physical behavior by the ordinary processes of analysis.

All of the above papers relate primarily to structural analysis and design, with particular reference to structural design. No designer can afford to be without the background and insight that Cross has made available to him in these research reports.

The remaining papers deal with three separate topics. The column analogy paper is the basis for a new insight into a relatively old method of analysis. Those who have learned the method from standard textbooks will find new ideas in this chapter. Similarly, Cross's paper on virtual work represents a new point of view which has not until recently been developed independently. It is well worth study to obtain a physical picture of the powerful method of virtual work so often used in engineering analyses.

The paper on analysis of flow is an unusual simplification for the solution of a difficult engineering problem which was developed at the request of some of his colleagues, done rather quickly, and which has had an extremely wide application in engineering practice. Again, reference to the original source may clarify and illuminate certain points which have become obscure in the standard textbooks describing the method.

Hardy Cross was a truly great teacher, one of the few so outstanding that in the memory of many of his students he had no peer. In the classroom he was an actor and artist of consummate skill. Each lecture was a performance planned and studied in detail to create the atmosphere, the impression he wanted, and no less a perfect performance because it seemed so impromptu, so natural. He never used notes or referred to his papers in class. He might conduct a class for an entire semester by calling on the same student, time after time, to go to the board and think a problem through. He might stage an impatient exit after ten minutes in class because no one had attempted a certain problem, and then ask a few minutes later in his office, with a twinkle in his eye, "How did it go over?"

My first contact with him came when I was a graduate student in the fall of 1931, when he was near the peak of his career. For nearly two years I walked with him many evenings after school to a small park midway between our homes, discussing meanwhile every sort of technical as well as non-technical topic. My part in this discussion must have been audible for blocks, as Cross was quite deaf.

He used his deafness to advantage in class. Even when he could hear, he might cup his hand to his ear and ask the hapless student to shout anew his hazarded answer to a question about which he was completely unsure. As a result his students learned to make up their minds, to admit their ignorance rather than to bluff it through at the top of their lungs, to be concise, direct, and explicit.

I shall always remember the occasion of my oral prelims when Cross asked a question, the details of which I do not now recall, but probably about the choice of a design criterion, which seemed to me to be so controversial I could not think of an answer. The only reply I could think of was, "I don't know!" Slowly that ineffable grin spread across his face; he replied, "That's the correct answer. It may well be the most correct answer you've given today. But don't be discouraged. Neither does anyone else know."

As one of his students I have much to be thankful for, including the knowledge learned from him that the simple, direct approach may be the most profound. Yet I found it necessary to avoid being carried away by some of his generalizations which he used for emphasis, perhaps for overemphasis, and I sometimes shudder when I hear his words parroted by others who do not realize the limitations that Cross always kept in mind. When he preached, "You must learn to think as the structure thinks," in his design courses, I used to tease him about his anthropomorphic concepts of structures. But he came closer to teaching judgment to his students than any other teacher I have known. And some of this comes through in his papers.

The careful reader will find tucked away little gems of wisdom, and often novel explanations that clarify many problems. For example, in "The Column Analogy" there is a paragraph or two on an extremely simple and useful approach to the analysis of curved beams that has never been published elsewhere.

Cross was not a particularly strong mathematician but he had a deep physical insight that led him to the appropriate mathematical solution of the problems he was concerned with in structural analysis. His strong background in the classics and liberal arts showed in his writing, even on technical subjects. The reader who is interested in his non-technical papers will find most interesting a collection of excerpts from some of his papers and talks, "Engineers and Ivory Towers," published by the McGraw-Hill Book Co. in 1952. His views on engineering education are even today sound and forward looking.

I hope that this collection of Cross's technical papers will acquaint many who did not know him personally with America's greatest teacher of Structural Engineering.

NATHAN M. NEWMARK

1

ANALYSIS OF CONTINUOUS FRAMES
BY DISTRIBUTING FIXED-END MOMENTS

Synopsis

The purpose of this paper is to explain briefly a method which has been found useful in analyzing frames which are statistically indeterminate. The essential idea which the writer wishes to present involves no mathematical relations except the simplest arithmetic. It is true that in order to apply the method it is necessary to determine certain constants mathematically, but the means to be used in determining these constants are not discussed in the paper, nor are they a part of the method. These constants have been derived by so many writers and in so many slightly different ways that there is little occasion to repeat here the whole procedure.

The reactions in beams, bents, and arches which are immovably fixed at their ends have been extensively discussed. They can be found comparatively readily by methods which are more or less standard. The method of analysis herein presented enables one to derive from these the moments, shears, and thrusts required in the design of complicated continuous frames.

Definitions

For convenience of reference, definitions of three terms will be introduced at once. These terms are "fixed-end moment", "stiffness", and "carry-over factor".

By "fixed-end moment" in a member is meant the moment which would exist at the ends of the member if its ends were fixed against rotation.

"Stiffness", as herein used, is the moment at one end of a member (which is on unyielding supports at both ends) necessary to produce unit rotation of that end when the other end is fixed.

If one end of a member which is on unyielding supports at both ends is rotated while the other end is held fixed the ratio of the moment at the fixed

NOTE.—Written discussion on this paper will be closed in **September, 1930**, *Proceedings*.

end to the moment producing rotation at the rotating end is herein called the "carry-over factor."

Effect of Joint Rotation

Imagine any joint in a structure, the members of which are being deformed by loads, or in some other way, to be first held against rotation and then released. Call the algebraic sum of the fixed-end moments at the joint the "unbalanced fixed-end moment". Before the joint is released this unbalanced fixed-end moment will not usually be zero; after the joint is released, the sum of the end moments at the joint must be zero. The total change in end moments, then, must equal the unbalanced fixed-end moment. This may be stated in another way by saying that the unbalanced fixed-end moment has been "distributed to" the connecting members in some ratio.

When the joint is released all connecting members rotate through the same angle and this rotation at the end is accompanied by a change in end moment. The change in end moments is proportional to the "stiffness" of the members.

Hence, it may be said that when the joint is released the unbalanced fixed-end moment is distributed among the connecting members in proportion to their stiffness.

The rotation of the joint to produce equilibrium induces moments at the other ends of the connecting members. These are equal in each member to the moments distributed at the rotating joint multiplied by the carry-over factor at the rotating end of the member. This follows from the definition of "carry-over factor".

Moment Distribution

The method of moment distribution is this: (*a*) Imagine all joints in the structure held so that they cannot rotate. Compute the moments at the ends of the members for this condition; (*b*) at each joint distribute the unbalanced fixed-end moment among the connecting members in proportion to the constant for each member defined as "stiffness"; (*c*) multiply the moment distributed to each member at a joint by the carry-over factor at that end of the member and set this product at the other end of the member; (*d*) distribute these moments just "carried over"; (*e*) repeat the process until the moments to be carried over are small enough to be neglected; and (*f*) add all moments —fixed-end moments, distributed moments, moments carried over—at each end of each member to obtain the true moment at the end.

To the mathematically inclined the method will appear as one of solving a series of normal simultaneous equations by successive approximation. From an engineering viewpoint it seems simpler and more useful to think of the solution as if it were a physical occurrence. The beams are loaded or otherwise distorted while the joints are held against rotation; one joint is then allowed to rotate with accompanying distribution of the unbalanced moment at that joint and the resulting moments are carried over to the adjacent joints; then another joint is allowed to rotate while the others are held against rotation; and the process is repeated until all the joints are "eased down" into equilibrium.

BEAM CONSTANTS

This method of analysis is dependent on the solution of three problems in the mechanics of materials. These are the determination of the fixed-end moments, of the stiffness at each end, and of the carry-over factor at each end for each member of the frame under consideration. The determination of these values is not a part of the method of moment distribution and is not discussed in this paper.

The stiffness of a beam of constant section is proportional to the moment of inertia divided by the span length, and the carry-over factor is — $\frac{1}{2}$.

The proof or derivation of these two statements and the derivation of formulas for fixed-end moments is left to the reader. They can be deduced by the use of the calculus; by the theorems of area-moments; from relations stated in *Bulletin 108* of the Engineering Experiment Station of the University of Illinois (the Slope-Deflection *Bulletin*); from the theorem of three moments; by what is known to some as the column analogy method;* or by any of the other corollaries of geometry as applied to a bent member. Formulas for fixed-end moments in beams of uniform section may be found in any structural handbook.

SIGNS OF THE BENDING MOMENTS

It has seemed to the writer very important to maintain the usual and familiar conventions for signs of bending moments, since these are the conventions used in design.

For girders the usual convention is used, positive moment being such as sags the beam. For vertical members the same convention is applicable as for girders if the sheet is turned to read from the right as vertical members on a drawing are usually read. The usual conventions for bending moments are, then, applicable to both girders and columns if they are looked at as a drawing is usually lettered and read.

Moments at the top of a column, as the column stands in the structure, should be written above the column and those at the bottom of the column, as the column stands in the structure, should be written below the column when the sheet is in position to read the columns. This is necessary because positive moment at the right end of a beam and at the top of a column both represent tendencies to rotate the connected joint in the clockwise direction.

It makes no difference whether girder moments are written above or below the girder. Either arrangement may be convenient. Confusion will be avoided by writing column moments parallel to the column and girder moments parallel to the girders.

When any joint is balanced the total moment to the right and to the left of the support is the same, both in absolute value and in sign. The unbalanced moment is the algebraic difference of the moments on the two sides of the joint.

LIMITATION OF METHOD

From the fact that the terms, "stiffness" and "carry-over factor", have been defined for beams resting on unyielding supports, it follows that direct

---

* "The Column Analogy," by Hardy Cross, M. Am. Soc. C. E., *Bulletin 215*, Eng. Experiment Station, Univ. of Illinois, Urbana, Ill.

application of the method is restricted to those cases where the joints do not move during the process of moment distribution. The method, however, can be applied in an indirect way to cases in which the joints are displaced during the moment distribution, as indicated later.

As the method has been stated, it is restricted only by this condition that the joints are not displaced. If this condition is satisfied it makes no difference whether the members are of constant or of varying section, curved or straight, provided the constants, (a) fixed-end moments at each end, (b) stiffness at each end, and (c) carry-over factor at each end, are known or can be determined. Such values can be derived by standard methods and may be tabulated for different types of members and conditions of loading.

It will be found that in most cases accuracy is needed only in the fixed-end moments. It does not ordinarily make very much difference how, within reason, the unbalanced moments are distributed, nor, within reason, how much of the distributed moments are carried over.

In the illustration which follows it has been assumed that the members are straight and of uniform section. The stiffnesses, then, are proportional to the moments of inertia, (I), divided by the lengths, (L), but the relative values given for $\dfrac{I}{L}$ in this problem might quite as well be the relative stiffness of a series of beams of varying section. In this latter case, however, the carry-over factors for the beams would not be — $\frac{1}{2}$.

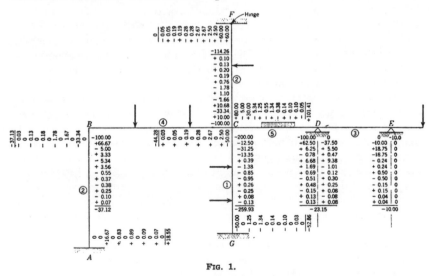

FIG. 1.

ILLUSTRATION

The illustration given (Fig. 1) is entirely academic. It is not intended to represent any particular type of structure nor any probable condition of loading. It has the advantage for the purpose of this paper that it involves all the conditions that can occur in a frame which is made up of straight members and in which the joints are not displaced.

The loads on the frame are supposed to be as indicated. The relative values of $\dfrac{l}{L}$ for the different members are indicated in circles.

The fixed-end moments in all members are first written. In this problem they are arbitrarily assumed to be as shown, as follows: at A, 0; at B, in $B\,A$, 0, and in $B\,C$, — 100; at C, in $C\,B$, — 100, in $C\,F$, + 80, in $C\,D$, — 200, and in $C\,G$, — 50; at F, + 60; at G, — 50; at D, in $D\,C$, — 100, and in $D\,E$, 0; at E, in $E\,D$, 0, and in the cantilever, — 10.

Before proceeding to a solution of the problem, attention may be called to the arrangement of the computations. The moments in the girders are written parallel to the girders; those in the columns, parallel to the columns. The original fixed-end moments are written next to the members in which they occur, the successive moments distributed or carried over being written above or below these, but farther from the member.

The arrangement of the moments in the columns in positions above the columns, when the paper is turned into a position to write these moments, for the top of the columns (at B, F, and C), and in positions below the columns for the bottom of the columns (at A, C, and G), is an essential part of the sign convention adopted.

The moment at C in the girder, $B\,C$, is written above the girder in order to get it out of the way. Otherwise, it makes no difference whether the moments are written above or below the girder.

The signs of the fixed-end moments are determined by observing the direction of flexure at the ends of the members due to the loads. In order to apply to the columns the ordinary conventions for signs of bending moments it is necessary to turn the drawing of the structure.

The reader should realize that the solution is built up step by step. It is always the last figures showing that are to be operated on—distributed or carried over—so that in ordinary framework there is little chance for confusion as to what step should be taken next.

Distribute at each joint the unbalanced moment, as follows:

1.—At A there is no moment.

2.—At B there is an unbalanced moment of — 100 on one side of the joint. This moment is distributed to $B\,A$ and to $B\,C$ in the ratio, 2 : 4, so that the distributed moment to $B\,A$ is $\dfrac{2}{2+4}\,100 = 33.33$ and to $B\,C$, $\dfrac{4}{2+4}\,100 = 66.67$. The signs are written in the only way possible to balance the joint by giving the same total moment (— 33.33) both to left and right of the joint.

3.—At C, the unbalanced moments are, in $C\,B$, — 100, and in $C\,G$, — 50, giving a total of — 150 on the left of the joint; in $C\,F$, + 80, and in $C\,D$, — 200, giving a total of — 120 on the right of the joint. The total unbalanced moment at the joint, which is the difference between the total moment on the left and on the right of the joint, is 30. This is now distributed in the respective proportions, as follows:

To $C\ B$,

$$\frac{4}{4 + 2 + 5 + 1}\ 30 = 10$$

to $C\ F$,

$$\frac{2}{4 + 2 + 5 + 1}\ 30 = 5$$

to $C\ D$,

$$\frac{5}{4 + 2 + 5 + 1}\ 30 = 12.5$$

and, to $C\ G$,

$$\frac{1}{4 + 2 + 5 + 1}\ 30 = 2.5$$

There is only one way to place the signs of the distributed moments so that the total is the same on both sides of the joint. This is done by reducing the excess negative moment on the left and increasing the negative moment on the right.

4.—At F, the unbalanced moment is $+ 60$. The hinge has no stiffness. The moment, then, is distributed between the member, $F\ C$, and the hinge in the ratio, 2 : 0; all of it goes to the member. The total balanced moment is $+ 60 - 60 = 0$, as it must be at a free end.

5.—At G, the abutment is infinitely stiff and the unbalanced moment, $- 50$, is distributed between the member, $G\ C$, and the abutment in the ratio, $1 : \infty$. The member gets none of it; the end stays fixed.

6.—At D, the unbalanced moment, $- 100$, is distributed to $D\ C$ and to $D\ E$ in the ratio of 5 : 3.

7.—At E, the unbalanced moment is $- 10$ in the cantilever. Since the cantilever has no stiffness, this unbalanced moment is distributed between the beam, $E\ D$, and the cantilever in the ratio, 3 : 0. This means that all of it goes to $E\ D$.

All joints have now been balanced. Next, carry over from each end of each member one-half the distributed moment just written, reverse the sign, and write it at the other end of the member. Thus, carry over, successively, in $A\ B$, 0 from A to B and $+ 16.67$ from B to A; in $B\ C$, $- 33.34$ from B to C and $- 5.0$ from C to B; in $C\ F$, $+ 2.5$ from C to F and $+ 30$ from F to C; in $C\ G$, 0 from G to C and $- 1.25$ from C to G; in $C\ D$, $+ 6.25$ from C to D and $- 31.25$ from D to C; and in $D\ E$, $+ 18.75$ from D to E and $+ 5.00$ from E to D.

Distribute the moments just carried over exactly as the original fixed-end moments were distributed. Thus, at A, $+ 16.67$ is distributed 0 to $A\ B$ (fixed-ended); at B, $- 5.0$ is distributed as $- 1.67$ and $+ 3.32$; at C, the unbalanced moment is $(- 33.34 + 0) - (+ 30.00 - 31.25) = - 32.09$ which is distributed as $+ 2.67$, $+ 10.68$, $- 5.34$, and $- 13.35$; at F, $+ 2.50$ is distributed as $- 2.5$ to the member; G is fixed-ended; at D, $+ 1.25$ is distributed as $- 0.78$ and $+ 0.47$; at E, the unbalanced $+ 18.75$ is distributed to the member as $- 18.75$.

The moments distributed are now carried over as before and then re-distributed; and the process is repeated as often as desired. The procedure should be stopped after each distribution, however, and a check made to see that statics ($\Sigma M = 0$) is satisfied.

When it is felt that the process has gone far enough, all moments at each end of each member are added to give the total moment at the joint. After the moments at the joints have been determined, all other quantities, such as moments and shears, may be obtained by applying the laws of statics.

CONVERGENCE OF RESULTS

The distribution herein has been carried out with more precision than is ordinarily necessary, in order to show the convergence of the results. To show the rate of convergence, the successive values of the moments at the joints after successive distributions are given in Table 1.

TABLE 1.—CONVERGENCE OF RESULTS.

Successive values of bending moment at joint.		After one distribution (two rows of figures).	After two distributions (four rows of figures).	After three distributions (six rows of figures).	After four distributions (eight rows of figures).	After five distributions (ten rows of figures).	After six distributions (twelve rows of figures).
A	....	0	+ 16.67	+ 17.50	+ 18.39	+ 18.48	+ 18.55
B	....	— 33.34	— 35.01	— 36.79	— 36.97	— 37.10	— 37.13
C	In C B	— 90.00	—112.66	—113.22	—114.24	—114.23	—114.26
	" C F	+ 75.00	+ 99.66	+100.36	+101.32	+101.36	+101.41
	" C D	—212.50	—257.10	—258.09	—259.89	—259.88	—259.93
	" C G	— 47.50	— 44.83	— 44.55	— 44.36	— 44.31	— 44.28
D	....	— 37.50	— 32.03	— 23.66	— 23.48	— 23.15	— 23.15
E	....	— 10.00	— 10.00	— 10.00	— 10.00	— 10.00	— 10.00
F	....	0	0	0	0	0	0
G	....	— 50.00	— 51.25	— 52.59	— 52.73	— 52.88	— 52.86

For most purposes the computations might as well have been stopped after the second distribution. Had this been done, the solution would have appeared as shown in Fig. 2.

For any practical purpose the computation might in this case have been stopped after the third distribution. In general, two or three distributions are sufficient. This is not true in all instances, but in any case the exactness of the solution at any stage will be indicated by the magnitude of the moments carried over in the members.

VARIATIONS OF THE METHOD

The writer has developed and used at different times several variations of the method shown, but the original method is itself so simple and so easy to remember that he finds himself inclined to discard the variants.

One variant is perhaps worth recording. It is rather tedious to carry moments out to the end of a member which is free to rotate and then balance the moment and carry it back again. This may be avoided by releasing the free end once for all and leaving it free. In this case, for beams of constant section, the stiffness of the beam is to be taken three-fourths as great* as

---

* The moment needed to produce a given rotation at one end of a beam when the other end is free is three-fourths as great as if the other end is fixed.

the relative $\dfrac{I}{L}$-value would indicate. After the end of the beam is once released, no moments are carried over to it.

CORRECTING FOR SIDE-SWAY

Single square or trapezoidal frames, portals, L-frames, box culverts, and similar structures act as simple continuous beams if there is no transverse deflection. If they are symmetrical as to form and loading, they will not deflect sidewise and if they are restrained against sidewise movement, they cannot so deflect.

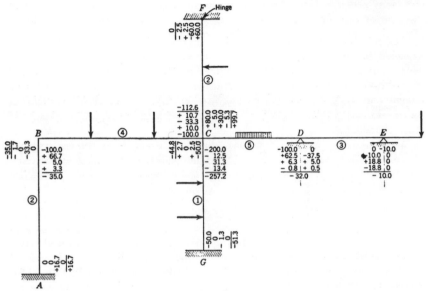

FIG. 2.

Side-sway of frames due to dissymmetry of the frame is rarely an important factor in design. Correction for side-sway may be made by a method which may be applied also in cases of transverse loading on bents. The method is to consider that the bent does not sway sidewise and analyze it as a series of continuous beams. The total shear in the legs will not now, except by accident, equal the shear which is known to exist. The difference must be a force which prevents side-sway.

Now, assume all joints held against rotation, but the top of the bent moved sidewise. Assume any series of fixed-end moments in the legs such that all legs have the same deflection. In this case for members of uniform section fixed-end

moments in columns vary as $\dfrac{I}{L^2}$. Distribute these fixed-end moments and find

the total shear in the legs. The changes in moments due to side-sway will then be to the moments just computed in the same algebraic ratio as the total unbalanced horizontal shear in the legs due to side-sway, when the frame is analyzed as a continuous girder, is to the shear just computed.

Multi-Storied Bents

Bents of more than one story, subject to side-sway, either as a result of unbalanced loading or due to horizontal forces, may be solved by this method. It is understood that exact solution of such problems is not commonly of great interest. It is the approximate effect that is desired rather than exact analysis.

To analyze by this method a two-story bent it will be necessary to make two configurations—one for each story. From the assumed shear in each story (producing, of course, shears in the other stories), a set of moment values may be obtained. These may be combined to obtain the true shears, and from the true shears the true moments follow.

General Application of the Method

The method herein indicated of distributing unbalanced moments may be extended to include unbalanced joint forces. As thus extended it has very wide application. Horizontal or vertical reactions may be distributed and carried over and thus a quick estimate made of the effect of many complicating elements in design. The writer has used it in studying such problems as continuous arch series, the effect of the deflection of supporting girders, and other phenomena.

An obvious application of moment distribution occurs in the computation of secondary stresses in trusses. Many other applications will doubtless suggest themselves, but it has been thought best to restrict this paper chiefly to continuous frames in which the joints do not move.

Conclusion

The paper has been confined to a method of analysis, because it has seemed wiser to so restrict it. It is not then an oversight that it does not deal with: (1) Methods of constructing curves of maximum moments; (2) methods of constructing curves of maximum shears; (3) the importance of analyses for continuity in the design of concrete girders; (4) flexural stresses in concrete columns; (5) methods of constructing influence lines; (6) the degree to which continuity exists in ordinary steel frames; (7) continuity in welded steel frames; (8) plastic deformation beyond the yield point as an element in interpreting secondary stress computations; (9) the effect of time yield on moments and shears in continuous concrete frames; (10) plastic flow of concrete as a factor in the design of continuous concrete frames; (11) whether in concrete frames it is better to guess at the moments, to take results from studies made by Winkler fifty years ago, or to compute them; (12) the effect of torsion of connecting members; (13) the relative economy of continuous structures; (14) the relative flexibility of continuous structures; (15) the application of methods of continuous frame analysis to the design of flat slabs; (16) probability of loading and reversal of stress as factors in the design of continuous frames; (17) the relation of precision in the determination of shears and moments to precision in the determination of fiber stresses; and a dozen other considerations bearing on the design of continuous frames.

The writer has discussed several of these questions elsewhere. He hopes that readers will discuss some of them now.

A method of analysis has value if it is ultimately useful to the designer; not otherwise. There are apparently three schools of thought as to the value of analyses of continuous frames. Some say, "Since these problems cannot be solved with exactness because of physical uncertainties, why try to solve them at all?" Others say, "The values of the moments and shears cannot be found exactly; do not try to find them exactly; use a method of analysis which will combine reasonable precision with speed." Still others say, "It is best to be absolutely exact in the analysis and to introduce all elements of judgment after making the analysis."

The writer belongs to the second school; he respects but finds difficulty in understanding the viewpoint of the other two. Those who agree with his viewpoint will find the method herein explained a useful guide to judgment in design.

Members of the last named school of thought should note that the method here presented is absolutely exact if absolute exactness is desired. It is a method of successive approximations; not an approximate method.

ANALYSIS OF CONTINUOUS FRAMES
BY DISTRIBUTING FIXED-END MOMENTS
(CONTINUED)

DISCUSSION

HARDY CROSS, M. AM. SOC. C. E. (by letter).[149] —The writer is indebted to those who have been kind enough to discuss the paper and have added so much to its value by illustrating the application of the principle involved.

Mr. Pilkey thinks the paper too brief. In the Seventeenth Century, Pascal wrote: "I have only made this letter rather long because I have not had time to make it shorter." (Provincial Letters, December 14, 1656.) The writer took time to make the paper short; as he looks at the mass of technical literature on his desk, he sincerely hopes the idea becomes popular. He thought best to confine the paper strictly to the fundamental principle and method involved, and not digress into the unlimited variations of this method or the unlimited applications of it. Secondary stresses, wind stresses, Vierendeel girders, continuous arches on elastic piers are special problems; while the elementary procedure is applicable to them, certain modifications are advantageous. The writer has indicated subsequently some of these modifications, but he has not felt justified in elaborating them in this closure.

Questions raised in some of the discussions have been clearly answered in others. The questions of Mr. Lyman have been answered in detail by Professors Martel, Morris, and Witmer, and Messrs. Pilkey, Black, Wessman, and Wilson. The limitations of the method suggested by Mr. Nielsen have also been discussed by others.

NOTE.—The paper by Hardy Cross, M. Am. Soc. C. E., was published in May, 1930, *Proceedings.* Discussion of the paper has appeared in *Proceedings,* as follows: September. 1930, by Messrs. C. P. Vetter, L. E. Grinter, S. S. Gorman, A. A. Eremin and E. F. Bruhn; October, 1930, by Messrs. A. H. Finlay, R. F. Lyman, Jr., R. A. Caughey, Orrin H. Pilkey. and I. Oesterblom; November, 1930, by Messrs. Edward J. Bednarski, S. N. Mitra, Robert A. Black, and H. E. Wessman; January, 1931, by Messrs. Jens Egede Nielsen, F. E. Richart, and William A. Oliver; February, 1931, by Messrs. R. R. Martel, and Clyde T. Morris; March, 1931, by Francis P. Witmer, M. Am. Soc. C. E.; May, 1931, by Messrs. T. F. Hickerson, F. H. Constant, W. N. Downey and E. C. Hartmann; September, 1931, by Messrs. Thomas C. Shedd, David M. Wilson, and Marshall G. Findley; November, 1931, by Messrs. George E. Large, and Sophus Thompson and R. W. Cutler; January, 1932, by Alfred Gordon, Assoc. M. Am. Soc. C. E., March, 1932, by Messrs. A. W. Earl, A. Floris, I. M. Nelidov, E. A. MacLean, George M. Dillingham, and Donald E. Larson; and April, 1932, by J. A. Van den Broek, Assoc. M. Am. Soc. C. E.

[149] Received by the Secretary April 25, 1932.

Mr. Osterblom's discussion is interesting and valuable, especially his explanation of the fundamental simplicity of Maxwell's method and of the difficulties which arise in applying it.

The discussions of Professor Shedd and Mr. Oliver call for little special comment. The writer appreciates them and heartily concurs in Professor Shedd's remarks with regard to formulas.

With the discussion of Mr. Vetter, the writer differs in practically every statement. Mr. Vetter seems to have some serious objection to the method, but he does not make it clear. His interest in the vertical reactions at F and G is entirely academic. Of course, the total vertical reaction at C may be found by statics. This reaction is distributed between CF and CG in proportion to the "vertical stiffness" of these paths if "vertical stiffness" is defined as the vertical force at C along either path necessary to produce unit vertical deflection at C. Presumably it all goes to CG, unless CF is a "skyhook." If the members are of constant section and immovable at G and F, the vertical stiffness is $\dfrac{1}{AEL}$, and it should involve no difficulties if the section varies.

The effect of shearing distortions is not involved in the problem of the distribution of the total vertical reaction at C between the points, F and G. In the paper the writer makes no assumption at all as to the effect of shearing distortions; if they are taken into account, the fixed-end moments, the stiffness values, and the carry-over factors are different from those used if these distortions are neglected. Of course, they should be neglected except perhaps in the most unusual cases. In the rare cases in which their effect in beams should be included, one should be guarded in accepting the conventional mechanics of internal stress in beams.

Whether longitudinal distortions shall be neglected depends on circumstances. It is a simple matter to correct for the effect of shearing and of longitudinal distortions by the method indicated in the paper. After the end moments are found in the beams, one computes the shears and the longitudinal forces and from these the distortions produced. He then finds that the frame is distorted by these displacements so that discontinuities would exist. The fixed-end moments needed to eliminate such discontinuities are then applied and these moments distributed throughout the frame. Theoretically, the procedure should be repeated, but except in the most unusual case, one trial will show the complete futility of the computation.

Mr. Vetter thinks that the engineer should "hitch his wagon to a star." He would do better to keep his feet on the ground. The conception of "mathematical accuracy" of the man on the street is decidedly amateurish; what the engineer needs is to get an answer with the requisite degree of accuracy without a prohibitive amount of labor.

The idea held by Mr. Vetter, that in some way (which he does not make clear), the method of moment distribution is approximate and involves assumptions which the theory of least work and the method of slope deflection escape, shows a fundamental misconception of these methods. Any one who computes the moments in a frame of reinforced concrete will make many assumptions as to the properties of materials, conservation of plane sections, and other matters; E has no definite value and I has no definite meaning in the analysis of frames of reinforced concrete.   This is true by whatever method the frame is analyzed.   Whether the computer knows that such assumptions are made is quite another matter.

Mr. Vetter seems also to object to the writer's list of incidental problems involved and states that he could add a great many more, "which have just as much, or more, to do with the subject under discussion [moment distribution?]"   That is excellent, or it would have been excellent had he done so; one of the things needed in connection with continuous frames is a clear recognition of the complications involved.   Another need is for a simple method of studying the effect of such complications; moment distribution is such a method.   The three samples of complications furnished by Mr. Vetter are not of the type listed by the writer.   Change in length of members due to shrinkage and to change of temperature and the settlement of supports are clearly recognized phenomena, the effect of which, for given data, are easily evaluated by moment distribution exactly as indicated in the text, thus:

"Imagine any joint in a structure, the members of which are being deformed by loads, or in some other way, to be first held against rotation and then released."

The method is not restricted to analysis for loads on the structure.

Mr. Eremin thinks that,

"In the limitations of his method, the author omitted to state that the modulus of elasticity of materials was considered to be constant for all members of the frame and also that the lateral rigidity of the members of a continuous frame is sufficient to prevent buckling."

The writer thinks that the first statement is in error.   One does not necessarily assume either that E is constant for all members or from section to section in any one member or over any one cross-section of the member.   It is merely necessary to have an accurate stress-strain diagram for the material.   If it is first assumed that E is constant and all stresses are computed on this basis, the fixed-end moments, stiffness values, and carry-over factors may then be revised for the values of E indicated by these stresses.   The operation may be repeated to any degree of precision.   The problem is evidently one for research, not for the office.   The writer has studied it in relation to the effect of chance variation of the modulus of elasticity,[150] the effect of plastic flow and time yield in concrete, and the effect of secondary stresses beyond the elastic limit of steel.   The common assumption of the constant, E, is a matter of convenience, and is not a limitation of method.

The statement that the method is restricted by the assumption that the members do not buckle seems to the writer to mean that the method will give the moment in a member if the member is still there—if it has not failed. This is correct.

---

[150] "Dependability of the Theory of Concrete Arches," *Bulletin 203*, Eng. Experiment Station, Univ. of Illinois.

Mr. Mitra deplores the fact that the method does not lead to any general equation. Since the avoidance of such general equations was the object of the paper, the writer is pleased by the comment. That the method of slope deflection and the graphical method of conjugate points are more accurate is not true; that these methods are quicker and easier to use is opposed to the experience of hundreds of engineers in the United States.

Professor Hickerson evidently does not like the paper at all, even though he "commends the author." Consequently, he introduces the subject of "Tabular Coefficients." Of course, it is better to use the answer previously determined for a problem than it is to re-work the problem, provided one is sure that the answer is correct and provided the answer is easily found. The trouble with tabular coefficients is that one cannot be sure, unless he checks them, that they are correct, however distinguished their author, and that the one using them may not agree with the basis on which they are computed. Unfortunately, few published tables explain clearly the basis on which they are prepared. Even so careful a scholar as Professor Hickerson fails to state whether the negative moments which he has computed are at the face of the support or at the center, and what allowance, if any, he has made for the increased flexural resistance of the members between the faces of any support.

Professor Hickerson gives a coefficient for an arch frame uniformly loaded between columns. He then states that "if the entire load is concentrated at the central ridge, * * * the foregoing values would be multiplied by $\dfrac{3}{2}$."

This is not quite correct either here or in general. In this case it is nearly true but any one using the tables must determine for himself when it ceases to be approximately true. Thus, any one using the "tabular coefficients" will still need a method of analysis.

Mr. Floris thinks that the idea of using fixed-end moments in the analysis of a continuous frame is not new. Of course it is not, but Mr. Floris has gone far afield for his references. Fixed-end moments have been used in slope deflection in this country for years and apparently by Manderla before that and probably by others before Manderla. Mr. Floris, moreover, has overlooked the paper presented by Professor W. M. Wilson at the World Engineering Congress at Tokyo. The book in Japanese is not available to the writer and would do him little good if it were. The method of the late Professor Ostenfeld referred to by Mr. Bednarski and by Mr. Floris is apparently an extension of slope deflection along the lines indicated by the writer in his monograph on the column analogy.[151] The presentation by Mr. Bednarski is, unfortunately, not very impressive. The writer fails to find anything like the method of the paper in Hartmann's "Statisch Unbestimmte Systeme."

Two conventions of sign are possible for moments at the ends of the members of a frame. The convention of rotation for statical moments is indicated where rotations are involved in the solution and, therefore, is used in the method of slope deflection. The alternative convention is for bending

---

[151] "The Column Analogy," *Bulletin 215*, Eng. Experiment Station, Univ. of Illinois.

moments. Where a structure is to be designed from the moments found by the analysis the writer still feels that it is best to adopt throughout the analysis the convention commonly used in design. Several who have preferred the convention of rotation have used it in connection with problems of wind stress or of secondary stress. In such problems the writer also prefers the convention of clockwise rotation, for with wind stresses and secondary stresses it usually makes no difference which side of a member is in tension. The object of analyses for secondary stresses is to determine whether they are too high, not to use them in design; the wind may blow in either direction. In any case, one should consistently follow one method, as Mr. Gorman notes.

Some misunderstanding has appeared in the discussions and some misstatement has appeared elsewhere as to the restriction given in the paper for the method. The writer does not confine the method to frames in which the joints do not move, but merely states that these movements must take place in finite jumps so that "the joints do not move during the process of moment distribution." The method is applicable, without special complication, to all frames for any condition of loading, transverse as well as vertical, and for any condition of deformation, whether due to shrinkage, change of temperature, or settlement of support. Several discussions illustrate such applications.

The first part of the paper is restricted to structures in which the joints do not move. The writer explained that if such movement actually takes place, allowance may be made for it as indicated later in the paper. This procedure has been explained in considerable detail by several contributors. With regard to this movement of the joint (referred to in the paper as side-sway), four questions are important: (1) Can side-sway occur in the structure? (2) Does side-sway occur for those conditions of loading which control the design of the structure? (3) Is this side-sway a matter of importance in design and is an approximate solution sufficiently accurate? (4) How shall one determine the exact moments produced by this side-sway?

In most structures side-sway produced by vertical loads only is either impossible or improbable. Thus, the probability of the lateral movement of a floor of a building due to vertical loads is negligible. Even where the forces act transversely, side-sway of individual bents is commonly either prevented or checked. Analysis for the moments produced by crane loads in a mill-building bent are often incorrect. If the load produces side-sway of each individual bent, there would occur, as the load moves, so much lateral vibration as to impair, seriously, the usefulness and the durability of the structure; such movement must be prevented or checked by some system of bracing and the bent then is not free to sway sidewise. Similarly, the bent of an elevated railway is not free to sway because of vertical live loads, but is restrained by horizontal bracing of the girders which frame into or rest upon the bent. The writer has also seen solutions presented for stresses produced in lateral frames of bridges due to unsymmetrical loading of the floor-beams which neglected the restraint against relative movement of the planes of the top and bottom chords of the bridge offered by lateral bracing.

In those cases in which side-sway due to the vertical loads is possible, it is frequently most improbable. An unsymmetrical vertical load may indicate lateral movement of any one loaded bay in a building of reinforced concrete, but for such lateral movement to occur freely it would be necessary for the entire floor to be loaded in this same way; the probability is that lateral sway will not occur.   Attention should be called to the fact that side-sway is often a mitigating influence tending to decrease the maximum stress in certain parts of the structure, especially in the more highly stressed column; the assumption of side-sway where it does not exist may be on the side of danger.

In those cases in which side-sway may occur, it is neither necessary nor desirable to take account of it for each condition of loading.   It is more convenient to correct for it only for those combinations of loading which produce maximum controlling moments.

Side-sway is much like the effect of wind.   If a frame is analyzed on the assumption that the joints do not move and movement of the joints will actually occur, it will be found that the sum of the shears in the columns is not equal to the known shear.   Movement of the joints must then have been prevented by forces acting at these joints.   These forces reversed in direction may then be treated as wind loads.   Moments may then be found by some of the approximate methods of wind-stress analysis to determine how large are the stresses involved.

In many cases side-sway does not exist; in other cases, it is of no importance; in most of the remaining cases. it is sufficiently unimportant to justify the use of approximate methods of wind-stress analysis without hesitation. In the remaining cases in which it requires precise analysis an indirect method may be used.

"Assume any series of fixed-end moments in the legs such that all legs have the same deflection. * * * Distribute these fixed-end moments and find the total shear in the legs."   Add these moments to those assuming no side-sway in such ratio that statics is satisfied.   The subject has interested several contributors.   The procedure may be by direct proportion as indicated by the writer in another paper,[152] and as shown by several discussers; it may be by finding first the effect of unit shear in one story at a time and combining the solutions by a method of successive convergence, as suggested by Professor Grinter; one may write a series of formal equations, as Professor Constant suggests; or one may use successive approximations to the true values, as indicated in detail by Professor Morris.

It does not seem to the writer that any one of these variations of technique has any general advantage; sometimes one and sometimes another is the more useful.   Thus, in a single-story frame, it is undoubtedly more expeditious to find the effect by direct proportion, but in a high building the method used by Professor Morris offers some advantages.

Another variation of method saves time in analyses for wind stresses.   The joints are not assumed to be fixed-ended, but it is assumed that all joints not fixed have the same rotation, the moments in the girders being proportional to their K values and the moments in the columns, due partly to rotation of

---

[152] "Continuity as a Factor in Reinforced Concrete Design," by Hardy Cross, *Proceedings*, Am. Concrete Inst., 1929.

the joints and partly to displacement of the floors, being those determined by the shears. If the ratio of girder moments to K values is chosen with discretion, all the joints may often be nearly balanced before any moments are distributed. In the columns in the first story an adjustment must be made for the fixation at the base.

Fig. 75 shows the revised computations for the building discussed by Professor Morris. Only one distribution and one shear adjustment have been made. The moments given by Wilson and Maney are also given on the diagram (in brackets, thus: [24.0]); it will be seen that the agreement for girder moments is much more satisfactory than in Professor Morris' solution. Too many conclusions should not be drawn from this case, however; the building is too regular to be taken as typical of those variations of framing arrangement which present, in modern design, the real problems of wind stress.

In Fig. 75, two devices have been used to simplify the procedure. In the first place certain moments proportional to K have been thrown arbitrarily into the girders so that to begin with, all joints are nearly balanced. These represent the effect of equal rotations at all joints except the bases of the columns; this exception is provided for in the columns of the bottom story by use of the factor, $\dfrac{1}{C}$, discussed later.

In the second place, the analysis is abbreviated by writing only the moments carried over and making one distribution at the end of the procedure. The moments produced by each distribution which would need adjustment to balance the shears are evidently equal to three times the moment carried over in the columns in any story.

The solution is presented here as an interesting variation of the technique of moment distribution and not necessarily as a procedure recommended for the analysis of wind stresses in all cases.

A valuable by-product in wind-stress analyses is the direct determination of deflections. Each addition of fixed-end moments in any column represents a relative deflection of the floors at the ends of that column equal to $\dfrac{Mh}{6\,EK}$, in which, M is the fixed-end moment at one end of the column. In the solution just given the total moment added in a column is due partly to rotation and partly to displacement. That due to rotation is $\left(\dfrac{K}{2} + \dfrac{K}{10}\right) = 0.6\,K$ in columns above the first story. Hence,

$$\Delta = \left(\frac{M}{6\,K} + 0.1\right)\frac{h}{E}$$

in stories above the first, in which, M is the total added moment at one end of the column. In the first story,

$$\Delta = \frac{Mh}{6\,EK}$$

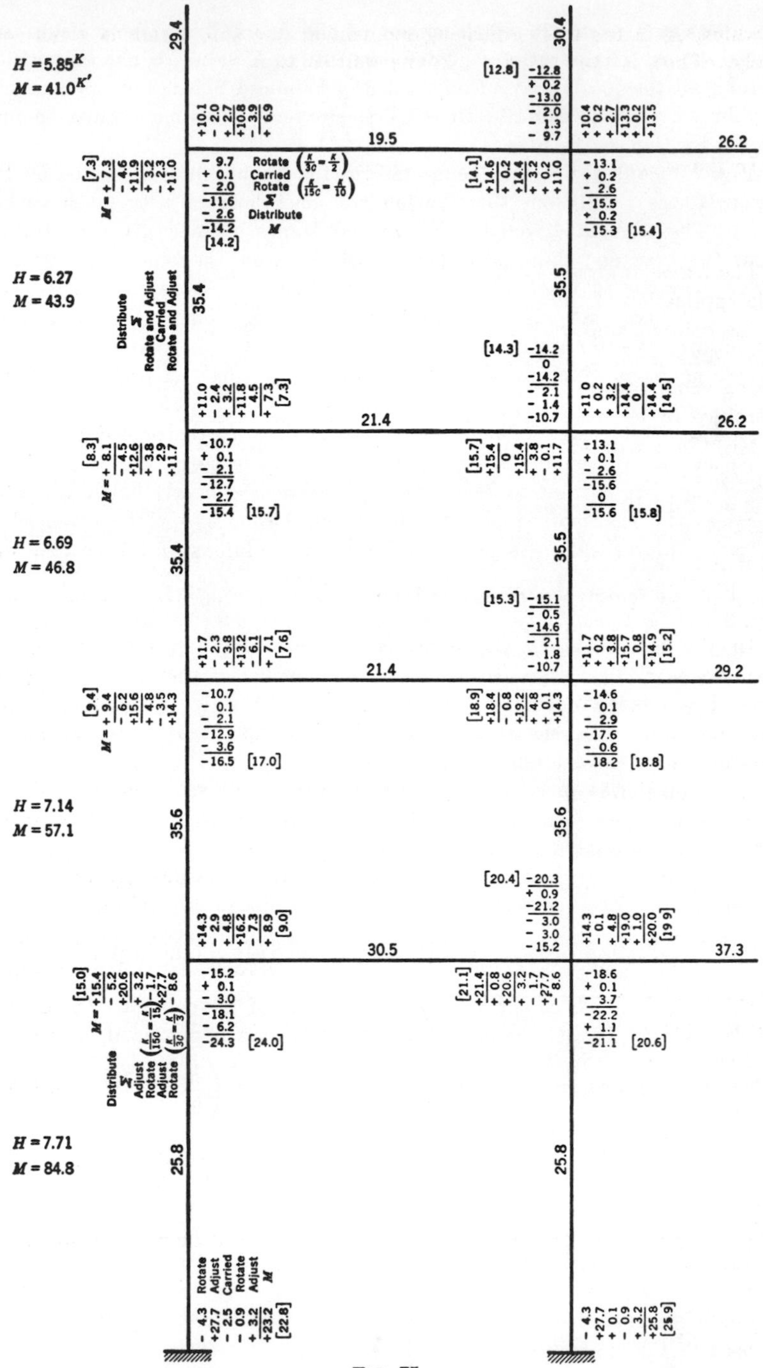

$H = 5.85^K$
$M = 41.0^{K'}$

$H = 6.27$
$M = 43.9$

$H = 6.69$
$M = 46.8$

$H = 7.14$
$M = 57.1$

$H = 7.71$
$M = 84.8$

29.4   30.4

[12.8] −12.8
+ 0.2
−13.0
− 2.0
− 1.3
− 9.7

+10.1
+ 0.1
+ 2.7
+10.8
− 3.9
+ 6.9

+10.4
+ 0.2
+ 2.7
+13.3
+13.5

19.5   26.2

M = +7.3
[7.3]
+ 4.6
+11.9
− 3.2
− 2.3
+11.0

− 9.7   Rotate $\left(\frac{k}{30} = \frac{k}{2}\right)$
+ 0.1   Carried
− 2.0   Rotate $\left(\frac{k}{15c} = \frac{k}{10}\right)$
−11.6
− 2.6   Distribute
−14.2   M
[14.2]

[14.1] +14.6
+ 0.2
+14.4
+ 3.2
+ 0.2
+11.0

−13.1
+ 0.2
− 2.6
−15.5
+ 0.2
−15.3 [15.4]

Distribute
Σ
Rotate and Adjust
Carried
Rotate and Adjust

35.4   35.5

[14.3] −14.2
0
−14.2
− 2.1
− 1.4
−10.7

+11.0
− 2.4
+ 3.2
+11.8
− 4.5
+ 7.3 [7.3]

+11.0
+ 0.2
+ 3.2
+14.4
0
+14.4 [14.5]

21.4   26.2

M = +8.1
[8.3]
− 4.5
+12.6
+ 3.9
+11.7

−10.7
+ 0.1
− 2.1
−12.7
− 2.7
−15.4 [15.7]

[15.7] +15.4
0
+15.4
+ 3.8
− 0.1
+11.7

−13.1
+ 0.1
− 2.6
−15.6
0
−15.6 [15.8]

35.4   35.5

[15.3] −15.1
− 0.5
−14.6
− 2.1
− 1.8
−10.7

+11.7
− 2.3
+ 3.8
+13.2
− 6.1
+ 7.1 [7.6]

+11.7
+ 0.2
+ 3.8
+15.7
− 0.8
+14.9 [15.2]

21.4   29.2

M = +9.4
[9.4]
− 6.2
+15.6
+ 4.8
− 3.5
+14.3

−10.7
− 0.1
− 2.1
−12.9
− 3.6
−16.5 [17.0]

[18.9] +18.4
− 0.8
+19.2
+ 4.8
+ 0.1
+14.3

−14.6
− 0.1
− 2.9
−17.6
− 0.6
−18.2 [18.8]

35.6   35.6

[20.4] −20.3
+ 0.9
−21.2
− 3.0
− 3.0
−15.2

+14.3
− 2.9
+ 4.8
+16.2
− 7.3
+ 8.9 [9.0]

+14.3
− 0.1
+ 4.8
+19.0
+20.0 [19.9]

30.5   37.3

M = +15.4
[15.0]
− 5.2
+20.6
+ 3.2
+27.7
− 8.6

−15.2
+ 0.1
− 3.0
−18.1
− 6.2
−24.3 [24.0]

[21.1] +21.4
+ 0.8
+20.6
+ 3.2
− 1.7
+27.7
+ 8.6

−18.6
+ 0.1
− 3.7
−22.2
+ 1.1
−21.1 [20.6]

Distribute
Σ
Adjust   Rotate $\left(\frac{k}{15c} = \frac{k}{15}\right)$
Rotate
Adjust   Rotate $\left(\frac{k}{30} = \frac{k}{3}\right)$
Rotate

25.8   25.8

− 4.3   Rotate
+27.7   Adjust
− 2.5   Carried
− 0.9   Rotate
+ 3.2   Adjust
+23.2 [22.8]   M

− 4.3
+27.7
+ 0.1
− 0.9
+ 3.2
+25.8 [26.9]

FIG. 75

in which, M is the total adjusting moment at one end, which is given separately. Thus, is the first story, in the wall column,

$$\Delta = 12 \ (27.7 + 3.2) \ \frac{h}{6 \, EK} \ = 0.0211 \text{ in.}$$

In the second story, in the wall column,

$$\Delta = 12 \left[(14.3 + 4.8) \, \frac{1}{6 \, K} + 0.1 \right] \frac{h}{E} = 0.0146 \text{ in.}$$

The frame analyzed by Mr. Nelidov offers an interesting illustration of the wide application of the method. The problem however, is solved more readily by the column analogy, as are probably all cases of an arch or bent of one span. The method of moment distribution has the advantage, however, of raising some question as to whether horizontal movement at B, C, and D is restrained by horizontal bracing, as it should be.

Mr. Nelidov divides frames into two classes according to the interrelation of possible linear movements of the joints. It is probably better to classify them according to the number of independent movements possible. Thus, the frame of Fig. 1 may be said to have no freedom of joint movement (assuming that D, say, is a fixed bearing); Fig. 5 has no joint freedom (A is fixed); also, Fig. 7 has one degree of freedom of joint movement; Fig. 8 has one; Figs. 9 and 10, two; Fig. 12, two; Fig. 22, one; Fig. 31 may well be treated as one span with no joint freedom (at A or A'); Fig. 32 has four degrees of joint freedom; Fig. 33 may well be treated as two spans with one degree of joint freedom; and Fig. 65 has two degrees of joint freedom. The degree of joint freedom is important in that it determines the number of simultaneous equations that must be solved in some way to satisfy the equilibrium of linear forces.

Mr. Bruhn suggests that the method has important applications in the field of airplane design. The writer knows that this is true, but is not sufficiently familiar with the problems involved in this field to illustrate its usefulness; he hopes that Mr. Bruhn will find time to do so. Certainly the method should facilitate the analysis of continuous struts subject to flexure. As Mr. Bruhn suggests, there is no difficulty in extending the method to include torsional effects. The writer has used the method in special problems of space frames in which the effect of torsional resistance is included in the analysis.

Mr. Downey has presented an interesting discussion of the application of successive convergence to the method of slope deflection. Slope deflection has more than justified its place in America and Mr. Downey has made a valuable addition to this literature. If, however, Mr. Downey will arrange his computation in the way shown by the writer and, further, if in using moment distribution one writes only the moments carried over in each member, it will be found that his computations parallel closely those of moment distribution; but in slope deflection the moments are first translated into rotations which are finally translated back into moments and this represents additional work not used in the method of moment distribution.

These relations are brought out by the problem shown in Fig. 76. This problem has been solved by slope deflection (Fig. 76(a)) and by moment distribution (Fig. 76(b)). As an additional check it has been solved also by the abbreviated method of moment distribution for a three-span beam in which the converging series are summed at once (Fig. 76(c)). By the method of slope deflection, using the method of successive convergence, the values of ϕ are first found. These values of ϕ are next converted into moments and added to the original end moments. In moment distribution the unbalanced

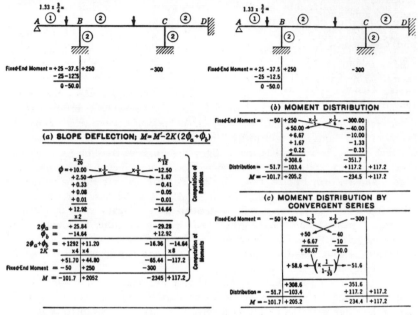

FIG. 76.

moments are carried over just as the ϕ values were carried over, the amount of computation being the same; but in moment distribution the quantities dealt with are always moments, which are the thing sought; by the method of slope deflection these moments are converted into rotations, from which the moments must be recomputed in the end.

Any frame must satisfy two general groups of conditions. The forces acting on it must satisfy the laws of statics so that the frame shall be in equilibrium. The forces acting on it must also satisfy the conditions of geometry, so that the rotations produced in the frame by these forces shall maintain continuity in the frame. The moments at the joints may be expressed either in terms of the joint rotations in the first place and these rotations found from the equations of static equilibrium at the joints, or the rotations may be expressed in terms of the moments and these moments found from the conditions of continuity at the joints. The latter method is that used in developing the theorems of three moments and of four moments. The former method has been used in the United States by writers on slope deflection. The method of moment distribution clearly belongs in the class with the theorems of Clapeyron, but it should be obvious that all kinds of combinations of the equations of statical equilibrium and of geometry are possible, and that it is worse than futile to discuss whether a method introduces any principle in this field which is not implied in principles already known. There will be no new principles in this field, but by varying the form or arrangement of the equations and by more convenient methods of solution a clearer picture of the procedure of analysis can be found and the labor involved may also be reduced substantially.

What has just been written with regard to the theorem of three moments and the method of slope deflection is equally applicable to the method of work. The method of work is simply a deduction from elementary geometry.

Professor Richart suggests modification of the K values in certain stock cases. General relations to be used in direct distribution may be stated as follows. The moment needed to produce unit rotation at one end of a member may be written in terms of the physical properties of the member and the ratio of the changes in end moments in the member due to rotation.

Let $M_a =$ change in moment from the fixed-end condition at the end, A, under consideration;

$M_b =$ change in moment from the fixed-end condition at the other end of the member, B;

$S_a =$ stiffness of the member at A, defined as the moment necessary to produce unit rotation at A when B is fixed;

$r_a =$ carry-over factor at A (from A to B); and,

$r_b =$ carry-over factor at B (from B to A).

Then, for unit rotation at A,

$$M_a = S_a \; \frac{1 - r_a r_b}{1 - r_b \dfrac{M_b}{M_a}} = S_a \frac{1}{C}$$

If, then, the ratio, $\dfrac{M_b}{M_a}$, is known for all members at a joint, the unbalanced moment at that joint may be distributed directly.

In certain cases the ratio, $\dfrac{M_b}{M_a}$, is known from inspection. When the member is fixed at B, $\dfrac{M_b}{M_a} = r_a$; when the member is free at B, $M_b = 0$; in cases symmetrical as to form and loading, $M_b = M_a$; and in anti-symmetrical cases, $M_b = - M_a$.

Values of the constant, $\dfrac{1}{C}$, are shown in Table 21. The general expression may be deduced, of course, in several ways; many will deduce it from area moments. This general relation leads also to a check on the analysis. It is easy to see whether the conditions of statics are satisfied by observing the balance of the joints. The conditions of geometry are satisfied if $M_a - r_b M_b$ is proportional to $\dfrac{S_a}{1 - r_a r_b}$, or, in the case of beams of constant section, if $M_a + \frac{1}{2} M_b$ is proportional to K at any joint.

As one uses the method of moment distribution it soon becomes evident that it is not necessary to write the distributed moment each time. One may write only the moment carried over and make all distributions in one opera-

TABLE 21.—VALUE OF CONSTANT, $\dfrac{1}{C} = \dfrac{1 - r_a r_b}{1 - r_b \dfrac{M_b}{M_a}}$

Description of beam	Unsymmetrical haunching, $r_a >$ or $< r_b$	Symmetrical haunching, $r = r_a = r_b$	Uniform section, $r_a = r_b = -\frac{1}{2}$
Beam fixed at far end............................	1	1	1
Beam simply supported at far end.............	$1 - r_a r_b$	$1 - r^2$	$\frac{3}{4}$
Symmetrical...................................	$\dfrac{1 - r_a r_b}{1 - r_b}$	$1 + r$	$\frac{1}{2}$
Anti-symmetrical..............................	$\dfrac{1 - r_a r_b}{1 + r_b}$	$1 - r$	$\frac{3}{2}$
Beam continuous at far end....................	$(1 - r_a r_b)$ to 1	$(1 - r^2)$ to 1	$\frac{3}{4}$ to 1

tion at the end of the process. Time is saved, since almost one-half the figures are omitted, but the simple physical picture of the operation is considerably obscured.

This procedure may be carried further in any case where the value, $\dfrac{1}{C}$, is known for all spans but one in a frame. Carry over the proper proportion of the unbalanced moment in this span and repeat. Let a and b be the proportions carried over at the two ends. If the procedure of carrying over moments is continued it will be seen that they run to an infinite converging series the sum of which equals $\dfrac{1}{1 - ab}$ times the sum of the first two terms. Thus, the total moments carried over may be written after two terms and the total unbalanced moment may be distributed.

Fig. 76(c) shows the procedure. The unbalanced moments at B and C are carried over twice. The sum of the moments thus carried over is then multiplied by $\dfrac{1}{1 - ab} = \dfrac{1}{1 - \dfrac{1}{5} \times \dfrac{1}{6}}$. The sum thus found for the moments carried over is then added to the original fixed-end moments and the total is distributed at the joint.

This method of writing at once the sum of the converging series may be extended to frames in which the value, $\dfrac{1}{C}$, is unknown for more than one span in the frame. The general procedure of exact moment distribution by summing the convergent series is of great interest and, in some cases and for some purposes, of great value; but such methods are not properly a part of a paper the object of which is to present a single general method involving no special paraphernalia.

It is interesting to note that to determine moments in any span any system whatever may be reduced with close approximation to an equivalent structure of three spans, such as $A\ B\ C\ D$ in Fig. 76, by estimating or computing the fixation of the outer ends of all members except BC. Professor Van den Broek indicates the use of such substitute frames; so also does Professor Richart. The writer also used the concept of equivalent stiffness in his paper, "Continuity as a Factor in Reinforced Concrete Design," previously mentioned.

As another illustration, in the truss analyzed by Mr. MacLean the members meeting at C are known to remain fixed at the end at this joint; also, the member, BD, is known to be symmetrically distorted and $\dfrac{1}{C} = \dfrac{1}{2}$. The value, $\dfrac{1}{C}$, is then known for all members except the end posts. By twice carrying over distributed moments in this member and then summing the series by multiplying by $\dfrac{1}{1-ab}$, the total change in end moment due to carry over is at once determined and can be directly distributed.

In secondary stresses this method of convergence is usually only of academic interest. In the problem solved by Messrs. Thompson and Cutler it is not applicable, but the procedure used by them is much shortened if all distribution is made once for all at the end of the analysis.

Extension of the method of moment distribution to the study of the effect of gusset-plates on the secondary stresses is of some interest and presents no great analytical difficulty, the members being treated as of varying section. Any one who has analyzed on this basis will recognize more clearly the futility of great precision in computations on the usual basis.

Mr. Hartmann suggests that time may be saved by distributing unit unbalanced moments at the individual joints and then combining for any combination of loading. Mr. Dillingham uses the method in connection with moving load systems. This procedure has much merit where many combinations of loading are to be considered. It is not necessary, however, to distribute a unit moment in each member, but only at each joint. The distribution at each joint being known, any unbalanced moment from any of the members meeting at that joint may be distributed at once. The writer always uses this method where moving concentrated loads are under consideration. The fixed-end moments are found from influence lines. These are available for beams of varying section in a recent paper by Mr. L. T. Evans.[153] The unbalanced end moments are then distributed by the factors already found. On a string polygon for the load system, one then lays off the end moments at the supports, draws the closing lines in each span, and thus constructs the entire curve of moments for any position of the loads.

---

[153] "The Modified Slope-Deflection Method," by L. T. Evans, *Journal*, Am. Concrete Inst., October, 1931.

This procedure may be abbreviated by distributing moments at a support near the center of the structure. This joint is then held rigid while distribution is made at adjacent joints on either side, the resulting unbalanced moment at the first joint being then distributed from the values already found. Thus, the distribution of individual moments becomes more rapid as the ends of the structure are approached.

Fig. 77 shows the application of this procedure to the problem solved in the original paper. An unbalanced moment is first distributed at B. Then, when unbalanced moments are distributed at A and C, B is first treated as fixed and the values previously found are used to distribute the unbalanced

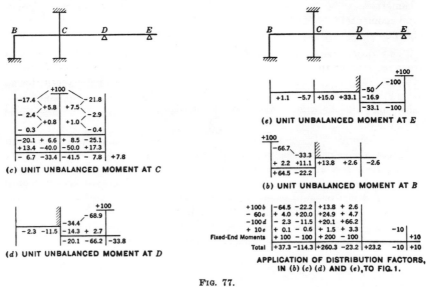

Fig. 77.

moment at B. Similarly, when an unbalanced moment is distributed at D, Joint C is first treated as fixed. The total end moments got by distributing the unbalanced fixed-end moments are shown at the end of the problem. The advantage of the method, however, seems to be chiefly in those problems where many different combinations of moments are to be considered. The abbreviated method of distributing moments only once is used; the convention of signs herein is that for statical moments.

Mr. Larson has made a valuable addition to the paper. The method of moment distribution is applicable to beams which are curved as well as to those which are straight, and is applicable to the distribution of forces as well as of moments. In order to use it conveniently, however, it is important that the convergence be rapid.

In the solution indicated by Mr. Larson it will be seen that the convergence is not very rapid. This is due to the large unbalanced thrusts and moments thrown back into the system each time by the pier. This disturbing factor may be avoided by distributing moments not about the pier top, but about some point so chosen that when the moments are distributed by rotation of the pier top about this point, the resulting thrusts are also balanced. It will also be true that there will be no unbalanced moment produced about this point due to distribution of unbalanced thrusts.

If this is done the pier may then be neglected during the process of distributing thrusts and moments. Indeed, the side arches may be neglected also, since only those thrusts and moments are distributed that are carried over from adjacent joints, none being carried over from the fixed ends. If it is desired to treat either one of the end arches or a pier as hinged at the foundation, its elastic properties may be determined for this condition and then it may be neglected during the procedure of distributing thrusts and moments.

The procedure indicated, then, is as follows:

(a) Locate a point (referred to subsequently as O) on the pier axis so that rotation of the pier top about this point (the other ends of the pier and the connecting arches being immovable), will produce no unbalanced thrust.

(b) Determine the thrust needed in each member alone to produce unit horizontal displacement at the pier top without rotation. Determine from this the distribution factors to the connecting arches.

(c) Determine the moments needed in each member alone to produce unit rotation of the end of the member about the point, O. Find from these the distributing factors for moments about O for the connecting arches. Locate also the thrust lines for such rotations. From the percentage of unbalanced moment distributed to each arch find the percentage carried over to the other end.

This gives all the essential data to be used in the distribution of the thrusts and moments. Now, proceed as follows:

(1) Distribute and carry over the unbalanced thrusts. Do not write the distributed values, but only the values carried over. Continue to convergence and find the total thrusts carried over.

(2) These thrusts produce unbalanced moments equal to the thrust multiplied by the vertical distance from the point, O, to the thrust line.

(3) Distribute and carry over the unbalanced moments just found, together with the original unbalanced moments about the points, O. Write only the moments carried over. Continue to convergence and find the total moments carried over.

(4) These moments produce unbalanced thrusts equal to the moments divided by the vertical distance from O to the thrust line.

Repeat the cycle to any desired accuracy. Next, by addition, find the total thrusts produced by displacements and the total thrusts produced by rotations. Since their lines of action are known, any other quantities may be determined by statics.

Since it is now necessary to deal only with the arches during the process of distribution, a somewhat more convenient convention of signs for thrusts than that used by Mr. Larson may be adopted. If the usual convention of signs is followed for moments used in the design of arches and girders that positive moment produces tension on the lower side, then a thrust acting above the axis—on the positive side—produces positive moment. Thrust in the arch is positive and tension negative. This makes it possible to add thrusts carried over to opposite ends of the arch without confusion.

Fig. 78 shows the solution of the problem given by Mr. Larson, using this technique. The percentages to be carried over and the lever arms of the thrusts have been determined from the data given by Mr. Larson. The final

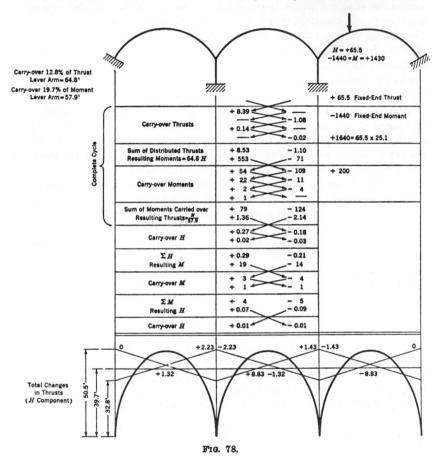

FIG. 78.

solution is obtained by adding the different thrusts and is indicated at the bottom of the diagram. The solution is shown here only to illustrate how, in this special case, a modification of the technique facilitates the convergence. The writer hopes to elaborate this procedure, elsewhere. It has a wide field of application in studies of continuous arch series in bridges or in buildings and of combinations of girders and arches.

It is not the function of this paper to discuss methods of deriving the elastic properties to be used in distributing the fixed-end moments and thrusts to the piers and arches. The writer prefers to use the theorems of the column analogy, according to which, the stiffness values and lines of thrust are defined as follows: (1) The stiffness for thrust is the stress at unit vertical distance from the neutral axis of the analogous column section for unit moment about the horizontal axis of this section; (2) the stiffness for moment is the stress on the analogous column section at the center of rotation for unit load at this center; and (3) the lines of thrust are the neutral axes of the analogous column section for these loadings. These theorems are equally applicable whether the arches are symmetrical or unsymmetrical.

The point about which rotation should be applied in order that the resulting thrusts shall balance may be found as "the centroid of the values for horizontal stiffness," or so that the sum of the products of vertical distances to the thrust lines for displacement multiplied by the horizontal stiffness shall equal zero.

Messrs. Large, Earl, and Gordon have discussed cases in which the moment of inertia of the members is variable. As stated in the paper, there is no difficulty in applying the method to such structures; the fixed-end moments, the values for stiffness, and the carry-over factors are different if the members are of varying I. It may be well to observe that, at least in reinforced concrete, the case of variable section is the rule rather than the exception, although this fact is not yet generally recognized. Even where the members seem to be of constant section, the moment of inertia is very much increased beyond the faces of the supports. Note carefully that the sum of fixed-end moments at the center of intersections is to be distributed, not the sum of moments at the faces of supports. Neglect of this requirement of statics invalidates the entire analysis. Tables or curves that purport to give the moment at the face of the supports of continuous frames without reference to the ratio of the width of support to span length are necessarily incorrect and may be very seriously in error. Note, also, that traditional practice in the use of moment coefficients is based on the clear span, as is pointed out by Mr. Wessman in his interesting discussion.

The writer has discussed elsewhere the computation of the constants for beams of varying section, and thought it best to exclude such material from the paper.[151][152] There is no great difficulty in determining these constants. In any given case five quantities are involved, the area, centroid and moment of inertia of the $\dfrac{1}{EI}$ diagram, and the area and centroid of the $\dfrac{M}{EI}$ diagram, in which, M is from any trial moment curve. These quantities are then to be combined. There are evidently endless variations of detail in doing this, the principal rule being to follow a definite procedure and avoid repetition of computation. The writer prefers to use the column analogy which converts the entire procedure into the familiar process of computing fiber stresses in beams.

In his paper previously mentioned, Mr. Evans has given constants for members of varying sections. It will be of interest to those who use moment distribution to note that the values for moment coefficients given by Mr. Evans are for fixed-end moments, the beam coefficients, C_1 and C_2, are for stiffness, and the carry-over factor at one end is $\dfrac{C_2}{C_1}$, and at the other end, $\dfrac{C_2}{C_3}$.

Curves and constants for the properties of haunched beams of reinforced concrete based on the assumption that I varies as the cube of the beam depth, however, should not be taken too literally. The effect of cracking, and the action of the flange in tension and in compression, introduce many uncertainties.

All kinds of ingenious tricks may be used to shorten the procedure. This is all right for the specialist who is engaged daily in this field. The general method presented in the paper originated from studies made by the writer in the analysis of three-span frames and is his final choice for ordinary daily use from many variations of method that he has developed and used. Any one can develop an unlimited number of such variations. Their novelty is no virtue; what is wanted for daily use is maximum simplicity consistent with reasonable facility. Such variations present a fascinating occupation to dilettantes who amuse themselves in the field of indeterminate structures; for the ordinary designer who analyzes such frames not as a vocation or for amusement, but as a passing incident to the design of the structures, it is essential that the procedure be simple and without special exceptions. The structural engineer has so many things to think about that it seems very unfortunate to load up his "tool chest" with a great many pretty but rather complicated "gadgets." Although developed in a class-room, the method of this paper was intended for use in offices.

The writer is especially pleased that so many have found the method useful in the design of actual structures. Professor Caughey and others have given estimates showing savings of from 80 to 90% of the time required by other methods; the writer knows of cases in which complete studies have required only one-twentieth of the time formerly used.

The writer is indebted to Mr. Findley for emphasizing the accuracy of the method. The writer called it a method of successive approximation; a better term which the writer has often used in this connection is "successive convergence." As Professor Van den Broek states, the word "except" scarcely has a place in the engineer's vocabulary; but the term "approximate" is one which many people misunderstand. The quest of the absolute is a beautiful thing; but he who seeks in engineering analysis a precision that cannot be ultimately translated into such units as pounds of steel and yards of concrete is misled. Structures are analyzed so that they may be designed; not for the pleasure or practice of analyzing them. As Professor Findley well states, "between the analysis of a given structure, which is essentially mathematics, and the design of a required structure, which is essentially art, lie many difficulties."

2

CONTINUITY AS A FACTOR
IN REINFORCED CONCRETE DESIGN

INTRODUCTION

The purpose of this paper is to explain a rapid and accurate approximate method for analyzing continuous girders and frames of reinforced concrete for bending moments, shears, and reactions and to bring together certain questions and considerations which bear on the interpretation of such analyses. The whole subject has often been confused on the one hand by too crude approximations and on the other by too fussy mathematical theory. The consequence of the mathematics has frequently been that the theory has occupied so prominent a position as to shut out from consideration certain practical aspects, and the problems solved often bear little resemblance to actual construction.

It is important to recognize that continuity in reinforced concrete construction is a fact—not a theory. It is obvious to anyone that a concrete beam can not bend without deforming the girders and columns connected to it. It is more important to recognize this fact clearly than it is to evaluate the effect with great precision. Provision must be made in some way for this bending and the resulting shears.

Perhaps the title chosen is too broad, for the paper raises rather than discusses some of the questions involved, and it has been found necessary to omit several phases of the subject entirely, especially the effect of specifications on economical type of design.

THE CONVENTIONAL RULES

Scarcely any idea seems more definitely entrenched in concrete literature and practice than the conventional moment coefficients. Until recently these have been confined in most cases to $\frac{1}{10}$ in the end span and $\frac{1}{12}$ in interior spans. Later specifications suggest $\frac{1}{16}$ at the center of the beam in special cases. The writer has never seen a complete history of the evolution of these coefficients. They probably originated from the work of Winkler about 1885 and have been inherited by English and American engineers from that source.

These rules are generalizations from elastic analysis of a series of beams of equal spans with ratios of live to dead load varying between 1 to 3 and 3 to 1. They should not be extended beyond this. An important point is that they depend upon elastic analysis and do not carry weight of independent authority or experimental evidence. They have recently been attacked in a number of technical articles and have been criticized in some recent texts. Careful examination of them shows that they are fairly satisfactory for such regular cases as usually occur in building practice. They should not be extended to irregular span lengths, they should not be extended beyond the range of live-dead ratios indicated above; within these ranges they are not so bad.

It seems unfortunate that the practice of designing live and dead load together became established in concrete practice but, having become established, it gives a reasonably satisfactory basis for comparative designs in certain standard cases.

There are many cases in which the designer will not be satisfied with these coefficients. It is becoming more common to make complete studies in cases of irregularity. The method now to be suggested is approximate but will give needed results within a few per cent of the "exact" results.

Note that the normal problem in design is the determination of maximum moments and shears and sometimes of maximum reactions rather than the determination of the moments or shears for any single condition of loading.

Maximum Moments In Continuous Spans

In securing data to draw curves of maximum moments we load one span at a time successively with live load and determine the end moments. In order to do this we find first the end moments in the span on the assumption that the ends are fixed.

Fixed end moments may be found in beams of uniform section from the general rule that the moment at one end of a fixed ended span due to a concentrated load is equal to the moment which would exist under that load if the beam were simply supported, times the proportional distance of the load from the other end of the span. If several concentrated loads occur the end moment should be determined for each and the results added. For uniformly distributed loads the fixed end moments are $\frac{1}{12}$ WL. For cases of non-uniform distributed load either simple calculus may be applied or the load may be broken up into a series of concentrated loads and the end moments computed as just indicated. The effect of haunches is discussed later.

In general these fixed end moments will not be balanced on the two sides of a joint. Distribute the unbalanced moment at the joint among the connecting members in proportion to the ratio of moment of inertia to span length. Carry over with opposite sign to the next joint one-half of such distributed moment and there distribute again in proportion to the I/L values and carry this out to the end of the series. Add the distributed moments to the original fixed end moments, and this will give the moments at the joints.

This procedure should be followed for live load in each separate span. Addition of the results will give the effect of live load in all spans and if the distribution of the dead load is the same as for the live, dead-load moments may now be found by proportion. Otherwise they must be computed separately.

The whole procedure may be checked by separately distributing unbalanced moments due to full uniform load.

In drawing curves of maximum moment, draw one curve of moments for dead load in all spans plus live load in alternate spans beginning with the first and another curve of moments for dead load in all spans plus live load in alternate spans beginning with the second. The portions of these two curves which lie between points removed about 0.2[1] of the span

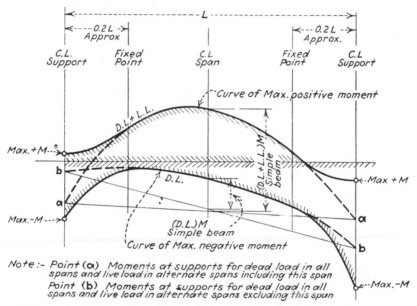

FIG. 1. A PROCEDURE FOR CONSTRUCTING CURVES OF MAXIMA—
SINGLE SPAN

length from the supports are portions of the curves of maximum positive and maximum negative moments.

At the supports maximum positive and maximum negative moments may be found by adding all positive or all negative live load moments just found at these supports to the dead load moment. Curves of maxima may now be completed by connecting the curves just mentioned to the maxima at the supports.

The whole construction is shown in Fig. 1 for a single span and in Fig. 2 for a series of spans. The shape of the curves will depend on the type of loading, the curves of moment for simple beams being drawn on the *a-a* or *b-b* lines (see Fig. 1) as bases. Both Figs. 1 and 2 are drawn for uniform loads. If the loads are concentrated at panel points, the

---

[1] These points are the fixed points used by Fidler, Ostenfeld, and others.

curves of maximum will break once at each panel point, once at each fixed point and once between each fixed point and the support for each panel point (see Fig. 5).

Signs.—The usual conventions of signs should be used in the girders.[1] The writer finds it convenient to apply this convention of signs also to the columns. The girders are read from the bottom up, the columns from the right hand side of the sheet—in other words, girders and columns are looked at as a drawing is ordinarily read. Moments in the girders are written parallel to the girders; moments in the columns parallel to the columns, above the column at its top and below at its bottom.

A joint will be balanced when the total moment on each side (left and right sides looking from the bottom of the page) of it is the same both numerically and in sign.

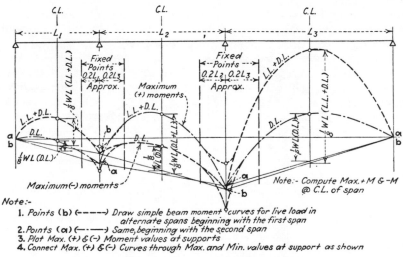

Note:-
1. Points (b) (-----) Draw simple beam moment curves for live load in alternate spans beginning with the first span
2. Points (α) (—·—) Same, beginning with the second span
3. Plot Max. (+) & (-) Moment values at supports
4. Connect Max. (+) & (-) Curves through Max. and Min. values at support as shown

FIG. 2.   A PROCEDURE FOR CONSTRUCTING CURVES OF MAXIMA— SERIES OF SPANS.

It seems to the writer very important that the same convention of signs be used in analysis as is used in design and that its application be as nearly automatic as possible.

DERIVATION OF MOMENT DISTRIBUTION PROCEDURE

The writer has used the method of moment distribution in various exact and approximate forms and has explained different phases and applications of it for the past five years.[2] Of all the variations that he has used, the above procedure seems the simplest and most rapid adequate method for concrete structures.

---

[1] Positive moment "sags" the beam; negative moment "hogs" the beam.
[2] Various aspects of moment distribution are discussed in the writer's Notes on Statically Indeterminate Structures, mimeographed, 1926.

It is evident that fixed end moments would exist if all joints were held so that they could not rotate and that the joints tend to rotate because the fixed end moments are in general not balanced.

Consider the influence of any one of these unbalanced moments on the system. If all of the members connected to that joint were fixed against rotation at their far ends it is easily shown from the theory of elasticity that this unbalanced moment would be distributed among them in proportion to their I/L[1] values and also that there would be produced at the other end of each member a moment of opposite sign and equal to one-half of this distributed moment.[2] If any one of these connected members were free at its far end, its stiffness (measured by the moment necessary to produce unit rotation) would be only three-fourths as great as if it were fixed ended.[3] This would alter somewhat the distribution of the unbalanced moment among the connected members. Some of the members may be fixed, some may be free and some may be continuous at their ends and the exact distribution of these unbalanced moments among them will depend upon this degree of fixation.

We will assume all members at any joint to be partly fixed at their other ends—to use a loose term, half fixed and half free. If they are completely fixed, they will be about 14 per cent stiffer and if actually free they will be about 14 per cent less stiff. But in reinforced-concrete construction the relative values of EI are uncertain to a greater extent than 14 per cent and the fixed end moments are themselves uncertain to the extent of 5 or 10 per cent. The quest for precision greater than is given by this method seems to neglect essential physical elements in the problem.

The approximate method indicated above in which the unbalanced moments at the joints are distributed among the connecting members in the ratio of their I/L values irrespective of the stiffness of the far ends gives results within the limits of accuracy possible from the physical data—about 5 per cent of the unbalanced moment at the joint.

It is possible that some engineers will not agree that this is satisfactory. Those who wish greater "precision" may vary the increase or decrease according to the stiffness of the connecting spans. In the next section an exact method of doing this is indicated.

The writer feels satisfied that any such attempt at precision in concrete structures is entirely unwarranted. In many cases, after the fixed end moments are computed, it is scarcely worth while to pick up a slide rule to get such facts as a designer needs.

---

[1] All fixed ended beams loaded with moments at their ends will have moment curves of the same proportions. The end slope is proportional to the end shear due to the M/I curve as a load, if the beam formula holds. Hence the end slope varies as ML/I and the moment necessary to produce a given end slope varies as I/L.

[2] Since the end slope is proportional to the end shear due to the M/I curve as a load, the end slope of a simple beam AB with a moment at one end A, is twice as great at the end A as at the end B. Hence a moment at B half as great as that at A and of opposite sign is needed to eliminate slope at B.

[3] This follows from the concept of moment distribution. Thus rotate end A of a beam, end B being fixed. Hold A and release B and carry over half of Mb with opposite sign. At A we now have $Ma - \frac{1}{2}Mb = Ma - \frac{1}{2}\frac{Ma}{2} = \frac{3}{4}Ma$.

In general the absolute error in the distributed moment in per cent of the unbalanced end moment will be less than one-fourth of the percentage error in relative stiffness. In Fig. 3 is shown the error in per cent of the unbalanced moment in the extreme case of one girder free and one fixed for various ratios of I/L of the two spans.

This fact, that a considerable error in the relative stiffness of the members makes so small a difference in the result is to the writer the most interesting and important fact connected with moment distribution. If this were not true, moments due to continuity in concrete would, because of the large and erratic variations in E, be as indeterminable as some theorists have alleged them to be.

Comparison of Exact and Approximate Values.—In Table 1 are shown comparisons of exact and approximate solutions for seven typical cases.

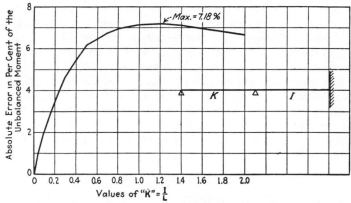

FIG. 3. CURVE SHOWING ERROR BETWEEN EXACT AND APPROXIMATE METHODS OF MOMENT DISTRIBUTION.

It will be noted that the errors are quite small. In general the relative error varies with the relative variations in span length and stiffness and with the relative intensity of the live load. Notice, further, that the proper basis of measurement of the relative error is the largest fixed end moment at the joint. The result cannot be more accurate than is this moment; no mathematics, no series of tests, no models can possibly eliminate this uncertainty as to bending moments in reinforced-concrete construction. It should be noted that the error in end moments may appear in the center moment as a somewhat larger relative error.

EFFECT OF HAUNCHES

Haunches at the ends of a beam increase the fixed end moments. They also affect the distribution factors—the relative stiffness of the members—and also the carry-over factors—the proportion of the distributed moment which is carried to the next joint. But we have already seen that the relative distribution is less important than the fixed end

TABLE 1 - MAXIMUM POSITIVE AND NEGATIVE MOMENT VALUES BY THE EXACT AND APPROXIMATE METHOD OF MOMENT DISTRIBUTION

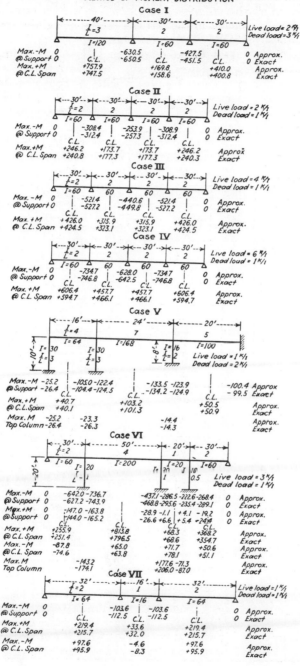

Case I

Max.-M	0	-630.5		-427.5	0 Approx.
@ Support	0	-650.5		-451.5	0 Exact
Max.+M		+757.9	+169.8	+410.0	Approx.
@ C.L. Span		+747.5	+158.6	+400.8	Exact

Case II

Max.-M	0	-308.4	-253.9	-308.9	0 Approx.
@ Support	0	-312.4	-257.3	-312.4	0 Exact
Max.+M		+246.2	+173.7	+173.7	+246.2 Approx
@ C.L. Span		+240.8	+177.3	+177.3	+240.3 Exact

Case III

Max.-M	0	-521.4	-440.6	-521.4	0 Approx.
@ Support	0	-527.2	-449.8	-527.2	0 Exact
Max.+M		+426.0	+315.9	+315.9	+426.0 Approx.
@ C.L. Span		+424.5	+323.1	+323.1	+424.5 Exact

Case IV

Max.-M	0	-734.7	-628.0	-734.7	0 Approx.
@ Support	0	-746.8	-642.5	-746.8	0 Exact
Max.+M	+606.4	+457.7	+457.7	+606.4	Approx.
@ C.L. Span	+594.7	+466.1	+466.1	+594.7	Exact

Case V

Max.-M	-25.2	-105.0 -122.4	-133.5 -123.9	-100.4	Approx
@ Support	-26.4	-104.4 -124.5	-134.2 -124.9	-99.5	Exact
Max.+M	+40.7		+103.2	+50.5	Approx.
@ C.L. Span	+40.1		+101.3	+50.9	Exact
Max. M	-25.2	-23.3	-14.4		Approx.
Top Column	-26.4	-26.3	-14.3		Exact

Case VI

Max.-M	0	-642.0 -736.7	-437.1 -286.5 -222.6 -268.4	0	Approx.
@ Support	0	-627.2 -743.9	-468.8 -295.6 -235.4 -289.1	0	Exact
Max.+M	0	-147.0 -163.8	-28.9 -1.1 +4.1 -19.2	0	Approx.
@ Support	0	-144.0 -165.2	-26.6 +6.6 +5.4 -24.4	0	Exact
Max.+M	+255.9	+813.8	+68.3 +368.2		Approx.
@ C.L. Span	+251.4	+796.5	+68.6 +354.7		Exact
Max.-M	-87.8	+65.0	+71.7 +50.6		Approx.
@ C.L. Span	-74.6	+63.8	+78.1 +51.1		Exact
Max. M		-143.2	+177.6 -71.3		Approx.
Top Column		-174.1	+206.0 -87.0		Exact

Case VII

Max.-M	0	-103.6	-103.6	0	Approx.
@ Support	0	-112.5	-112.5	0	Exact
Max.+M	+219.4	+33.6	+219.4		Approx.
@ C.L. Span	+215.7	+32.0	+215.7		Exact
Max.-M	+97.6	-4.6	+97.6		Approx.
@ C.L. Span	+95.9	-8.3	+95.9		Exact

TABLE 2 – COMPARISON OF EXACT AND APPROXIMATE CONSTANTS FOR HAUNCHES AND VARIATION OF FIXED-ENDED MOMENTS FOR UNIFORM LOAD IN PER CENT OF THE FIXED-ENDED MOMENT FOR A PRISMATIC BEAM

A' = % Added Area

%L	%d	%A'	Haunched One End Only — Haunched End	Un-Haunched End	Haunched Both Ends	Method	Type of Haunch
15	19	2.8	105	97	105 / 103	Exact / Approx.	Straight
		1.9	104	98	104 / 102	Exact / Approx.	Parabolic
	49	7.4	115	93	110 / 107	Exact / Approx.	Straight
		4.9	110	95	108 / 105	Exact / Approx.	Parabolic
	71	10.7	121	89	113 / 111	Exact / Approx.	Straight
		7.1	114	93	110 / 107	Exact / Approx.	Parabolic
	102	15.3	131	85	115 / 115	Exact / Approx.	Straight
		10.2	120	90	112 / 110	Exact / Approx	Parabolic
20	19	3.8	113 / 108	95 / 96	106 / 104	Exact / Approx.	Straight
		2.5	109 / 105	96 / 97	104 / 103	Exact / Approx.	Parabolic
	49	9.8	125 / 120	88 / 90	113 / 110	Exact / Approx.	Straight
		8.5	120 / 117	91 / 91	110 / 109	Exact / Approx.	Parabolic
	71	14.2	133 / 128	84 / 86	116 / 114	Exact / Approx.	Straight
		9.5	126 / 119	88 / 90	112 / 110	Exact / Approx.	Parabolic
	102	20.4	144 / 141	81 / 80	119 / 120	Exact / Approx.	Straight
		13.6	132 / 127	86 / 86	115 / 114	Exact / Approx.	Parabolic
25	19	4.8	113 / 110	94 / 95	107 / 105	Exact / Approx.	Straight
		3.2	109 / 106	95 / 97	105 / 103	Exact / Approx.	Parabolic
	49	11.3	131 / 123	87 / 89	115 / 111	Exact / Approx.	Straight
		7.5	122 / 115	88 / 92	111 / 108	Exact / Approx.	Parabolic
	71	17.8	141 / 136	82 / 82	118 / 118	Exact / Approx	Straight
		11.9	131 / 124	86 / 86	114 / 112	Exact / Approx.	Parabolic
	102	25.5	151 / 151	78 / 74	122 / 126	Exact / Approx.	Straight
		17.1	139 / 134	83 / 83	118 / 117	Exact / Approx.	Parabolic

moment and evidently the proportion which is carried over is less important than the proportionate distribution.   The writer has found it
surprisingly satisfactory to correct the fixed end moments for the effect
of haunches, and otherwise to neglect the haunching.   This will not be
true in the case of very large haunches but very large haunches are rarely
justified and if the case be important more exact studies can be made.

There is a remarkable relation between the increase in end moment
due to haunching and the increase in area of the side elevation of the
beam.   At a haunched end the fixed end moment is increased relatively
about as much as the area of the side elevation of that half of the beam
is increased and at the other end the fixed end moment is decreased

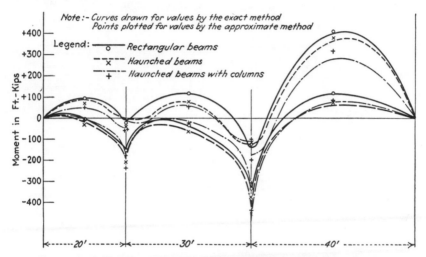

FIG. 4. CURVES OF MAXIMA—COMPARISON OF THE EXACT AND
APPROXIMATE METHODS OF MOMENT DISTRIBUTION
AND SHOWING EFFECTS OF HAUNCHING AND
COLUMNS ON THE MOMENTS.

about half as much relatively as this increase in area.   The effects of
haunching both ends are additive.   Table II gives data to support this
approximation.

Fig. 4 gives a comparison in one case of results by this approximate
method with those by "exact" analysis.   The writer has on file many
other comparisons, but a discussion of and interpretation of all these
would involve mathematical relations not here presented.   He does not
wish to present the above as a general rule for all extremes of haunching,
but in the usual case, where span lengths do not differ too greatly and
haunches are not very large and are not dissimilar, the rule will make
reasonable allowance for haunching.[1]

[1] The writer has discussed the exact analysis of haunched beams in a paper dealing with
the general theory of moment distribution.   This paper is now in the hands of another technical society.   It was submitted in February, 1928, but at this writing (December), their
committee on meetings and publications has not passed on it; for this reason, as well as for
brevity, the treatment of haunched beams is here restricted to the approximate method.

Shears and Reactions

Maximum shears have been neglected to a large extent in the literature of continuity. In case of equal spans maximum shear at the inner end of the end span may readily be 20 per cent greater than if the span were simply supported. A theorist may find even greater shears than this. Consider, for example, the first interior girder from the corner of the building. The continuity of beams and slabs will increase the load coming to this girder probably 20 per cent. The continuity of the girder with the next girder will increase the shear at the first interior column by another 20 per cent, and the maximum shear at the end of this girder may be 40 or 50 per cent greater than if there were no continuity in the frame work. The writer does not know why the increase in shear in the

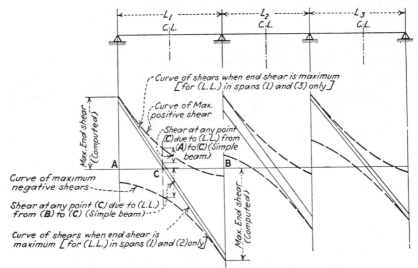

FIG. 5. TYPICAL CURVES OF MAXIMUM SHEARS (APPROXIMATE)
FOR UNIFORM LOAD.

end span was neglected and the increase in moment so carefully defined when the conventional rules were first stated.

Maximum end shear will occur for the same loading that gives maximum end moment in a girder. The end moments may be taken from the tabulations already made for moment computations. The difference between the moments at the two ends of a span divided by the span length represents the change in end shear from that which would exist were the span simply supported. If the negative moment is greater at that end of the span than at the other, the shear at that end will be increased. Computations for maximum end shear seem worth making, though not with great precision.

Curves of maximum shear in a span are tedious to determine because the maxima require different partial loadings of the span in question. The writer has found that a very satisfactory rule for drawing these curves is to add to the curves of shears which exists in the span when the end shear is maximum, the shear at the point in question due to live loads between this point and the end, computed on a simple span.   The construction is shown in Fig. 5.   As indicated later, however, it is not quite clear how to use these curves when they are available, though it is certainly important to have some idea of their shape.

Maximum reactions may be determined by adding maximum shears on two sides of a support to any loads which occur at this support.

ILLUSTRATION I.   (SIMPLE CASE.)

The example here shown is for a simple case with uniform live and dead load and no columns.   The values of I/L are first computed.

Live load is now applied in the first span and the fixed end moments computed $\frac{1}{12} wL^2 = \left(\frac{1}{12}\right)2 \times 40 \times 40 = -267$.   The free end is released and half the released moment brought over and added to give a total unbalanced moment of -400 at the first interior support.

This unbalanced moment is now distributed as follows:

$$\left(\frac{2}{2+3}\right)400 = -160.$$

Carry over, change sign, and distribute again $\left(\frac{160}{2}\right)\left(\frac{2}{2+2}\right) = +40$

For live load in the second span there are two unbalanced moments to distribute.

At left end $\left(\frac{3}{3+2}\right)$ 150 = -90 to the left end span
$+60$ to the interior span.

Carry over, change sign, and distribute $\left(\frac{60}{2}\right)\left(\frac{2}{2+2}\right) = -15$

At the other end $\left(\frac{2}{2+2}\right)$150 = -75 to the right end span
$+75$ to the interior span

Carry over, change sign, and distribute $\left(\frac{75}{2}\right)\left(\frac{3}{2+3}\right) - 22.5$

Adding, total at left end of span = -112.5
at right end of span = -90.0

The right end span is treated as was the left end.

Adding all totals gives the moment at supports for uniform load over all girders of 2k/ft.   Multiplying by $\frac{3}{2}$ gives dead load moments at supports.

All negative moments at supports due to live load are now added to the corresponding dead load moments to give maximum negative moments at supports.   Similarly all positive live load moments at supports are added to the corresponding dead load moments to give maximum positive moments at supports.   Due to the relatively great intensity of dead load, the maximum positive moments at supports (minimum negative moments) are both negative.

ILLUSTRATION I
THE APPROXIMATE METHOD FOR MAXIMUM MOMENTS

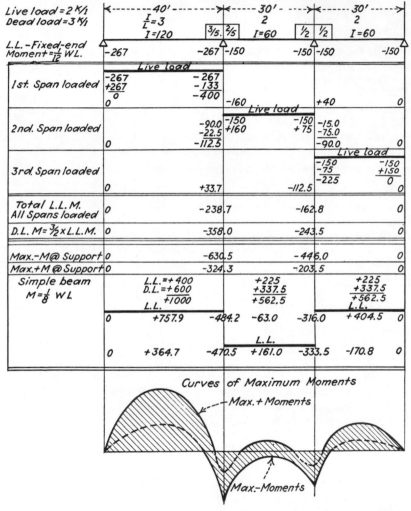

Now add dead load moments at supports to moments at supports for alternate spans loaded with live load beginning with the first span (in this example the left end span and the right end span) to get moments at the supports for this condition.   The average moment at the ends added to the moment which would exist at center on a simple beam for the corresponding loads (live and dead in end spans, and dead only in center span) gives maximum moments at centers of the spans. These are positive maxima in the end spans and negative maximum in the center span.

Similar computations are made for live load in the center span (alternate spans beginning with the second.)

ILLUSTRATION II
THE APPROXIMATE METHOD FOR MAXIMUM MOMENTS

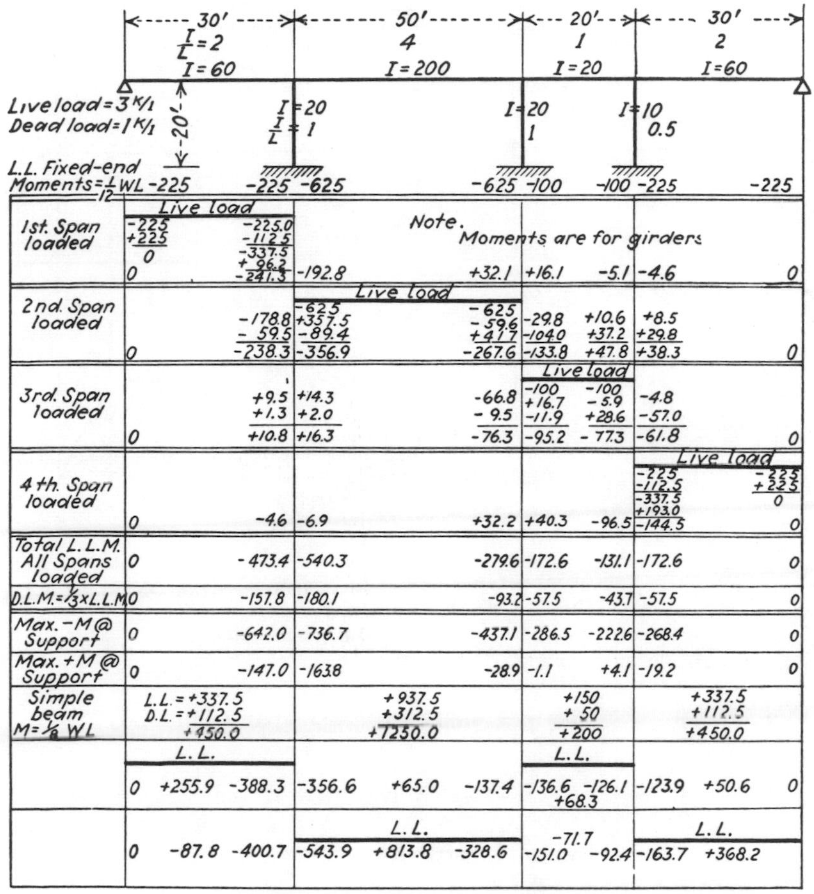

Frame dimensions and properties:

- Span 1: 30', $\frac{I}{L}=2$, $I=60$
- Span 2: 50', 4, $I=200$
- Span 3: 20', 1, $I=20$
- Span 4: 30', 2, $I=60$

Live load = $3\,^{k}/_{ft}$ Dead load = $1\,^{k}/_{ft}$ Columns: height 20'

Columns: $I=20$, $\frac{I}{L}=1$; $I=20$, 1 ; $I=10$, 0.5

L.L. Fixed-end Moments $=\frac{1}{12}WL$	-225	-225	-625	-625	-100	-100	-225	-225

Row	A	B (30' side)	C (50' side)	D (50' side)	E (20' side)	F (20' side)	G (30' side)	H
1st Span loaded (Live load)	-225 / +225 / 0	-225.0 / -112.5 / -337.5 / +96.2 / -241.3	-192.8	+32.1	+16.1	-5.1	-4.6	0
2nd Span loaded (Live load)	0	-178.8 / -59.5 / -238.3	+357.5 / -89.4 / -356.9	-625 / -59.6 / +41.7 / -267.6	-29.8 / -104.0 / -133.8	+10.6 / +37.2 / +47.8	+8.5 / +29.8 / +38.3	0
3rd Span loaded (Live load)	0	+9.5 / +1.3 / +10.8	+14.3 / +2.0 / +16.3	-66.8 / -9.5 / -76.3	-100 / +16.7 / -11.9 / -95.2	-100 / -5.9 / +28.6 / -77.3	-4.8 / -57.0 / -61.8	0
4th Span loaded (Live load)	0	-4.6	-6.9	+32.2	+40.3	-96.5	-225 / -112.5 / -337.5 / +193.0 / -144.5	-225 / +225 / 0
Total L.L.M. All Spans loaded	0	-473.4	-540.3	-279.6	-172.6	-131.1	-172.6	0
D.L.M.=⅓ x L.L.M.	0	-157.8	-180.1	-93.2	-57.5	-43.7	-57.5	0
Max.−M @ Support	0	-642.0	-736.7	-437.1	-286.5	-222.6	-268.4	0
Max.+M @ Support	0	-147.0	-163.8	-28.9	-1.1	+4.1	-19.2	0

Note. Moments are for girders.

Simple beam $M=\frac{1}{8}WL$:

Span	30'	50'	20'	30'
L.L.	+337.5	+937.5	+150	+337.5
D.L.	+112.5	+312.5	+50	+112.5
Total	+450.0	+1250.0	+200	+450.0

L.L. rows:

0	+255.9	-388.3	-356.6	+65.0	-137.4	-136.6 / +68.3	-126.1	-123.9	+50.6	0

0	-87.8	-400.7	-543.9	+813.8	-328.6	-71.7 / -151.0	-92.4	-163.7	+368.2	

The curves of maximum moments are shown but details of their construction are omitted. (See Figs. 1 and 2.)

Maximum shears and reactions have not been computed for this case.

ILLUSTRATION II. (WITH COLUMNS.)

The procedure is the same as in the first illustration. Different girder moments, however, must be carried on two sides of the column at any support.   The details of the distribution may need a little more explanation.

Consider live load in the second span.   Fixed end moments are $\left(\dfrac{1}{12}\right)3 \times 50^2 = -625.$ Distributing at left end gives $\left(\dfrac{2}{2+1+4}\right)625 = -178.8$ to first span and $\left(\dfrac{4}{2+1+4}\right)625 = +357.5$ to second span.

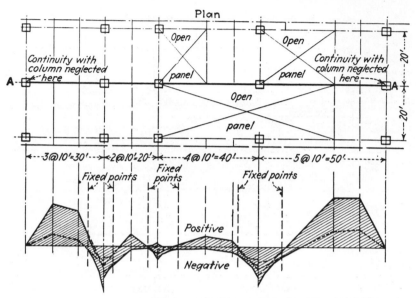

FIG. 6.   CURVES OF MAXIMUM MOMENTS FOR GIRDES ON LINE AA
IN A PLATFORM CONTAINING OPEN PANELS AS SHOWN

Change sign, carry over and distribute

$$\left(\frac{357.5}{2}\right)\left(\frac{1+1}{4+1+1}\right) = -59.6 \text{ in second span (right end)}$$

$$\left(\frac{357.5}{2}\right)\left(\frac{1}{4+1+1}\right) = -29.8 \text{ in third span (left end)}$$

Change sign, carry over, and distribute

$$\left(\frac{29.8}{2}\right)\left(\frac{2+0.5}{1+2+0.5}\right) = +10.6 \text{ in third span (right end)}$$

$$\left(\frac{29.8}{2}\right)\left(\frac{2}{1+2+0.5}\right) = +8.5 \text{ in fourth span (left end)}.$$

Since the procedure is approximate it may as well be done on the upper scale of the slide rule and need never be taken out of the slide rule till all distributions in one direction have been made.

Note that signs are such as will balance the joint—that is, will make the total values the same on both sides in value and in sign. The column moments, however, are not written until the end, when they may be found by subtraction, if needed. They have not been computed here.

This represents a girder in a platform having blank panels as shown in Fig. 6. All dead load has for simplicity been assumed as concentrated at panel points. The outer ends of the girders have been treated as freely supported.

ILLUSTRATION III APPROXIMATE METHOD

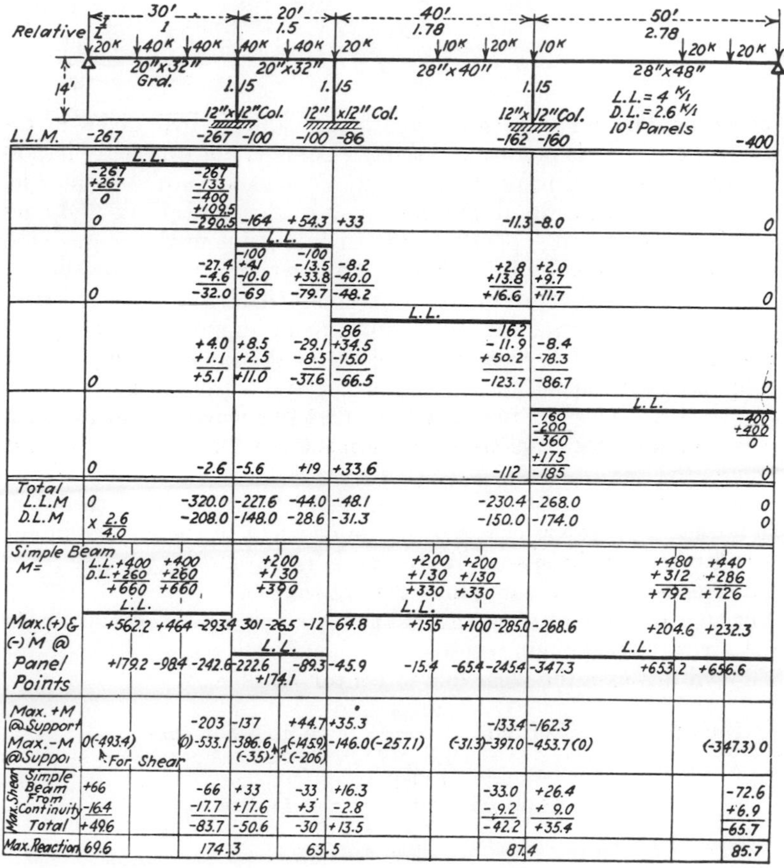

ILLUSTRATION III.   (IRREGULAR LOADING.)

The computation of fixed end moments deserves notice.

In the first span $40\left(\dfrac{20 \times 10}{30}\right)\left(\dfrac{2}{3}+\dfrac{1}{3}\right) = -267$

In the second span $40 \times \dfrac{20}{4} \times \dfrac{1}{2} = -100$

In the third span $20 \times \left(\dfrac{10 \times 30}{40} \right)\left(\dfrac{1}{4} \right) = -36 \times 3 = -112$

$$10 \times \left(\dfrac{40}{4} \right)\left(\dfrac{1}{2} \right) = \qquad \dfrac{-50}{-86} \qquad \dfrac{-50}{-162}$$

In the fourth span $40 \times \left(\dfrac{10 \times 40}{50} \right)\left(\dfrac{1}{5} \right) = -64 \times 4 = -256$

$$20 \times \left(\dfrac{20 \times 30}{50} \right)\left(\dfrac{2}{5} \right) = \dfrac{-96}{-160} \times \dfrac{3}{2} = \dfrac{-144}{-400}$$

The procedure for moment computations follows that given in the two cases above. It is interesting, though perhaps not especially important, to note that the curves of maximum moment are not straight lines from the support to the first beam but break at the fixed points and once between fixed point and support for each panel point in the span. The exact location of points on this curve is, however, rarely worth while.

The computation of maximum shears and reactions deserves attention. When the maximum negative moments at supports are computed the moments at the other ends of the beams for the same loading are also computed and written in brackets. For the end support, since there is no moment, it is necessary to understand that live loads should be in the end span and alternate spans beyond; moments for this case have already been computed.

The end shears are now computed assuming the spans to act as simple beams. These are changed by the quotient of the change in end moment divided by the span. When the negative moment is greater at the end considered, the shear is increased at that end.

The sum of the maximum shears at any support plus loads over the support gives the maximum reaction.

Thus in this case the shear due to continuity is

In the first span—Left end $\quad \dfrac{493.4 - 0}{30} = 16.4$ decrease

Right end $\dfrac{533.1 - 0}{30} = 17.7$ increase

In the second span—Left end $\quad \dfrac{386.6 - 35}{20} = 17.6$ increase

Right end $\dfrac{206.0 - 145.9}{20} = 3.0$ decrease

Curves of maximum shears have not been computed. They may be determined by finding shears for each individual load, or may be approximated as explained elsewhere.

ILLUSTRATION IV
MOMENT DISTRIBUTION BY THE APPROXIMATE METHOD
FOR CURVES OF MAXIMUM MOMENTS
WITH HAUNCHED BEAMS AND WITH COLUMNS

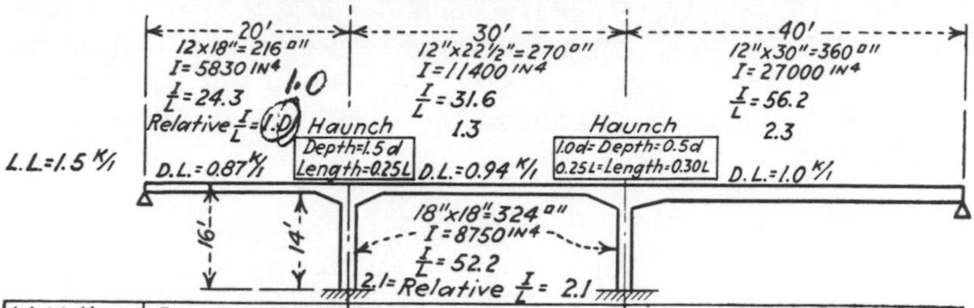

Diagram labels:

```
--- 20' ---        --- 30' ---         --- 40' ---
12"x18"=216 □"     12"x22½"=270 □"     12"x30"=360 □"
I=5830 IN⁴         I=11400 IN⁴         I=27000 IN⁴
I/L=24.3           I/L=31.6            I/L=56.2
Relative I/L=1.0   1.3                 2.3
L.L.=1.5 K/₁       Haunch              Haunch
D.L.=0.87 K/₁      Depth=1.5d          1.0d=Depth=0.5d
                   Length=0.25L        0.25L=Length=0.30L
                   D.L.=0.94 K/₁       D.L.=1.0 K/₁

16'   14'
18"x18"=324 □"
I=8750 IN⁴
I/L=52.2
2.1=Relative I/L=2.1
```

L.L.M=1/12 W.L.	-50	Added area	-50	-112.5	Added area	-112.5	-200	Added Area	-200
Effect due to haunches	+18.8=	37.5%×2=37.5		-84.6=2× 37.5% = +42.3 +28.1= 25 % x2= -56.2			-60 = 2 × 15% = +30		
Total L.L.M	-31.2		-87.5	-169.0		-125.4	-260		-170
1st. Span loaded	Live load -31.2 +31.2 0		-87.5 -15.6 -103.1 +23.4 -79.7	-30.4		+11.7	+6.1		0
2nd. Span loaded	0		-38.4 - 3.3 -41.7	Live load -169 + 30 -10.1 -129.1		-126.4 - 18.5 + 28.8 -115.6	-97 -51.0 -60.7		0
3rd. Span loaded	0		+8.9	+27.7		-78.6	Live load -260 - 85 -345 +139 -206	-170 +170 0	0
Total L.L.M	0		-112.5	-131.8		-182.5	-260.6		0
D L M	0	×0.87/1.5	- 65.3	-82.4	×0.94/1.5	-114.2	-173.6	×I/1.5	0
Max.-M @ Support	0		-186.7	-241.9		-308.4	-440.3		0
Max.+M @ Support	0		-56.4	-54.7		-102.5	-200.0		0
Simple beam M=1/8 WL		L.L.=+75 D.L.=+43.5 +118.5		+168.8 +105.7 +274.5			+300 +200 +500		
	0	L. L. +50.5	-136.1	-85.1	-27.4	-181.1	-373.5	L.L. +313.3	0
	0	-10.0	-107.0	-211.5	L. L. +53.9	-229.8	-234.3	+82.9	0
Values for Max. M Curves	+M	C.L. +50.5	-56.4	-54.7	C.L. +53.9	-102.5	-200.0	C.L. +313.3	
	-M	-10.0	-186.7	-241.9	-27.4	-308.4	-440.3	+ 82.9	

Illustration IV.   (Haunched Beams.)

This problem illustrates the application of the approximate method of allowing for the effect of haunches. The solution is not correct as regards the columns, no allowance having been made for the changed stiffness of columns produced by flare at their tops.

The fixed end moments are first computed as if the girders were not haunched. For each haunch the moment is increased at the haunched end by the same percentage as the side elevation of that half of the girder is increased by the haunching and at the other end is decreased by half this percentage.

TABLE 3 - VALUES FOR CURVES OF MAXIMA IN (FIG. 4)
BY THE EXACT AND APPROXIMATE METHOD
OF MOMENT DISTRIBUTION

	←------ 20' ----→		←-------- 30' --------→		←----------- 40' ----------→
Case I Rectangular beams	C.L.		C.L.		C.L.
+M Exact	+93.6	−16.4	+116.0	−134.0	+399.0
+M Approx.	+91.5	−23.1	+115.0	−124.7	+406.2
−M Exact	−5.2	−148.0	−40.9	−352.0	+112.0
−M Approx.	−8.3	−152.5	−36.7	−339.6	+113.7

Case II Haunched beams					
+M Exact	+84.0	−2.1	+72.2	−126.9	+363.0
+M Approx.	+68.7	−41.5	+73.0	−121.2	+377.2
−M Exact	−19.5	−192.7	−65.7	−426.5	+60.4
−M Approx.	−32.4	−210.1	−67.0	−375.6	+74.5

Case III Haunched beams with columns							
+M Exact	+49.3	−48.9	−10	+59.3	−111.4	−183.5	+279.5
+M Approx.	+50.5	−56.4	−54.7	+53.9	−102.5	−200.0	+313.3
−M Exact	−4.5	−186.0	−206	−19.2	−352.0	−507.0	+72.3
−M Approx.	−10.0	−186.7	−241.9	−27.4	−308.4	−440.3	+82.9

Thus, in the second span, the fixed end moment for a prismatic beam is $\left(\dfrac{1}{12}\right)1.5 \times 30^2 = -112.5$. The effect of the haunch at the left end, which has a depth 1.5 times as great as at the center (total depth at end 2.5 times center depth) and extends to the quarter point of the span is to increase the area of side elevation of this end of the beam 75 per cent. The fixed end moment at this end is therefore increased 75 per cent of 112.5 = 84.6 and that at the other end is decreased 42.3. Allowance is made in the same way for the haunch at the right end of the beam. The effects of both haunches are then added to the moment originally computed.

The distribution of unbalanced moments at supports and combination of these moments to give maximum moments then follows the procedure for beams of uniform section, the I values being computed for the depth at the center.

Fig. 4 shows a comparison of maxima computed for this case by this method with curves of maxima arrived at by theoretically exact analyses. It indicates also the effect on maximum moments of haunching and of columns. The same data are given in tabular form in Table 3.

ILLUSTRATION V   APPROXIMATE METHOD

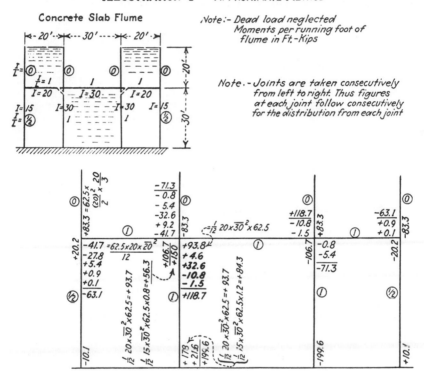

Concrete Slab Flume

Note:- Dead load neglected
Moments per running foot of
flume in Ft.-Kips

Note.- Joints are taken consecutively
from left to right. Thus figures
at each joint follow consecutively
for the distribution from each joint

ILLUSTRATION V. (SIGN CONVENTIONS.)

The structure shown here represents a series of water conduits having continuous walls and bottom slabs, the upper and lower reservoirs being connected so that the lower reservoir is under a static head. The problem is devised to bring out clearly the convention of signs used.

Use the usual moment conventions on both girders and columns looking at them as a drawing is usually read.

Write girder moments parallel to the girder. In this case the girder moments are written below the girder at the right end and above at the left end in order to avoid interference with the rows of figures for the columns. Usually it makes no difference whether girder moments are written above or below the girders.

Write column moments parallel to the columns, above the column at the top and below at the bottom. This is an essential part of the sign convention used.

A joint will be balanced when the total moment to left and to right of the joint (the sheet being held in its usual position) are the same both in value and in sign.

The fixed end moments are first written for the vertical walls and for the girders. The first projecting wall on the left is bent $)$ and the moment is +83.3; the wall of the bottom tank is bent $)$ at its ends and the moment is

due to uniform load

$$\left(\frac{1}{12}\right)20 \times 62.5 \times 30^2 = \qquad 93.7 \text{ at top} \qquad 93.7 \text{ at bottom}$$

due to triangular load [1]

$$\left(\frac{1}{12}\right)15 \times 62.5 \times 30^2 \times \frac{8}{10} = \underline{\quad 56.3 \times 1.5 \quad} \qquad \underline{84.3 \text{ at bottom}}$$

Total...................... +150.0 at top   +178.0 at bottom

In the girders the end moments are ⌒ −41.7 in the end girder and ⌣ +93.8 in the interior girder.

Unbalanced moments are distributed in succession beginning at the left end. The moments distributed to girders only are written and column moments found later by balancing joints.

At the left end +83.3 − 41.7 = +41.6 is unbalanced. Girder takes $\left(\dfrac{1}{1 + \frac{1}{2}}\right)41.6 = 27.8$, the stiffness of the vertical projecting wall being zero. The moment to the girder is negative because this tends to reduce the positive moment on that side of the joint and so balance the joint.

Carry over and change sign $\left(\dfrac{1+1}{1+1+1}\right)\left(\dfrac{27.8}{2}\right) = +9.2$ and $\left(\dfrac{1}{1+1+1}\right)\left(\dfrac{27.8}{2}\right) = +4.6$.

Carry over and change sign $\left(\dfrac{1}{1+1+1}\right)\left(\dfrac{4.6}{2}\right) = -1.5$ and $\left(\dfrac{1}{1+1+1}\right)\left(\dfrac{4.6}{2}\right) = -0.8$

---

[1] Fixed end moments with triangular loading are 20 per cent greater at one end and 20 per cent less at the other than if the load were uniformly distributed.

Carry over and change sign $\left(\dfrac{0.5}{1+0.5}\right)\left(\dfrac{0.8}{2}\right) = +0.1$

Distributing unbalanced moments at the second joint, we have

$$\left.\begin{array}{c}-41.7\\ +150.0\end{array}\right) \text{ on the left}$$

$$\left.\begin{array}{c}-83.3\\ +93.8\end{array}\right) \text{on the right}$$

Total $+97.8$ unbalanced on the left.

Each girder takes $\left(\dfrac{1}{3}\right)\left(97.8\right) = 32.6$. On the left this is negative, on the right positive to balance the joint. These moments are then distributed, thus

$+5.4 \longleftarrow -32.6 \quad\big|\quad +32.6 \longrightarrow -10.8 \quad\big|\quad -5.4 \longrightarrow +0.9$

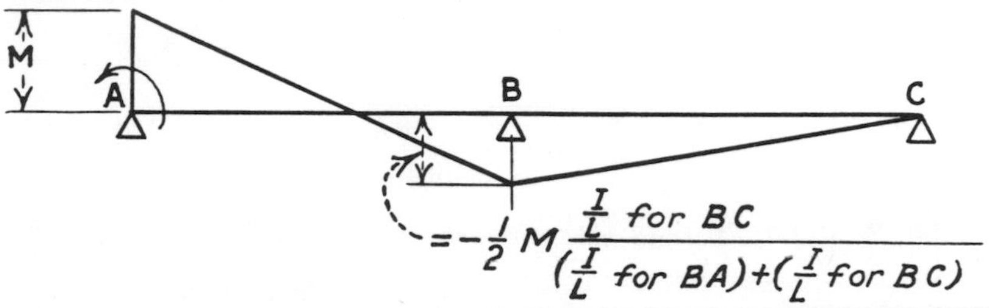

$$=-\frac{1}{2}\,M\,\frac{\frac{I}{L}\ for\ BC}{\left(\frac{I}{L}\ for\ BA\right)+\left(\frac{I}{L}\ for\ BC\right)}$$

FIG. 7. MOMENT CURVE OF TWO-SPAN BEAM SHOWING DISTRIBUTION BETWEEN SPANS.

Distributions from the third and fourth joints are, of course, as above. Addition now gives total end moments in the girders.

Moments in the columns are now found by balancing the joints.

At the left joint, $\left.\begin{array}{c}+83.3\\ -63.1\end{array}\right)$ on the right is balanced by $+20.2$ written on the left of the column. At the next joint $\left.\begin{array}{c}-83.3\\ +118.7\end{array}\right)$ on the right and

-71.3 on the left are balanced by $+106.7$ in the column (total each side $+35.4$). This is a change of $106.7 - 150.0 = -43.3$ in the column, half of which is carried to the bottom to give a total there of $+199.6$.

EXACT METHOD OF ANALYSIS

Many engineers will wish a convenient exact method as a basis for comparison with the approximate method shown.

Consider any two-span beam ABC, as shown in Fig. 7. Apply at A a moment M. Assume B held rigidly against rotation. The moment at B is now $-\dfrac{M.}{2}$ Now let joint B rotate.   The moment at B is distributed between BA and BC in proportion to their I/L values, the resulting total moment at B being

$$-\tfrac{1}{2}M\frac{\text{I/L for BC}}{\dfrac{I}{L}\text{for BA} + \dfrac{I}{L}\text{for BC}}.$$

The final moment curve on the beam is now as shown in the figure.

The rotation at A is $\dfrac{1}{EI}$ times the shear at A due to this moment curve as a load on AB.

$$\text{Rotation} = M\frac{L}{EI}(1 - \tfrac{1}{4}\frac{\text{I/L for BC}}{\dfrac{I}{L}\text{ for BA} + \dfrac{I}{L}\text{ for BC}})$$

Hence the moment needed to produce unit rotation at A is proportional to

$$\frac{I}{L}\text{for BA}\frac{1}{1 - \tfrac{1}{4}\dfrac{1}{1+\dfrac{\text{I/L for BA}}{\text{I/L for BC}}}} = \frac{\text{I/L for BA}}{C}$$

Values of the function $(I/C - 1)$ expressed as percentage increase for various ratios of the I/L values are shown in Fig. 8.   The values have been plotted in terms of the ratio of the larger to the smaller I/L in order to increase the accuracy for small values of $\dfrac{\text{I/L for BA}}{\text{I/L for BC}}$

If there are several connecting members at B, some of which are stiffened by continuity at their far ends, I/L for BC will be replaced by $\Sigma\dfrac{I/L}{C}$ of all connecting members.   The distribution at B is in the ratio of I/L for BA to $\Sigma\dfrac{I/L}{C}$ for all members such as BC.

This gives an exact technique for "precise" analysis.   Starting at one end of the series, write $\dfrac{I/L}{C}$ values—adjusted I/L values—for the far end of each member to the other end of the series.   The values of 1/C may be computed or taken from the curve.

At any joint distribute the unbalanced moment in proportion to the adjusted I/L values of connecting members.   Carry over one half the moment distributed to any beam and at the other end of the beam distribute it in the ratio of the I/L of this beam—not the adjusted value —and the adjusted values of I/L for connecting beams.

Unbalanced moments at successive joints are thus distributed and all distributed moments added to the original fixed end moment, just as in the approximate method.

ILLUSTRATION VI.—EXACT METHOD.

The following procedure illustrates the process just explained. For simplicity, an unbalanced moment is assumed to exist at one joint only. All figures are shown. Most of the computation would be done mentally and need not be very accurate. It is important to note that in distributing moments which are carried over in a member, the I/L for that member and not its adjusted I/L is used. For other members connecting at that joint use the adjusted I/L values.

ILLUSTRATION VI EXACT METHOD

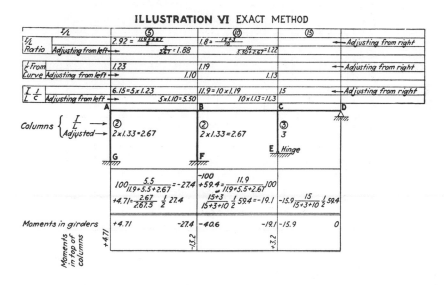

Beginning at the right end; member CD is hinged at the far end and its I/L value needs no adjustment; member CE is hinged and its I/L value needs no adjustment; for member BC, sum of I/L of connecting members at C = 15 + 3 = 18, ratio of I/L values $\frac{18}{10}$ = 1.8 from which $\frac{1}{C}$ = 1.19 is found from the curve or by computing

$$\cfrac{1}{1 - \frac{1}{4}\ \cfrac{1}{1 + \cfrac{1}{\text{I/L for member} + \Sigma\left(\frac{I}{L}\ \frac{1}{C}\right)\text{for connected members}}}{\text{I/L for member}}}$$

$$= \frac{1}{1 - \frac{1}{4}\frac{1}{1 + 1.8}} = 1.19,$$

then $10 \times 1.19 = 11.9$ for the adjusted I/L value of BC at B.

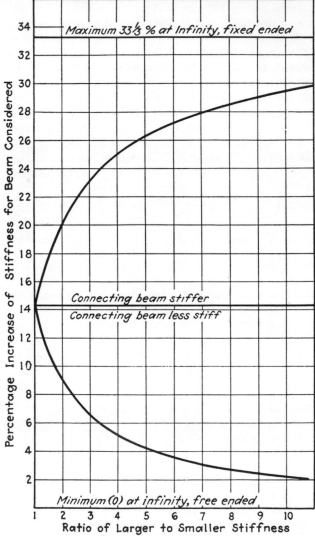

FIG. 8. CURVE GIVING PERCENTAGE INCREASE IN STIFFNESS OF A
BEAM DUE TO CONNECTING MEMBERS.

For AB, $\Sigma\frac{I/L}{C}$ for connected members at B = $11.9 + 2.67$, $\frac{I}{L}$ for
member BF being adjusted to 2.67 because of fixation at F; ratio at

$A = \dfrac{11.9 + 2.67}{5} = 2.92$, for which curve gives $1/C = 1.23$ and 5×1.23

$= 6.15$ is the adjusted I/L value for AB at A.

All I/L values are now adjusted in the same way, working from the

left end.   For AB, I/L ratio is $\dfrac{5}{2.67} = 1.88$ which gives $1/C = 1.10$

(the connected members are less stiff than the main member) and the adjusted I/L value for AB at B is $5 \times 1.10 = 5.50$.   Similarly the adjusted I/L value of BC at C is found to be 11.3.

Now distribute the unbalanced moment at B to the girders and column in the ratio of their adjusted I/L values at B (5.50 for AB, 11.9 for BC, 2.67 for BF).   Do not write the column value.   Carry over to joint C one-half of 59.4 and distribute there in the ratio of the I/L of BC and the adjusted values of I/L for CD and CE (in this case the adjusted values are the same as the I/L values because D and E are hinged).   Of course the moment in CB equals the sum of the moments in CD + CE and so we can write at once for the moment in CB

$\left(\dfrac{15 + 3}{10 + 15 + 3}\right)\left(\dfrac{59.4}{2}\right) = -19.1$ and then on the same slide rule setting

the moment in CD $\left(\dfrac{15}{10 + 15 + 3}\right)\left(\dfrac{59.4}{2}\right) = -15.9$.   Again the moment

in the column is not written.   Similarly the moment in BA is distributed to A.

Addition now gives the final moments in the girders.   Moments in the columns are then found by subtraction.

Note that signs are nearly automatic because the signs at any joint must be such that the sum of the moments on two sides of the joint are alike both in sign and value.   When moments are "carried over," they change signs.

ILLUSTRATION VII.

This shows another case in which the loads are fixed.

In actually using this method, the I/L ratios would be mentally figured and $1/C$ estimated.   This is certainly all that is needed.[1]

SIDE SWAY AND HORIZONTAL LOADS

The theory indicated above is based on the assumption that the joints of the structure do not move.   If the movement of the joints is due to settlement of foundations and can be predicted or determined in any way it can be allowed for as indicated below.   A symmetrical frame symmetrically loaded with vertical loads has no tendency to displace its joints if the foundations do not settle.   If it is restrained sideways its joints can not be displaced.

---

[1] A convenient approximation is to assume $1/C = 7/6$ for all interior spans.

If the frame is unsymmetrical or unsymmetrically loaded and subject to vertical loads it will be found that the solutions given above do not satisfy the laws of statics[1] because the sum of the shears on a horizontal section through the frame is not equal to zero. The frame will therefore move sideways until these shears are balanced. If there are several columns it will be found that this effect is negligible. In the case of isolated bents the effect may be worth evaluation.

The effect of this sideway can be evaluated as follows: Assume a sideway such as will produce a given consistent set of fixed end moments in the columns. If the columns are alike assume fixed end moments of 100 at each end of each column. If the columns are not alike the end moments should be proportional to $\dfrac{I}{L^2}$ for each column. Distribute these moments throughout the frame, compute the total shear existing in all

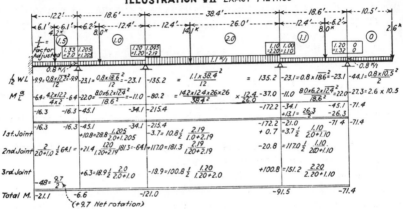

ILLUSTRATION VII EXACT METHOD

columns, multiply these moments by the ratio of the unbalanced shear to be corrected for to this total shear and subtract from the moments previously computed in the frame.

The same procedure may be followed in using moment distribution to compute moments due to lateral forces. Fixed end moments for the lateral forces are computed first, assuming no displacement of the joints. A consistent set of fixed end moments may then be assumed in the columns, distributed and the unbalanced shear produced by them computed as above. These moments may then be subtracted in proper proportion from the moments previously computed so as to satisfy the laws of statics.

This method will give a rapid, practical solution of many problems such as wind stresses in framed bents or traction stresses in viaducts. In nearly all cases, however, the girder is so relatively stiff compared with the column that its moment of inertia may be taken as infinite and fixed end moments in the columns therefore remain undistributed.

---

[1] Unless, by accident, the dissymmetry in loading balances the effect of unsymmetrical form.

ILLUSTRATION VIII.   (HORIZONTAL LOADS)

This illustrates a wide range of cases, the precise computation of which is not usually of great importance.

In this case fixed end moments are first computed on the windward column and then distributed.   This assumes that the joints do not move and hence the transverse shear at the top of the bent is unbalanced.

Now assume any consistent set of fixed end moments—that is, a set such that the fixed end moment in the columns is proportional to $\dfrac{I}{L^2}$, thus giving the same deflection at the top of each column.   In this case assume ± 100 in the windward column and $\pm(\tfrac{1}{2})(\tfrac{20}{25})(100) = \pm 40$ in the leeward column.   Distribute these moments.

ILLUSTRATION VIII   APPROXIMATE METHOD

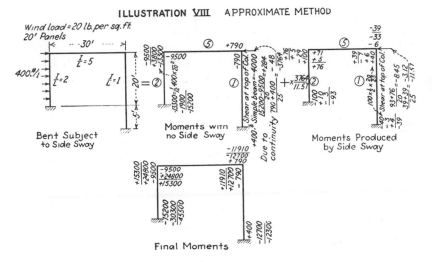

Bent Subject to Side Sway

Moments with no Side Sway

Moments Produced by Side Sway

Final Moments

Now add the second set of moments to the first set in such proportion as to make the total transverse shear at the top of the bent equal to zero.

The method may be applied in exactly the same way no matter how many columns the bent has and no matter what the condition of transverse loading.   It may be applied wherever the joints move.

The method may be extended to multiple story bents but the solution must be made carefully and simultaneous equations are needed to balance the shears.   Exact solutions in such cases are usually of academic rather than practical interest.

COLUMN MOMENTS AND THEIR EFFECTS

The effect of the girders on the columns is much greater than the effect of the columns on the girders.   Moments in the girders are the sum of the fixed end moments and the distributed moments.   Fixed end moment, though subject to some uncertainty as explained above, is pretty definitely known.   The column simply affects the distribution of the unbalanced moment and this unbalanced moment is only a part, and often a small part, of the total moment in the member.

But in general, the column has no transverse load and no fixed end moment and therefore the only moment in it is the distributed moment

TABLE 4 – VARIATION IN END MOMENTS OF A FIXED-ENDED BEAM FOR A VARIATION OF THE PHYSICAL PROPERTIES. (E) decreased $(33\frac{1}{3}\%)$ for designated Sections

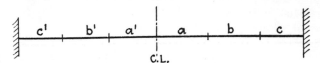

C.L.

For Full
Uniform Load

Normal
−18.0

M	% Variation	Sections Varied	% Variation.	M
−19.04	+6	a'b'b	+3	−18.55
−20.09	+12	a'b'abc	−4	−17.21
−20.12	+12	a'b'ac	−6	−16.94
−19.79	+10	a'b'bc	−8	−16.58
−16.72	−7	a'c'b	+8	−19.36
−16.94	−6	c'ac	−3	−17.45
−19.15	+6	a'ab	+7	−19.22
−17.23	−4	a'b'c'ab	+12	−20.11
−16.94	−6	a'c'ab	+12	−20.12
−17.04	−5	a'b'c'b	+7	−19.34
−19.53	+9	abc	−7	−16.75

For Unit
Load at
Center of Span

Normal
−1.50

M	% Variation	Sections Varied	% Variation.	M
−1.60	+7	a'b'b	+3	−1.54
−1.397	−7	a'c'ab	+16	−1.735
−1.65	+10	a'ab	+7	−1.61
−1.39	−7	a'b'c'ab	+16	−1.75
−1.40	−7	c'ac	−3	−1.46
−1.37	−9	a'b'c'b	+10	−1.65
−1.36	−9	a'c'b	+10	−1.65
−1.74	+16	a'b'abc	−7	−1.39
−1.74	+16	a'b'ac	−7	−1.40
−1.715	+14	a'b'bc	−13	−1.30
−1.67	+11	abc	−9	−1.36

which comes to it.   There is good reason, as shown later, to believe that the moments in the girders can be determined with reasonable accuracy but there seems equally good reason to doubt whether the moments in the columns can be determined with much accuracy.   Nevertheless an effort should be made to include the column effects in the analysis.

Accuracy of Girder Moments

The chief element affecting the end moments in the girders is the original fixed end moment. Now it is certain that the moment of inertia of a reinforced concrete girder varies along its length. At the center it normally acts as a T beam. At the end the T is on the tension side of the beam and while probably effective to some extent even up to failure, is not as effective as when in compression.

It becomes important, then, to ask whether uncertainty as to the variation of (EI) in a concrete girder arising from variation of the quality of the concrete or from uncertainty as to the physical action of the sections

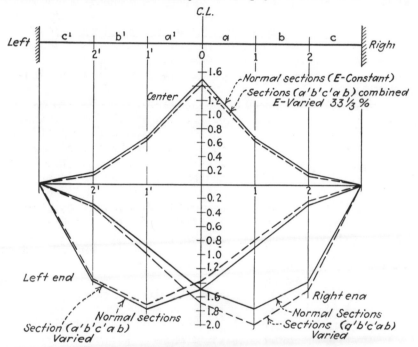

FIG. 9. VARIATION IN THE INFLUENCE LINES FOR MOMENT AT CENTER AND ENDS FOR A DECREASE OF THE MODULUS OF ELASTICITY OF 33⅓ PER CENT FOR SECTIONS INDICATED

may not seriously affect the computed fixed end moments. This question can be studied in a semi-empirical way by assuming different combinations of the EI values along the girder section and computing fixed end moments. After assuming properties for the girder we apply principles which are purely geometrical and in no way involve any theory of structural action.

Table 4 shows the result of such a study. A straight beam has been divided into six sections and some of these sections have been assumed one third stiffer than others. For certain selected combinations of stiff and flexible sections fixed end moments have been computed for a load at the center of the span and for uniform load.   For certain cases influence lines are shown in Fig. 9.   It will be seen that the error in the fixed end moment is not very large, but is not entirely negligible.   It should be said that some of the cases taken are quite unfavorable combinations of sections.

There is probably greater uncertainty as to the relative stiffness of adjoining members than there is with reference to their fixed end moments. We have already seen, however, that this uncertainty is not a very important source of error; nor is uncertainty as to the carry-over factors. The important fact seems to be that if the fixed end moments themselves can be determined it does not make so very much difference how within reason we distribute the unbalanced moment nor does it make very much difference how much of this distributed moment we carry over to the next joint.   It seems probable that the true moments in those continuous girders which are not affected by continuity of members crossing them can be determined quite as accurately as in most problems in structural analysis.

Two other factors affect the moments in girders continuous with members framing into them.   In the case of ordinary slab and girder construction there must be a considerable restraint at the ends of beams which frame into heavy girders because of torsional effects in the girders and some torsional restraint of the girders from their connecting beams. We know very little about the matter.   There seem to be practically no published data indicating the comparative stiffness of concrete girders in bending and in torsion.   But it is not difficult to imagine that twisting a concrete girder must require a moment quite comparable with the necessary to bend it, especially where the girder is continuous with a slab which practically prevents torsional distortion at the top.   The effect of this torsion is evidently to make all beams more nearly fixed ended than one would at first suppose.

In addition to this torsion there is in slab and girder construction some variation in the loads brought to the girders from the beams.   If two adjacent panels are completely loaded and the outer ends of the beams are free, the girder should receive about 25 per cent more load from the beams than it is ordinarily assumed to carry.   The outer ends of the beams are rarely free but there will in general be some increase in the load on the girder due to the influence of the continuity of the beams and some increase in the load brought to the beams by their slabs.

The torsional rigidity of members framing in at the ends of the span tends to make each span act as an isolated fixed ended beam and therefore not subject to additional moments brought into it from other spans, while the continuity of slabs over beams or of beams over girders tends to increase somewhat the load carried by the member under consideration.   In the case of large members of long span these elements are usually less important; certainly the torsional element is relatively of less importance.

These elements are pointed out here as a warning against too naive comparison between conventional coefficients and academic theoretical values for the moments. While the moments in an isolated frame work may perhaps be determined within 10 or 15 per cent other uncertainties enter into the action of typical slab and girder construction and still others into flat slab construction.

Moreover it is well to be warned against a comparison of the moments determined by the application of the conventional coefficients to the moments on the clear span with the results obtained at centers of supports by theoretical analysis. Moments at the center of intersection of the members must be reduced in order to determine the moment at the face of the column. It is in the moments at the face of the column that we are interested and we can not tabulate and compare these with the moments determined by conventional methods unless we assume a certain definite ratio of column width to span. Comparison becomes especially unsatisfactory if we undertake to compare the moments given by conventional rules for haunched beams with moments which theory would indicate.[1]

The moments at the column face may be got from moments at the column center by sketching in the curves of moment maxima as shown above.

Time yield of the concrete is often cited as an important source of uncertainty in determining moments in continuous construction, especially in the case of dead load moments. The idea seems to the writer to have little to support it. To enter accurately into the question here would lead too far afield. The idea seems to be based on the conception that a column, for example, subject to heavy moment from dead load of connecting girders will slowly yield and get rid of its moment. This seems to neglect the fact that the girders also yield, follow up the column and so continue to apply a moment to it. These terms are vague, but it may be said in passing that theoretical studies[2] show no reason to suppose that time yield seriously affects moments produced by loads. That it does affect in an important way moments produced by temperature or by settling supports is another matter.

Other sources of uncertainty, the effect of the stiffness in the joints themselves and temperature and shrinkage effects are mentioned in succeeding sections.

EFFECT OF THE JOINT

It is important to understand that the theory—any of the methods —of continuous girders assumes that rotation takes place about the center of intersection of the members. We have further assumed here, in treating members of constant section, that this constant section continues to this center of intersection.

---

[1] With whom did the conventional rules for effect of haunching originate? What is their basis?

[2] Such an investigation may be made by treating time yield as a reduction of the EI values at the yielding sections, making the reduction some function of the bending moment.

Actually, even where all axes intersect at a point, any member is very much enlarged in section after it joins another member. This is equivalent to a short and deep haunch at the end of the member. Very deep haunches, however, have little more effect than haunches of moderate depth. The effect is to increase the fixed end moment somewhat and to change somewhat the relative stiffness of the members and their carry-over factors. The effect on end moments in the girders is not commonly very great—about 5 to 10 per cent in ordinary cases. The stiffness of columns connected to deep girders is, however, very much affected, which adds further to the uncertainty of column moments.

Often the axes of the members do not meet in a point. Rotation must then take place about some compromise position. This will produce a longitudinal movement of some of the members as the joint rotates. If the far ends of the members were rigidly fixed and could not move and the eccentricity great, this would set up powerful shearing stresses in the joint. The fact seems academic, however, since unless some longitudinal movement is possible, temperature will soon tear the structure to pieces. The effect of such eccentricity in ordinary construction is probably small.

Temperature and Shrinkage Stresses in Continuous Frames

This subject should be mentioned here though it does not seem wise to go into it extensively. It is evident that these stresses exist both from uniform temperature change or shrinkage and from differentials of temperature between two sides of a member and from non-uniform shrinkage.

That these stresses may in some cases reach values of several hundred pounds per square inch in the concrete seems certain. For example, a temperature differential of 40 deg. between top and bottom of a series of similar beams or between inside and outside of a tier of columns would produce a stress in the concrete of over 200 lb. per sq. in. with a corresponding stress in the steel of about 3000 lb. per sq. in. Such stresses certainly make over-refined computations of other effects seem absurd.

Computation of moments and thrusts for an assumed set of conditions is not difficult by the method here shown. Some designers will find such studies enlightening.

Accuracy of Column Moments

The writer thinks that the moments in the columns can not be very accurately determined. We can make assumptions as to moments of inertia and we can go through certain analyses but it seems clear that we will not avoid fundamental difficulties thereby.

Perhaps this can be made plain as follows: Assume that at any joint in slab and girder construction we have two girders and two columns connected. Assume further, in order to simplify the picture, that both girders and columns are of the same length and are rigidly fixed at their far ends. Now assume that an unbalanced moment rotates this joint. The problem is to determine the fiber stress resulting in the column.

It will be seen that this problem is the same as that of a composite beam made up of these four members, namely, two girders with their connecting slabs and two columns. Both slabs are presumably in tension, in fact though not from the result of this rotation alone. It is now evident that the determination of true fiber stresses in such a section is scarcely practicable. It is true that the flanges of the girders are in tension but it does not follow, in fact it is almost certainly not true, that they are ineffective.

We can conveniently think about this question by applying the formula $f = \dfrac{Mc}{\Sigma I}$ where c is the half depth of the column and ΣI the sum of the moments of inertia of all connecting members. If the members are not of the same length, this becomes $f = \dfrac{Mc}{\Sigma I \dfrac{L}{L_1}}$, where L is the length of any one of the members and L_1 that of the column. In both cases M is the unbalanced moment at the joint.

This conception will give the same results as computation of the moments and subsequent stress analysis provided the two processes are consistent in the values used for I. The picture here presented, however, seems to point out more clearly the uncertainties of the problem.

This method also serves to distinguish two very different cases. If the column $\dfrac{I}{L}$ is small with reference to the value of $\dfrac{I}{L}$ for the girder, as in slab and girder construction, or in continuous viaducts, enlarging the column will usually increase c more rapidly than $\Sigma I \dfrac{L}{L_1}$ is increased and consequently the larger the column the greater the bending stress.

The reverse is true in flat slab construction. Here $\Sigma I \dfrac{L}{L_1}$ increases more rapidly than does c as the column size increases and the larger the column, the smaller the bending stress. In flat slab construction, however, there is uncertainty as to the value of M, the unbalanced moment in the above formula, as well as in the value of I for the slab. The fixed end moment at the wall column when the slab is loaded is less than $\dfrac{1}{12}$ L times the panel load. The value of this moment will evidently depend on the torsional rigidity of the wall beam if there is one.

The whole subject of types of loading to produce maximum column stresses and of the probability of such loading is also important. There is also a question whether high tension in the steel not accompanied by high compression in the concrete is especially dangerous.

The writer doubts whether one is at present justified in placing much faith in elaborate procedures for stress computation due to combined direct stress and bending in such cases as these. But he realizes that he is questioning a theory much honored in the breach, though little in the observance.

Value of Moment of Inertia

Different rules have been suggested by various writers for determining the moment of inertia of the members. Fortunately it is the relative and not the absolute values which are in question. Of course the term moment of inertia is used only in an analogous sense, simply as a measure of the relation existing between bending moment and angular deformation. It does not seem clear that measurements on the deflection of girders have anything particularly to do with the determination of the moment of inertia for computation of continuous frames.

Considerable discrepancy in relative moments of inertia does not very seriously affect our results and the rule which assumes I as proportional to bd^3 seems fairly satisfactory as regards the girders alone. In determining the relative moment of inertia of the girders and columns, however, there is considerable uncertainty because of their difference in shape. Evidently it is on the safe side as regards the moments in the columns to neglect the flange in computing the moment of inertia of the girder, but the writer is inclined to think that it is too far on the safe side.

If all girders have the same section, I/L varies as $1/L$; if the girder sections are designed for shear, girders of equal depth will have I/L nearly constant, for girders of the same shape (constant ratio $\dfrac{b}{d}$) $\dfrac{I}{L}$ will vary as L and for girders of equal width I/L will vary as L^2. From such relations the designer can often estimate the relative I/L values well enough before he makes an analysis for maxima.

Extensions and Modifications of Above Method

The method indicated may be extended to cover the case of settling supports. The problem is perhaps academic unless the designer wishes to assume certain values for these settlements merely to guide his judgment. In such a case fixed end moments may be computed in the girders equal to $6EI/L^2$ times the settlement assumed. It will at once be realized that there is considerable uncertainty in regard to the value of E. These fixed end moments may now be distributed through the frame. The same method applies to temperature stresses.

The treatment of moving concentrated loads by this method would justify a separate paper. The writer has found it as convenient as any method to simply move the train of loads across the spans, determine the fixed end moments for successive positions and distribute these through the structure, thus determining the moments at various points for successive positions of the loads and from these determining maxima.   A knowledge of the general shape of the influence lines will be found a convenient guide but the writer thinks influence lines are not essential here and believes that the problem can be solved more rapidly without constructing them.

This problem occurs in buildings in the determination of moments in continuous crane runways. The problem of viaducts subject to trolley car or railway loading is of course a problem in itself but the same methods can be conveniently applied there.   The technique can be systematized and simplified but it will not be elaborated here.

The method has an interesting application to open-web or Vierendeel girders, but the problem is not common.

Slabs

Perhaps it would be better not to mention slabs at all, for the principles here stated contribute only slightly to the study of continuous slabs. But these principles will, if judiciously applied, contribute something.

Tools available to the average engineer in thinking about slabs are the limitations imposed by statics upon the total moments, principles of symmetry and assymmetry, and mental pictures of the deflected slab as a means of judging of the variation of the moments along any given section.   The last tool, though inexact, is very powerful.   The writer finds the idea of distributing fixed-end moments useful in revising his mental pictures of the deflected slab when affected by continuity with other slabs or by discontinuities.   It is consoling to realize that there is considerable evidence that these pictures need not be very exact and that if the total statical limitations are met, the assumed distribution of the moments need not conform precisely to results of mathematical theory.

Design Aspects of Continuity

In discussing the effect of continuity upon the design of concrete members it is necessary to consider many questions besides the mathematical evaluation of moment shears and reactions.   In the first place we should consider the probability of occurrence of those split loadings which are indicated by loading alternate spans, more particularly in that fortuitous type of loading which is necessary in order to secure absolute maxima in building frames.   It has been generally recognized in structural design that the simultaneous occurrence of maximum live load over large areas is less probable than over small areas.   It is usually recognized in bridge design that simultaneous occurrence of maximum live load exactly spaced but discontinuous is less probable than is continuous load.   In preparing a design both factors are combined; in certain cases maxima occur only when large areas are loaded with large intensity of live load and intermediate areas are entirely unloaded with live load. The engineer is justified in taking these facts into account.

In long span construction the problem of bond becomes relatively unimportant. Probably the most convenient form of the bond relation[1] states that the maximum size of rod may be determined as

$$\phi_{\text{Max}} = 4\,\frac{u}{f_s}\cdot\frac{M}{V}$$

The largest permissible size of bar is determined, then, by the ratio of the maximum moment to maximum shear. It will be found that $1\frac{1}{4}$ in. bars will not usually exceed ordinary bond requirements in spans longer than 25 ft. The moments in the longer spans would seem to be more clearly defined because of the smaller importance of column and torsional action and the action of the beam seems more definite because of the absence of uncertainty as to bond slip. In fact the ordinary theories seem to become more clear in application as the span increases.

Recent specifications have introduced the question of anchorage conspicuously into concrete design. In the longer spans anchorage will not be necessary although it is probably desirable. It is difficult to define what constitutes adequate bond or adequate anchorage in continuous girders of irregular span length. There is no such thing as "the point of inflection" in a girder; each different type of loading gives rise to a different point of inflection. If we undertake to carry bars so far that the bond in them computed by the bond formula is not excessive under any conditions of loading, we are likely to find that we are attempting to provide bond on a tension bar for a shear which would be accompanied by compression in that bar. In such a case our bond would be only about half of what we supposed it to be. In order to precisely apply the ordinary bond formula to bars in continuous girders it would be necessary to determine the maximum shear at any point coincident with tension in the bars under consideration at that point. This presents an unusually elusive problem in structural analysis; to justify its solution would require much greater faith in the bond formula than the writer of this paper has.

If we reject the bond formula and substitute the theory of anchorages we find that the point beyond which we desire to anchor is also elusive. Anchorage to the third point of the girder seems to be as readily justified as rules involving theoretical analysis of each case.

Whether one thinks that curves of maximum shear are accurately applied in determining web reinforcement depends somewhat on the views which he holds as to the action of web reinforcement.[2] Practically all tests show an intimate relation between stresses on the horizontal bars, bond on the horizontal bars and shear failure. For those loadings which give maximum shears at points removed from the support, the stress in

---

[1] This relation may be derived directly from the classical bond formula.

[2] To the writer it seems a clear and adequate theory of web steel to say that after the concrete has cracked on a diagonal plane, the steel prevents the beam from dropping and makes $\Sigma V = O$ across this crack, being assisted to a variable extent by shear on the concrete still intact above the crack. Hence we should provide web steel for the maximum shear which can possibly occur at any section. Perhaps this is a case in which tests tell us what usually happens, whereas the designer's chief interest is in what may happen.

the longitudinal bars is not great because of the reduction of moment by partial loading. It seems probable that failure from web shear at points away from the support is less likely for the condition of partial loading which gives maximum web shear. The writer believes that some approximation to this maximum shear should be made but he does not believe that the facts justify very precise analysis for the maximum shear curves.

An outstanding uncertainty in design arises in connection with columns subject to bending. The writer has already indicated his doubts as to the precision with which moments are to be determined due to the deflection of connecting girders. It is to be noted that[1] the analysis of a reinforced concrete column subject to sufficient flexure to produce tension in the column is unique in structural design. This is the only case in structural analysis in which stresses due to live, temperature, wind and other loads can not be added in order to secure a total. To this is to be added the general uncertainty as to the action of concrete columns in any case and the noticeable lack of published data as to the action of concrete columns in flexure. The cubic equations which are exhibited in our literature for concrete columns in flexure seem to possess a mathematical rather than a factual background.

The writer has found that the beam formula,

$$\frac{P}{A} + \frac{M_c}{I}$$

with a proportional increase in allowable compressive stresses up to the point where tension occurs in the section and with no proportional increase beyond this point seems to agree pretty well with ordinary practice. This solution, however, is not entirely satisfactory. In the case of columns which are partly in tension due to heavy double flexure or irregular section, it is not practical to apply present methods of analysis at all; yet these cases are common enough.

The above comments on the difficulties of applying elastic analysis to actual design are not intended to be pessimistic. The writer believes that we know about all that it is necessary to know in order to secure sane economical and satisfactory designs for continuous concrete structures but he thinks a word of warning against a too naive and complacent admiration of the results of mathematical analysis may not be out of place.

Economy of Continuous Construction

As a general rule there is no great difference in costs between continuous and non-continuous construction. American structural literature has been much affected by two view points as to the economy of continuous construction. One group of engineers, which includes many of the older structural engineers in America, has maintained that continuous construction is necessarily uneconomical—that indetermination necessarily interferes with the efficiency of the structure. In some cases this

---

[1] With the exception of the deflection theory of suspension bridges.

is notably true; in a series of continuous girders, for example, the sum of the maximum reactions is considerably greater than the total load. But in most cases any theoretical self-interference does not appreciably effect economy.   On the other hand some engineers have undertaken to show that continuous construction is inherently economical.   This also is not true in any general sense.

Economy must be determined on its merits in each particular type of structure.   In the case of steel construction continuity introduces additional costs into the erection program; in concrete it is generally simpler and more economical to build the structure continuous than otherwise. Studies of continuous steel girders show potential economies of over 15 per cent in the materials in certain cases.

In the case of concrete any theoretical economy is not so easily attained if shear requirements control concrete volume; shears are increased rather than decreased by continuity.   It is true that the moments are decreased by continuity but while the area of steel required at any one section is smaller, the length of steel including anchorage is greater and no reduction in tonnage results in most cases.   Saving in concrete quantities may be secured by haunching the girder and this is a familiar device.   Studies made under the writer's direction indicate that haunching beyond the quarter point or to a depth greater than about the depth of the beam at the center will not promise economy.

It should be noted that any promised economy from continuity decreases in general as the relative intensity of the live load increases. The separation of the curves of maximum positive and maximum negative moment is a measure of the relative intensity of the live load.   If the live load is zero these two curves become identical and coincide with the curve of dead load moments.   This would be the ideal case for economy due to continuity.

STIFFNESS OF CONTINUOUS CONSTRUCTION

Continuous structures do not necessarily deflect less than those which are not continuous.   It is difficult to discuss definitely "rigidity" in any structure unless we define the term more carefully than is commonly done. Sometimes rigidity is measured by the total range of deflection due to live load, though the downward deflection only is more often used.   Certainly we are not especially interested in dead load deflection; we camber for that.   In reinforced concrete construction it is difficult to accurately predict deflection at all because of uncertainties as to the modulus of elasticity and as to the effect of residual tension in the concrete.

It is true that a continuous girder of the same section as a series of simple spans will give less maximum downward deflection under live load than will the simple spans.   If the total range of live load deflection is considered instead of the downward live load deflection alone, the deflection of the continuous span will be about the same as that of the simple span.

But continuous girders and simple girders will not be of the same section.   In the case of steel construction, if the beams are designed for the same maximum fiber stress and are of the same depth throughout, the deflection of the continuous span downward will be about the same as that of the simple span and its total range of deflection will be nearly twice that of the simple span.

Frequently, continuous construction will be made more shallow than simple construction, advantage being taken of the possibility of haunching. If the depth of the continuous span at the center is much less than that of the simple span the range of deflection of the continuous span will be considerably greater than that of the simple span, even if the downward deflection alone is considered.[1]

These figures are not directly applicable to concrete because so much of the material in concrete girders is idle in flexure but they serve to show that it will not do to generalize carelessly with reference to relative rigidity.

The writer doubts whether comparison of deflections is really very significant in judging stiffness.   This, however, seems to be the prevailing basis for comparison and here are the facts on this basis.   Acceleration due to moving loads, in many cases, is a better basis and on this basis continuous construction shows to great advantage.

The writer knows of no general relation between stiffness and economy.

SUMMARY

The studies in continuity here presented may be briefly summarized as follows:

A sufficiently accurate approximate analysis may be quickly made for any continuous frame including the effects of haunches and columns. This should give maximum curves of moment and maximum end shears.

In short span construction where torsional elements play a large part, it is doubtful whether moments can be determined with great precision. In general the tendency of the continuity of the whole structure is to increase the loads due to the continuity of connecting members and also to make the span act as an isolated fixed ended beam because of torsion.

Determination of the longitudinal steel required is quite satisfactory. Problems of bond and of web reinforcement are, however, less clear.   It is not possible to directly apply, without further investigation, the curve of maximum shears to determine bond by the bond formula nor to determine anchorage.

Stresses in columns due to continuity are quite uncertain.   It is quite doubtful whether the theory of continuity in such a case will give values closely enough in accordance with the facts to justify the elaborate theories applied in the analysis of such columns.

---

[1] Comparative studies of deflections are most readily made from the theorem that deflection at any point of a span is proportional to the bending moment on this span due to the f/y curve as a load.

Continuous structures are not necessarily more economical than are structures which are not continuous.

If a structure is continuous, as nearly all concrete structures are, it is essential to consider this continuity in the design.

Continuous structures will not as a general rule deflect less under load than those which are not continuous, provided the continuous structures are economically designed.   This rule may or may not have application in concrete construction depending upon whether there is necessarily a large amount of idle material.

3

SIMPLIFIED RIGID FRAME DESIGN

In the preparation of this report to which Professor Cross was assigned as author-chairman, he has had the benefit of criticism and suggestions from the critic members of Committee 301, Simplified Rigid Frame Design—Clyde T. Morris, Prof. of Structural Engineering, Ohio State University, Columbus; F. E. Richart, Research Associate Professor of Theoretical and Applied Mechanics, University of Illinois, Urbana; Albert Smith, Smith and Brown, Consulting Engineers, Chicago.

THE GENERAL subject of rigid frames could be discussed from several viewpoints. A comprehensive treatment would involve almost every phase of design and construction in reinforced concrete. It has seemed necessary, therefore, to restrict the scope of this report. The paper attempts to indicate the object of analysis of such structures and to recommend a method of analysis available for their design.

The first and the most important thing to recognize about rigid frames is that the design of these structures involves many inter-relations. Absolute precision in the solution of these problems is impossible. All that is possible and all that should be sought is a reasonably consistent basis of comparison of different structures or of different designs of the same structure, or of different parts of the same structure.

The writer of this report has discussed elsewhere the general problem of moments in continuous concrete structures.[1] It is

Author's Note—The writer of this report wishes to thank the other members of the committee for their interest in the problem and for their helpful criticisms. He is especially indebted to Professor Richart for unusually useful suggestions.

[1]"Continuity as a Factor in Reinforced Concrete Design," *Proceedings* A. C. I., 1929, Vol. 25, p. 669.

proposed here to state briefly a method of analysis recommended for ordinary cases.

It must be recognized that it is not safe to neglect continuity as an element in concrete design, and that it is vastly more important to make some consistent provision for continuity than it is to make that provision very precise.

Here, as elsewhere in structural analysis, any effort to substitute formulas and rules for a clear conception of the principles involved will prove dangerous.

It should be recognized that continuity may involve either flexure or torsion. This means that the rotation of the end of the loaded beam may be restrained either by its connection to other beams in line with itself, which will be bent by this rotation, or by continuity with beams or slabs running normal to its own length, which will be twisted by this rotation. The torsional element has, in the past, been frequently overlooked as an element in the problem.

WHAT IS A RIGID FRAME?

The term, "rigid frame," has been used in different senses by different writers. It may be taken to apply to all frames having rigid connections at the joints and would then include buildings, bents and viaduct structures. By some it has been restricted to those structures which are made continuous with the object of improving the design, as has been done in arched bents used for industrial buildings, hangars and similar structures and also for rigid viaduct frames at highway over-crossings having limited clearance.

In some structures continuity of columns with the girders is a distinct disadvantage to the designer because it complicates the design without saving material and is justified only by its convenience to the constructor; while in others continuity is definitely depended upon to produce economy of materials. The effect of continuity on the moments and stresses is in one case similar in some ways to what is referred to as secondary stress in steel construction, while in the other the moments produced by continuity are themselves primary. In one case we do not depend on continuity to support the load; in the other case we depend definitely on continuity to support the load.

WHAT CONSTITUTES A COMPLETE ANALYSIS?

Complete analysis of a rigid frame involves curves of maximum positive and negative moments on girders, curves of maximum shear on girders, determination of maximum tension and maximum compression in all columns, and of maximum stresses from a combination of torsion and flexure in girders. Such complete studies in ordinary cases are futile and impractical. Only in the most important structures are they justified.

It must be recognized that buildings differ from viaducts and that multi-story buildings differ from single story buildings, not only in the relative importance of the problems involved but also in complications which arise from uncertainties of loading and from improbability of certain combinations of loading.

SOURCES OF STRESSES

To be comprehensive, an analysis of a rigid frame should include the effect of live load, dead load and wind, of tractive, centrifugal, and other transverse forces, of temperature change and shrinkage, and perhaps of anticipated settlement of supports.

But it must be clearly understood that a mere tabulation and summation of effects from these sources, with no attention to the relation of factor of safety to probability, is largely a waste of time. For example, we should in general be satisfied if settlement combined with other causes does not produce stresses which threaten collapse.

SCOPE OF THIS REPORT

Because of the complications involved in several aspects of the subject, it seems desirable to restrict definitely the scope of this report.

The immediate need in this field seems to be a simplified procedure in analysis of rigid frames and this paper is restricted chiefly to an attempt to present such procedure. The discussion deals only with frames composed of straight members of uniform section.

The report is further limited to those cases in which the joints are not displaced in position. Except for the effect of transverse loads, the joints may be considered fixed in position in practically all rectangular frames.

Arched bents and arches, cannot be treated easily by the methods here indicated. In any case, their design seems to constitute a separate problem.

PHYSICAL ELEMENTS

Every one knows that the moments, shears and reactions in continuous construction depend on the relative stiffness of the members.

Stiffness may be definitely defined as a physical property of the beam proportional to the moment necessary to produce unit rotation of one end of a beam supported at both ends if the other end is fixed against rotation.

We do not know very accurately the relative stiffness of concrete members, nor does it seem probable that any laboratory data will ever give us precise knowledge in this respect. For important members carrying transverse loads, uncertainty as to relative stiffness does not affect the accuracy of computed results very much. The design of such members as columns, which carry either no transverse load or very little, is often much influenced by assumptions as to relative stiffness.

The stiffness of girders in bending depends on the dimensions of the stem and of any flanges present, on the modulus of elasticity of the concrete, the stiffening effect of the merging of beams and columns, the amount and disposition of steel, bond slip, if any, and span length.

Stiffness of columns is scarcely less complicated, the chief difference being in the absence of the flange.

As to stiffness of beams in torsion, we know almost nothing even in those cases where a beam is rectangular. Obviously the twisting of a T-beam is very much restricted by the presence of a flange, and its torsional stiffness very much increased thereby. It seems probable that concrete deck beams are quite stiff in torsion.

For beams of constant section to which the beam formula $f = \frac{Mc}{I}$ can be applied, the flexural stiffness is proportional to the "stiffness factor," $\frac{EI}{L}$, where E is the elastic modulus, I the moment of inertia and L the span length.

The moment of inertia of a beam of reinforced concrete and especially of a T-beam is a rather indefinite quantity. It has usually been recommended for rectangular members that I be taken as proportional to the product of the width by the cube of the depth. Reinforced concrete girders are, however, rarely rectangular and as to the effect of the slab of T-beams we know very little. Any assumptions on this point must of necessity be almost entirely arbitrary.

We may say, then, that the stiffness factor varies with $\frac{EI}{L}$ and write $\frac{EI}{L} \propto \frac{Ebd^3}{L} \propto EA\frac{d^2}{L} \propto \frac{EA^2}{L}\frac{d}{b}$

For square columns $\frac{d}{b} = 1$. For beams we may assume $b = \frac{d}{2}$ for the stem and if further we assume an arbitrary multiplier 5 for the effect of the flange, we derive as approximate relations for columns and T-beams of usual proportions.

Relative stiffness of a column $= E_c\frac{A^2}{h}$.

Where (A) is the area in square inches

(h) is the height in feet.

Relative stiffness of a girder $= 10E_c\frac{A^2}{L}$

Where (A) is the area of stem in square inches

(L) is the span in feet.

These rules are highly arbitrary, but are at least useable and are perhaps as near the facts as any. The girders are assumed to be T-beams of ordinary proportions. For girders with relatively thin slabs or relatively wide stems the stiffness should be reduced somewhat, but the writer does not pretend to know exactly how much.

Mr. Albert Smith has suggested to the writer that the arbitrary multiplier used for T-beams should be two or four and also that some provision should be made for the effect of the reinforcement. Probably both points are well taken, and the second suggestion is unquestionably correct but the writer knows of no data definitely applicable to the problem. For the purposes of this report, the writer has considered simplicity more desirable than precision in determining the stiffness factor.

SIGNS OF BENDING MOMENTS

It is recommended that for bending moments in horizontal members the same convention of signs* be used as is customary in design procedure and that the same convention be applied to

---

*Positive moment sags the beam; negative moment hogs the beam.

columns when they are looked at from the right as a drawing is usually read.

If the moments in columns are written to the left of the columns at the top of the columns and to the right at the bottom of the columns, a joint will be balanced when the algebraic sum of the moments on the right and left sides of the joint are equal.

Thus the joints shown at the bottom of Problem 2 are balanced. The direction of curvature of the members is shown by dotted lines.

If these conventions are followed no difficulty should be found in the signs, since for given fixed-end moments in the loaded members, there is only one way in which the signs of the distributed end moments can be arranged to balance the joint—that is, to give the same algebraic total moment to right and to left of the joint.

SPAN LENGTH

All methods of analyzing rigid frames assume that the moments are computed on a length of member, center to center of intersections, and further assume that all members at any joint meet at a point. It is important to understand that by none of these methods is it possible to use directly the clear span consistently in computations.

EXACT METHOD OF ANALYSIS

The method of analysis proposed here will give accurately the moments at the supports of any frame made up of straight members of uniform section, provided the joints are not displaced by loading and provided the physical properties of the structure and the conditions of loading are accurately known.

The method to be used involves the calculation of moments at the ends of all beams in the frame under certain artificial conditions of restraint, then a redistribution of unbalanced moments by arithmetical proportion when the artificial restraints are removed. A clearer conception of the method recommended can be had by thinking of moment distribution as a physical procedure than by considering the mathematical relations involved.

Consider a continuous frame of several spans, under given loading. Denoting the junctions of members as joints, if all joints are originally held against rotation, the end moments for each span can be found as fixed-end moments.* Suppose any one joint is now released; if the fixed-end moments at the joint do not balance each other, the joint will rotate, and since the ends of all members at that joint rotate through the same angle, the moment in each member accompanying such rotation will vary as the stiffness factor EI/L for that member, since this is proportional to the moment required to produce a unit rotation of one end of the member when the other end is fixed. Since, after the joint is released it will automatically come to equilibrium and be statically balanced, it follows that the sum of the newly induced moments equals the original unbalanced moment, and that by distributing the unbalanced moment among the members at the joint in proportion to their stiffness factors, the induced moments are determined.

In each of the members which has received its share of the unbalanced moment, there is produced a moment at the far end equal to $\frac{1}{2}$ of the distributed moment at the joint end, but of opposite sign. This follows because, if a member of uniform section, supported at the ends, is fixed at the end B and subjected to a bending moment at the end A, the moment produced at B is $\frac{1}{2}$ the magnitude of the moment at A, and of opposite sign. Thus the balancing of a single joint results in setting up additional unbalanced moments at the adjacent joints. The joint that has been balanced may now be held against further rotation while another joint is released and balanced in a similar way. The amount of unbalance is thus rapidly reduced at all joints, and the process is continued until the amount of unbalance remaining is made as small as desired. It is evident that the process may be carried to any desired degree of precision. If approximate results are sufficient, the process of distribution need be repeated only a few times. The various moments found and combined may be thought of as the terms of a rapidly converging series, for which the number of terms employed determines the precision of the result.

The above operations may now be systematized and the application of the process stated in a few words.

---

*The derivation of formulas for moments at the ends of "fixed" spans may be found in most texts on Mechanics.

1.   Compute the moments due to the given loading which would exist at the ends of each member of the frame if these ends were fixed, or held against rotation.

2.   At each joint distribute the unbalanced moment (the difference between the fixed-end moments for the members meeting at the joint) among the members at the joint in proportion to their stiffness factors, EI/L.

3.   For each member which has received a certain distributed moment at a joint, apply at the far end of the member a moment of opposite sign and one-half the magnitude of the distributed moment.   These may be called "carry-over" moments.

4.   If the carry-over moments at any joint are now unbalanced, again distribute these unbalanced moments and apply the carry-over moments as described in paragraphs 2 and 3 above.

5.   Repeat the process until the desired degree of precision (freedom from unbalanced moments) is attained. At each side of each joint add the original fixed-end moments, the distributed moments, and the carry-over moments. The sum is the true moment at the end of the member at the joint.

After the end moments on the members of the frame are known, all other quantities—moments at points other than the ends, shears, reactions—may be computed from statics.

ILLUSTRATIVE PROBLEMS

Problem 1—As an illustration of the application of the above method to a particular case, assume a continuous girder of three spans, with no restraint at the ends, as shown. The span lengths are successively 20, 30 and 40 ft. Assume the relative stiffness successively as 6, 4 and 3, which is correct if the girder is of constant section and material.   Assume the second span only to be loaded with a distributed load of 2,000 lb. per foot of length.   The fixed-end moments for this span are WL/12 =150,000 ft. lb., and are the unbalanced moments at the ends of the middle span.   For convenience, the moments will be expressed in ft.-kips, or thousands of ft.-lbs.

At the second support, distributing the unbalanced moment of 150 between the first and second spans in the ratio of 6 to 4, we have 90 on the left of the joint and 60 on the right of the joint.   At the third support, distributing the unbalanced moment of 150 between the second and third spans in the ratio of 4 to 3, we have 86 on the left and 64 on the right of the joint.   The signs of

PROBLEM-1
Girder without Columns

Relative Stiffness	20'	30'	40'
	6	4	3

Load-2 K/FT.

First Method

$-150 = \frac{1}{12} \times 2 \times \overline{30}^2 = 150$

	-90 +60	+ 86	-64	
+45	0 -43	- 30	0	+32
-45	-26 +17	+17	-13	-32
+13	+22 - 8	- 8	+16	+ 6
-13	-18 +12	+13	-11	- 6
0	-112 -112	-72	- 72	0

Second Method

	-150 -90 +60	-150 +86	-64	{+32 -32
+45 -45	0 -26 +17	-30 +17	0 -13	{+6 -6
+13 -13				
0	-116 -116	- 77	-77	0

PROBLEM-2
Girder with Columns

Relative Stiffness	6	4	3
	Each Column=1		

Load- 2 K/ft.

First Method

	-150 -75 +50	-150 + 67	-50	
+37	0 - 33	-25	0	+25
-28	-16 +11	+11	-8	-15
+8	+14 - 6	- 6	+8	+ 4
-6	-10 +7	+6	-5	- 2
+11	-87 -121	- 97	-55	+12

Second Method

	-150 -75 +50	-150 +67	-50	{+25 -15
+37 -28	-33	-25		
+8 -6	-16 +11	+11	-8	{+4 -2
	-91 -122	-97	-58	+12

Column Moments

+11   -87 -121   -97 -55   +12

these moments are so applied as to make the sums of the moments to right and left of the joint equal, or to balance the joint.

Now considering the first span the moment of –90 at the right end produces a carry-over moment of +45 at the left end. Similarly, carry-over moments are written for the ends of each span giving successive values of +45, 0, -43, -30, 0 and +32.

These carry-over moments now produce unbalance at all of the joints, and the process of distributing unbalanced moments must again be carried through. At the first and fourth supports we have assumed free ends of beam, hence moments of-45 and -32, respectively, must be added at these joints to produce balance (the zero moment assumed).* The six distributed moments then become -45, -26, +17, +17, -13 and -32. The six carry-over moments (½ of distributed moments at opposite end) are +13, +22, -8, -8, +16 and +6.

In distributing these moments, it is seen that the unbalanced moment at the second support is the algebraic difference between +22 and —8, or 30. This 30 is distributed in the proposition 18 and 12, with signs assigned which will produce balance at the joint. A similar distribution is made at the third support. The six distributed moments now are -13, -18, +12, +13, -11 and -6.

This procedure of distribution may be carried as far as seems desirable. If we stop at this point and add values we find end moments as follows: 0, -112, -112, -72, -72 and 0. In any case it is obvious that the procedure should be stopped after unbalanced moments have been distributed to balance the joints. Had we stopped after the first distribution, the moment at the second support is seen to be -90, after the second distribution it was -116, after the third, -112. If a fourth and fifth distributions were carried through, the values found would be -113 and -113.5. The exact value for this moment is -113.36. The third distribution is seen to give quite satisfactory precision in this case.

Problem 2—Assume the same beam and loading, but with beam supported on and rigidly connected to columns. The relative stiffness of each column is taken as 1.

The same procedure is followed as in the previous case. The distribution of moments will take into account the share of unbalanced moment to go to each column, but it will be more convenient to tabulate only the moments in girders, the moments in the columns to be found later by subtraction of girder moments at each joint.

The fixed-end moments are the same as before.

At the left end of the loaded span the fixed-end moment is distributed to the four connecting members in the ratio 6, 1, 1, 4 or 6/12 150 = 75 to the girder on the left, 4/12 150 = 50 to the girder on the right. (The joint appears not to be balanced because the column moments have not been written.)

At the right end of the loaded span, the fixed-end moment is distributed to the four connecting members in the ratio 4, 1, 1, 3, or 4/9 150 = 67 to the girder on the left of the joint and 3/9 150 = 50 to the girder on the right of the joint.

Now carry over one-half of these moments with opposite signs.

Distribute again. At the left end distribute in the ratio 1, 1, 6 or 6/8 37 = 28 to the girder. At the next joint distribute in the ratio 6, 1, 1, 4 or 6/12 33

---

*Note that there is nothing special about this procedure; the unbalanced moment is distributed among the connecting members, but there is only one member.

= 16 to the girder on the left and 4/12 33 = 11 to the girder on the right. At the next joint 4/9 25 = 11 is distributed to the girder on the left and 3/9 25 = 8 to the girder on the right. At the right end distribute in the ratio 1, 1, 3 or 3/5 25 = 15 to the girder.

Again carry over and again distribute. In this case at the first joint from the left we distribute 14 + 6 = 20 to the four connecting members. At the next joint we distribute 8 + 6.

Add all figures in each vertical column. The final end moment are 11, 87, 121, 97, 55, 12.

The column moments are, for the two columns at the left end, 11, for the next pair of columns 121 − 87 = 34, for the next pair 97 − 55 = 42 and for the pair at the right end 12. These moments are in each case distributed equally between the two columns in the pair because they are equally stiff. In any other case they would be distributed in proportion to the column stiffness. The signs of the column moments and the direction of curvature in the columns are as shown by the sketches.

FIXED-END MOMENTS

The fixed-end moment for beams of constant section and for uniform load is 1/12 WL where W is the load on one panel. Where the load is applied through floor beams, the fixed-end moment is C1/12 WL, where

for one intermediate floor-beam, $C = 3/4$

for two intermediate floor-beams $C = 8/9$

for three intermediate floor-beams, $C = 15/16$

For concentrated loads, the fixed ended moment at one end may be computed from the formula $\dot{M}' = a^2bPL$, where "a" is the fraction of the span by which the load is distant from the other support, and "b" is the fraction of the span by which the load is distant from the support considered—(a + b = 1)

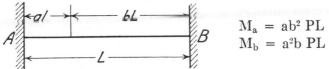

$$M_a = ab^2\,PL$$
$$M_b = a^2b\,PL$$

For a series of concentrated loads, the end moments should be separately computed and added.

RECOMMENDED APPROXIMATE METHODS

The method just indicated, though a method of successive approximation, is in no sense an approximate method because we can obtain by it results in which the error is made less than any assigned quantity.

Attempts at great precision in this work are usually futile, as explained elsewhere; consequently, the procedure can be conveniently abbreviated. This can be done by distributing only a few times as explained above. This method is simple but is not quite definite because we cannot specify how many distributions will be satisfactory.

Another approximate method which is perfectly definite and is usually about as accurate as is a few distributions in the method explained above is to distribute first at the unbalanced joints and then to carry-over and distribute always *away* from that joint, omitting to carry over the moments back toward the joint from which they originate.

Thus in the first problem solved above we follow the same procedure as before in distributing the original unbalanced fixed-end moments, and also in carrying over these moments and distributing the moments carried over so that the first three lines of the solution after writing the fixed-end moment are identical in the two methods. When these distributed moments are carried over, however, they are carried over in the same direction as before. The values +17 and +17 are, then, not carried over to give —8, —8 nor are the end values —45 and —32 carried over to give +22 and —16.

In the second illustrative problem, using this second method of approximation, the first three lines after the fixed-end moments are again identical with those previously found but the values +11, +11 are not carried over (carried back) nor are the values —28 and —15 carried over.

This second method of approximation is that given in the writer's paper "Continuity as a Factor in Reinforced-Concrete Design" before referred to. It is not as convenient as the first method where several spans are loaded. Maximum shears, moments and reactions, however, are most readily determined by combining results from loading individual spans. In this case the second method is rapid, can be readily condensed, and is sufficiently accurate for most purposes.

CONCLUSIONS

Experience has shown that the method here presented for determining moments at the joints of a rigid frame is easy to remember and rapid to apply. It is the writer's belief that it will be found convenient in design offices.

A rigid frame in which all the elements of distortion are taken into account is undoubtedly better designed than one in which arbitrary coefficients are used. This, however, does not seem to justify abrupt departure from existing practice in design specifications.

But considerations of continuity will be more and more forced on the attention of design offices. It is, therefore, recommended that our specifications be revised so as to make it permissive to use moment coefficients derived from elastic analysis in all cases provided adequate provision is made for the elements depended on in such analysis. Thus, where the stiffness of columns is depended on in computing girder moments, adequate provision must be made for the moments resulting in the columns, or where torsion of connecting members is depended on, adequate provision must be made for such torsion.

Evidently such a recommendation will ultimately require also workable recommendations as to what constitutes adequate provision for flexure in columns or for torsion in beams, but anyone who will consider the present status of design practice in rigid frames should see that the exact details of such provision are less important than is some method of encouraging designers to recognize the facts and to make any provision at all for them.

Such a change in specifications should result in appreciable reduction in the positive steel requirements in buildings. In the writer's opinion such reduction is perfectly proper where its basis is clearly recognized. New possibilities of economy will be opened to the skilled designer.

In considering the advisability of such specifications—especially from the viewpoint of building departments or of unscrupulous designers—it should be recognized that it simply makes permissive in the cases which are perfectly regular (Sections 708 and 709 of the Building Regulations)* that which is now permitted by the specifications in all other cases. (Section 710 of the Building Regulations.)

*Tentative Building Regulations for Reinforced Concrete," *Proceedings* A. C. I., 1928, Vol. 24, p. 791.

It has been suggested that curves be drawn giving coefficients for varying column stiffness similar to those now in use for cases of equal spans. The writer has not thought the idea very practical at this time. The present system of coefficients does not distinguish between live and dead load, and does not use the span length between centers of intersection of the members. Such curves as proposed would, then, involve four variables—ratio of dead to live load, ratio of girder stiffness to column stiffness, ratio of clear span to span length between intersection of members, and the moment coefficient. The difficulties involved in presenting curves having four variables are very great.

There exists some difference of opinion among designers as to what combinations of loads should be considered in determining maxima, especially in regard to the weight to be given in cases of split loading. This question at least should be settled before any attempt is made toward further standardization.

4

THE RELATION OF ANALYSIS
TO STRUCTURAL DESIGN

Synopsis

Confusion sometimes exists in structural design as to the use to be made of analyses. The designer soon realizes that precision is futile in some cases and important in others, and the experienced designer realizes fully that analysis of the conventional type is frequently a poor guide to proper proportions. That analysis shows a certain member to be overstressed commonly indicates that the member should be made larger; but the over-stress sometimes has little importance and may be disregarded. In some cases where the over-stress is serious, the best solution is not obvious; sometimes the structural layout should be changed entirely.

Critical study soon leads to recognition of important differences between load-carrying stresses and stresses which produce no appreciable resistance to the applied loads. The latter may be due either to external movement of abutments or to internal distortions, or they may be due to deformation induced in one part of a structure as a result of that in another part. The load-carrying stresses may also be divided into two groups. The distinction in this case, however, is based upon response to changes in design; these sub-groups are not always clearly distinguishable, but they have characteristics so widely different in certain cases as to force their differentiation.

A classification is presented herein, with the idea of suggesting a convenient arrangement of certain familiar characteristics rather than with any wish to define the groups formally. The designations suggested, therefore, are for convenience of reference only. The non-load-carrying stresses will be distinguished as Deformation Stresses and Participation Stresses; and the load-carrying stresses as those normal in their characteristics and those which are hybrid.

NOTE.—Presented at the meeting of the Structural Division, New York, N. Y., on January 17, 1935. Discussion on this paper will be closed in January, 1936, *Proceedings*.

Deformation stresses are a consequence of strain and strain is a consequence of internal or external movements not due to stress in the structure, such as abutment movements, shrinkage, or the effects of temperature change.

Participation stresses are similar to deformation stresses, but they are due to a quite different cause. They include what are known as "secondary stresses" in bridge trusses and "participation stresses" in bracing systems as special cases. The designation is used herein for want of a better one, but the term is used in a wider sense than usual.

The primary action of most structures is such that the stress in any one part is independent, or nearly independent, of that of the other parts. This is termed normal, structural action. The group indicated includes all structures statically determined and, for good reasons, it includes also most of the forms of indeterminate structure that experience has shown to be useful.

There is a type of structure in which one member cannot be designed separately but must be designed with due consideration for its effect on other members. Such action is referred to as "hybrid," because it has some of the characteristics both of normal structural action and of participation action. The group of structures seems to be quite large and to have characteristics of great importance to designers.

Although the designations assigned herein may be new, the concepts involved are not new. What the writer wishes to do is to classify and arrange certain views of structural design which have an honored tradition in American practice. The paper is not intended to be quantitative, except in so far as quantitative statements may help in defining qualitative action. The classification proposed has some value in reconciling discordant views held by practical designers and those held by theoretical analysts, and seems, further, to have value in reconciling conflicting views held by theoretical students in the field. It is also of value in anticipating the characteristics of proposed structural types.

I.—Types of Structural Action

Deformation Stresses.—The outstanding characteristic of deformation stresses is that the strains in the structure are fixed and that the stresses are deduced from the strains. The stresses themselves are not fixed at all, but depend entirely upon the stress-strain relation of the material.

Another important characteristic is that strength has nothing, or practically nothing, to do with the problem. The strains are fixed by the overall dimensions of the structure and by the amount of deformation to be accounted for. The designer finds it convenient to predetermine such strains, reduce them to equivalent stresses, and deduct these stresses from the working stresses available for load-carrying capacity.

Participation Stresses.—This term is used to include what are commonly known as secondary stresses in bridge trusses, participation stresses in bracing systems, participation stresses in cross-frames due to unequal deflection of trusses or girders, cross-flexure in the vertical members of trusses, secondary flexure in slender columns of bents, secondary flexure in slender spandrel columns of open spandrel arches, and secondary flexure in slender columns of buildings.

Participation stresses have many of the characteristics of deformation stresses: The strain is fixed; the stress is a consequence of the strain; and the strain, in general, can be affected in an important way only by changing over-all dimensions and not by changing the strength of the member. Thus, it is generally known that increasing the moment of inertia without changing the depth of truss members will affect the secondary stresses only as the primary stresses are affected.

Another important characteristic of these stresses is that they do not increase in proportion to the load up to rupture, but increase less rapidly after the yield point of the material has been passed. They are then clearly somewhat less dangerous than primary load-carrying stresses.

The interest of the designer in these secondary stresses is not to determine their value exactly but rather to be sure that this value is not too high. In order to find what value is too high, it is not sufficient to approach the problem from the analytical viewpoint. The values permissible in design vary with the material used, with the importance of the member involved, and with the type of failure that would result. At present, secondary stresses are accepted as a necessary evil. Try to keep them within a reasonable figure, and otherwise forget about them. Any effort to change this viewpoint represents a radical departure in thinking in the field of structural design. (In 1934, a valuable paper on the "Effect of Secondary Stresses Upon Ultimate Strength," was presented[2] by John I. Parcel, M. Am. Soc. C. E., and Eldred B. Murer, Jun. Am. Soc. C. E. Surely, the idea of discounting secondary stresses is not new in America; but accurate data as to the amount that may be discounted are much needed.)

An important difference between participation stress and deformation stress lies in their relation to the properties of the material. The two are affected in the same way by departures from Hooke's law for, in both cases, it is the strain that is fixed, the stress being a consequence of the strain. In so far as the ratio of stress to strain, however, changes with time (time flow of concrete) the effect is pronounced and direct in the case of deformation stresses, whereas time flow as distinguished from plastic flow has no effect at all in the case of participation stresses because, although the stress for a given participation strain is less as time goes on, the strain itself is in the same ratio greater because of flow under primary stress.

[2] *Proceedings*, Am. Soc. C. E., November, 1934, p. 1251.

If the participation strain is linear, as in the case of cross-bracing, the designer can control the stress only by changing the length of the member, which usually means that he cannot control it at all. If the strain is angular, the designer can control the maximum participation stress by changing the length of the member (which is usually impracticable), by changing the depth in the plane of flexure, and, to some extent, by changing the form or variation of section along the member.

Participation stresses are dangerous to the extent that they impair the primary load-carrying capacity of the member. Any generalization about them that does not consider the nature of failure from primary load is misleading.

Normal Structural Action.—The term is used herein to describe the action of those structures or structural parts in which it is possible to determine at the beginning the approximate magnitude of the forces in action, and in which the magnitude of these forces is affected comparatively little by the relative stress intensity in the parts of the structure.

The most obvious example is the ordinary statically determinate structure. In this type primary stress in one member is not affected at all by the stresses in any other member. All stresses are determined directly by statics, and the members are then proportioned for the forces which act upon them.

Most of the classical forms of indeterminate structures act normally, although their action is less definite than for structures statically determinate. A good example is the ordinary continuous truss, which, in practice, is often designed at once without any exact-analysis being made after the design is complete. The experienced designer knows that for these structures such analyses will not indicate any important changes in his design.

Other examples are ribbed arches and spandrel-braced arches of steel, the so-called "rigid frame" bridges hinged at footings so far as the forces and moments at the knee are concerned. Most cases of continuous girders are included in this type.

In these structures it is possible to follow the procedure recommended in the textbooks. The engineer is told to guess at the sections, analyze, revise, and re-analyze. A bad first guess does not make much difference; the series of designs converges rapidly. In these cases, however, the designer can do much better than a bad first guess. Preliminary studies of pressure lines and of the properties of influence lines will enable him to make a good first guess—so good that the revision is trivial.

Hybrid Structural Action.—The term is used herein to mean structural action in which two or more parts participate in carrying loads to such an extent that if the strength of one part is changed the forces acting on other parts are largely affected. Clearly, there is some interaction in all indeterminate structures; the difference here indicated between normal and hybrid action is one of degree, and the two classes merge into each other. Participation stresses also are directly affected by changes in the primary stresses, but the relation is not reciprocal.

Hybrid structural action may be divided into two classes from the viewpoint of the designer's knowledge: Those in which the nature of the structural action can be foreseen; and those in which it cannot be foreseen. This says nothing except that the designer either does or does not know what he is doing; but the distinction needs to be made.

This type of action may be further divided into two classes, depending on whether the structure can or cannot be designed efficiently as laid out. It is very important to know this at once, but the knowledge depends on the designer's understanding of the problem.

A very simple example of what herein is called hybrid structural action occurs where two parallel beams are connected so that their center deflections must be the same under a single load at the center. If they are of the same span, depth, and material, they share the load in proportion to their strengths, and load can be assigned to one or the other at will. Even if the spans are different, this is still true if the depth-length ratio is the same for the two beams.

In this case the designer can foresee the action. He then designs as he chooses and knows that the stresses will be as assumed without further analysis; the analysis precedes any designing. Moreover, the structure can be designed efficiently since the stresses in the two beams will be the same. If the depth-length ratio is different for the two beams, however, they cannot be designed efficiently. No matter what the designer does, the relative stresses will be proportional to this ratio; but he can still foresee this fact. This case is simple; frequently the action of the structure is not easily predetermined and, in many cases, the efficiency of the design must be considered for several conditions of loading.

Near the center of long trusses having two diagonals in each panel, the designer may predetermine the stress intensities in these diagonals pretty accurately. In any panel the stress intensities in the diagonals are in inverse ratio to the squares of the lengths of these diagonals if there is no stress in the posts and if the stress intensities in the chords are equal and opposite. For dead load, these conditions in chords and posts are nearly fulfilled; for isolated loads, they are only approximately correct.

Knowing this and considering for the present only dead load, the designer can assign areas to the diagonals at will. If the chords are parallel, the diagonals can be designed efficiently; if the chords are not parallel, one diagonal must be inefficient. Influence lines may be helpful, but they fail to furnish at once a very illuminating picture of the essential structural action. For single concentrated loads the effect of the stresses in the posts and of unequal stresses in the chords may be pronounced. If single moving concentrated loads dominate the design, exact proportioning seems hopeless.

In these cases—parallel beams and double diagonals—the textbook recommendation to guess at a section, analyze, and re-design, to convergence will not work very well. If the layout is efficient, analysis will show the first guess to be right—and will show any guess to be right—but if it is inefficient, repetition of analysis and design will eliminate the inefficient member—after many repetitions—and result in a simpler structure.

Similarly, the king post truss cannot be designed for given working stresses in beam and sag rods except for a small range of the ratio of beam depth to sag depth, which ratio can be predetermined. The chief interest in the king post truss is that, goemetrically, it is so obviously the familiar problem of a truss subjected to secondary stresses. Looking at the truss from this viewpoint, the engineer would first design it; then he would reduce the depth of the beam until the secondary stress in it was within safe limits, or he could, by adjusting the sag rods, produce initial stresses to offset the secondaries. If, however, he attempts to utilize these secondaries, to put them to work in carrying the load, an entirely different structural problem is presented, and new methods of study are required.

Hybrid structural action also occurs in the queen post truss, in systems of intersecting beams, in Vierendeel girders, probably in most slabs (at least where variation of depth is involved), in some problems of continuous beams, and in many problems of continuous frames. It is discussed subsequently, in the case of bents, of rectangular wind frames, and of arches integral with their spandrel structures.

Study of a Two-Legged Bent Illustrating the Types of Structural Action. —The distinctions herein presented are well illustrated by studies of a two-legged bent carrying vertical loads. It is assumed that the members are rectangular and homogeneous. It is proposed to study the flexural stresses in the columns. The girder section is assumed to be the same throughout the discussion but first the depth, and then the width, of the column is varied.

If the column is very narrow the girder acts practically as a beam simply supported. The rotation of the top of the column must be the same as that of the end of the girder. The angular strain in the column, therefore, is fixed, and the flexural stress varies almost directly with the depth. If the column is extremely rigid it takes nearly the full fixed-end moment in the girder and the flexural stress varies nearly inversely as the square of the column depth. Between these conditions is one in which the flexural stress in the column is nearly independent of the depth; the column is picking up moment as fast as it can take it.

If the width of the column is increased, it will be found that in the first stage (column slender) the flexural stress in the column is scarcely affected at all; in the last stage (column stiff) this stress varies inversely as the width; and in the transition stage, the increase in width reduces the flexural stress somewhat but not at all in proportion to the increase in strength.

The first stage represents a structure essentially statically determined (post and lintel or column and beam), but with participation stresses in the columns. When the column becomes very stiff the structure—so far as the columns are concerned—is normal in its action, the stresses in the columns being determined for a fairly definite moment. In the transition stage the structural action is hybrid and does not respond readily to ordinary design procedure; increase in depth may either increase or decrease the flexural stress or leave it unchanged; and increase in width (which amounts to increase in moment of inertia) produces comparatively little effect.

Deformation stresses would be produced in this structure by change of temperature. As the depth of column is increased, the deformation stresses at the top of the column would vary at first almost directly as this depth, but later would be relieved by flexure of the girder.

Perhaps the most important fact revealed in this case is that if the flexural stresses indicated in the hybrid stage are dangerously high, there does not seem ·to be very much that can be done effectively, as long as the girder section is constant. This column may be thrown from the hybrid stage into the normal· stage of action, however, by reducing the stiffness of the girder. In the rigid-frame bridge this is done by reducing the center depth of the girder.

II.—General Remarks on Hybrid Structural Action

It is difficult to identify hybrid action in an unfamiliar structural type, but after one has come to recognize the type he begins early to suspect its existence in certain cases. Probably the chief identifying characteristic of the type is that it responds sluggishly or erratically to traditional methods of structural design. Successive cycles of design and analysis may indicate a trend, but produce only slowly a definite and satisfactory conclusion. If there are discontinuities in this design procedure the traditional process may be quite misleading.

Traditional processes are not very helpful in this field, although they still have their place. In these cases there are usually many variables and the curves of variation present maxima and minima. It should not be necessary to point out to scientific men the extreme difficulty—the grave danger—of applying purely empirical methods to such problems. It is impossible, in such a case, to generalize or extrapolate beyond the range of data presented and it is almost impossible to classify the data for study no matter how numerous these data are, unless such arrangement is based on an adequate theory.

It makes a good deal of difference what the designer wants to do. Where the action is normal for given proportions, there is usually only one answer and that is easily approximated at once and easily determined accurately by cut and try. Where the action is hybrid there are many possible structures; the designer must make his choice. In a sense he tells the structure what he wants it to do, and the structure will try to do it. If, however, it is something that the structure cannot do at all, the designer has erred; if it is something that the structure cannot do efficiently, the design is penalized. To apply the more erudite terminology of mechanics to this conception, the fiber stresses desired may involve incompatible strains.

This type of structural action is often best approached from a direct study of the fiber stresses. H. V. Spurr, M. Am. Soc. C. E., has done this in his wind-frame studies,[3] and, without discussing herein whether his method of design is necessary, sufficient, or invariably satisfactory, the writer feels that his contribution to the direct method of attack is of great value.

Rigid-Frame Bent Subject to Vertical Loads.—Consider a bent of the so-called rigid-frame type sometimes used for building frames consisting of a roof girder, curved or polygonal, carried by two columns. The pressure

[3] "Wind Bracing", by H. V. Spurr, McGraw-Hill Book Co., 1930.

line for dead load in this structure may lie anywhere between that for a simple curved beam supported on columns and that for a three-hinged arch (hinges at the center of the girder and at the bases of the columns).

The action of the structure may be studied by either of two methods. Choose some pressure line which is expected to give a good distribution of material, determine the moments for this pressure line, and then vary the moment of inertia along the section so as to satisfy the conditions of continuity. The depths of the sections may then be varied by choice. By this method the designer tells the moments where he wants them and then decides whether he likes the result.

As an alternative procedure which has some advantage, he chooses the desired pressure line, selects working stresses along this line, and then varies the depths to provide the requisite conditions of continuity. This requires judgment, but may be done quite well by eye. The moments of inertia may then be determined for these moments, stresses, and depths. The important fact is that the design may be predetermined—and predetermined over a wide range.

If at three points of the structure the moments of inertia are intentionally reduced compared with the sections elsewhere, the structure now becomes a normal structure (a three-hinged arch) with participation stresses at the weakened sections, which now act as hinges.

Rectangular Wind Frames.—The problem of analyzing rectangular frames for horizontal forces due to wind or to earthquake accelerations continues to occupy an important place in structural literature. It seems particularly illuminating to discuss the problem from the viewpoint proposed herein. It is assumed that the columns have been designed for vertical loads and that their sections will not be changed; discussion, then, is directed entirely to the design of the girders. The effect of offsets is not considered.

It is not intended to discuss the participation stresses induced in the girders of upper floors by departures from planarity at floor levels. The writer's studies indicate that the problem is neither so important nor so difficult as some have indicated.

Assume that the girders have been designed by some of the conventional methods. An analysis is now made and it is found that some girders are overstressed and some under-stressed. Tradition indicates re-design by increasing the size of the overstressed girder and decreasing that of the girder under-stressed. However, analysis will show in many cases practically the same stresses as before; in other cases, it may show a slight improvement in the stress distribution which will be further improved by repeated re-design to a certain point; but numerous cycles of re-design may be necessary to produce much improvement.

The girders of a symmetrical rectangular frame, carrying horizontal loads, may be designed on the following assumptions: (a) Points of inflection are at the mid-points of all members; (b) column shears are proportional to moments of inertia of columns; and (c) design stresses in girders are proportional to depth-length ratios of girders. If so designed, it will act as designed except near the fixed base. The analysis precedes and dictates the design; after design, no analysis is needed.

If points of inflection in the columns and distributions of column shears are assumed throughout the building, the designer can, by working from irrotational footings, determine relative stiffness, or K-values for the girders all the way up the building. Negative values for K would indicate impossible assumptions and positive values of K might be unsatisfactory because, for a given working stress, too deep a girder would be indicated or, for a given depth, too great a fiber stress would result.

The object is not to recommend this method of design, although it has value, but rather to indicate that as an alternative to the procedure, now popular, of assuming a structure and, by analysis, determining the stresses in it, presumably with a view to re-design, the designer may predetermine the function that the bracing is to perform, design directly, and then see whether the design is satisfactory as regards girder depths or working stresses. Of the two procedures, the second is often the more satisfactory. Each method is useful for certain purposes.

Note that the sensitiveness of the procedure depends upon the relative stiffness of columns and girders. If the columns are very stiff relative to the girders the moments can be applied almost anywhere without disturbing the desirable condition of inflection points very near the mid-points of the girders; the moments in the girders will be proportional to their K-values.

It seems futile to ask which of several conventional methods of analysis most nearly conforms to the results of so-called exact analysis; the answer depends on the proportions of the structure. Special attention is directed, therefore, to the dangers of induction from specific data whether obtained by computation, from models, or from tests in a laboratory, unless the range of the data covers all variables.

Arches Integral with Their Spandrel-Structures.—An important example of hybrid structural action occurs in arches that are integral with their spandrel construction. It has long been recognized that there is interaction of the rib and the spandrels, but such interaction is commonly neglected in design.

In special cases applying to such structures, the engineer can see certain controlling relations. If the columns of an arch having open spandrels are quite flexible and very closely spaced, angular changes along the arch rib must be the same as those along the deck girder, since the vertical deflections of the two are every where the same. In this case, then, the entire structure could be designed at once as an arch made up of two members placed side by side as in a flitch beam. The relative flexural stresses in the rib and deck can be predicted and may be controlled by varying their relative depths.

Clearly, in this case, the designer may put all flexural resistance in the rib, or in the deck girder; or he may divide this flexural resistance between the two members at will; arches have been built of all three types—a stiff arch without stiffening girder; a flexible arch with stiffening girder; and a stiff arch reinforced with a stiffening girder. Of course, in any case, there must be some flexural resistance in the flexible member and some flexural resistance in the columns. These, however, will have the well-defined characteristics of participation stresses.

If the columns are not closely spaced the simplicity of the picture is marred both because the flitch-beam picture is less simple and also because the deck girder now has primary stresses as a continuous beam.

. As the columns become quite stiff, however, the picture becomes very complicated. Such a structure is clearly hybrid in its action and the nature of the inter-relations is not at once apparent. Methods of studying such cases have been developed by Nathan M. Newmark, Jun. Am. Soc. C. E.[4]

It is important to question whether it is good practice to change from normal structural action with participation stresses to hybrid action with obvious reduction in the factor of safety of the rib, with little promise of economy, and with much complication and uncertainty in design. There is little, if any, evidence that the participation stresses in these structures are dangerous or even objectionable. The idea of putting secondary stresses to work is not usually very promising.

III.—GENERAL REMARKS ON INDETERMINACY

Thirty-four years ago Mr. Frank H. Cilley presented a paper under the title "The Exact Design of Statically Indeterminate Frameworks. An Exposition of Its Possibility but Futility."[5] The main thesis was that "statical indetermination in a structure is always to be regarded as self-interference with efficiency." The paper followed a previous paper by the same author,[6] and revived a discussion of long standing as to the relative advantages of determinate and indeterminate systems. Two discussions of the paper were presented by distinguished American engineers and several by foreign engineers.

There is little question that Mr. Cilley's views represented those of many, and probably of a large majority, of the leading American structural engineers of his day. To-day, on the other hand, literature contains numerous articles extolling the virtues of indeterminacy and some writers even go so far as to attribute to indeterminate structures virtues which appear to be contradictory. They are referred to as "reservoirs of resilience," their rigidity is praised, as are their economy and their strength.

Since 1900, many indeterminate steel trusses have been built in America with claims, apparently well supported, of considerable economy. More important still, a new material—concrete—which is more conveniently made continuous, has come into general use.

The rather awkward methods of analysis current at the beginning of this century undoubtedly delayed the development of continuous structural types. At that time the analysis of some of the more complicated types now proposed

---

[4] Some phases of Mr. Newmark's extensive studies are reported in "Interaction Between Rib and Superstructure in Concrete Arch Bridges", by Nathan M. Newmark, Jun. Am. Soc. C. E. Thesis presented to the University of Illinois in 1934, in partial fulfillment of the requirement for the degree of the Doctor of Philosophy.

[5] *Transactions*, Am. Soc. C. E., Vol. XLIII (1900), p. 353.

[6] "Some Fundamental Propositions Relating to the Design of Frameworks", by Frank H. Cilley, *Technology Quarterly*, June, 1897.

was impracticable. The profession has made progress in this field. It may be well now to divert the attention of structural designers from the endless elaboration of analytical technique to the more important matter of interpretation of analyses.

It appears that Mr. Cilley's paper was directed too much to a consideration of what is herein termed hybrid structural action. The degree of self-interference in normal structures is quite negligible. Each normal indeterminate structure usually has a determinate analogue in comparison with which it has certain virtues and which has certain virtues in comparison with it. No generalization is possible, but the indeterminate structure has won consideration and is often indicated.

Structures in which hybrid action predominates are also sometimes indicated. If their action can be clearly foreseen and if they are designed for one controlling load condition, they may be designed economically. Often they are indicated for reasons entirely apart from structural efficiency, as in the case of rectangular wind-bracing; but where their action cannot be clearly visualized, conventional procedures of analysis by computation or by model may furnish little help.

IV.—CONCLUDING REMARKS

The paper has indicated four types of structural action the characteristics of which make their separate discussion worth while. These are (a) the action that produces deformation stresses; (b) that which produces participation stresses; (c) normal structural action; and (d) hybrid structural action. Deformation stresses and participation stresses have many characteristics in common, but are essentially different in cause and sometimes in action. Hybrid structural action represents a transition stage between participation stress and normal structural action.

Deformation stresses cannot be avoided except by avoiding the deformation that produces them. They may be slightly modified so that a little more strain takes place at one point and a little less at another, but about the same total strain—angular or linear— will inevitably occur. Linear strain due to angular strain may be reduced by decreasing the depth.

The designer's interest in participation stresses is that they shall not be too high; he does not want their exact values. If they are too high, he changes either the over-all dimensions or the details of construction. What is "too high" will always remain a matter of judgment. In normal structural types only is the traditional procedure, of first computing the forces and then designing for them, applicable.

Hybrid structures may be designed in many ways. In order that analysis may guide to design, it should precede design so that the designer may see in what ways the structure can act. Then, in a quite literal sense, he tells it how to act and makes it act in that way. The difficulty is that he may blunder in trying to have it act in a way in which it cannot possibly act or that, of the many ways in which it can act, he chooses an inefficient one.

Structures characterized by hybrid action are difficult to design and are often inefficient in any case. Study of them is made difficult by the inadequacy of traditional methods; it is almost hopeless, and may be dangerous, to study them by emprical methods.

Generalizations as to relative advantages of determinate and indeterminate systems are difficult in any case. Some conflicting opinions in the literature may be reconciled by recognizing the distinction indicated.

5

LIMITATIONS AND APPLICATION
OF STRUCTURAL ANALYSIS

I — AMID the many new developments in stress analysis, especially in the field of indeterminate structures, it is desirable to distinguish between analysis for research and analysis for design — Stress analysis for design should utilize familiar concepts, and the method should be flexible

Safe engineering means first of all correct calculation of stresses. This is true of a rigid frame or other indeterminate structure just as much as of a simple beam. Does it mean that the new systems of analysis brought out in recent years for the computation of stresses in intermediate structures are essential? Must the structural engineer use them? Do they assure safe building?

Professor Cross subjects these questions to searching scrutiny by dissecting the process of stress analysis into its elements. His conclusions are all in favor of simple, transparent methods as against complex and confusing procedure.

In the present first half of his study he proceeds on the view that a good method of analysis should use familiar concepts, should have a clear physical meaning at every stage and should be flexible. He holds that the quickest method is usually inferior to a slower but clearer one. He then tells what stress analysis really does and compares it with the process by which a picture puzzle is worked out. Incidentally he shows that the geometrical and the energy or least-work methods are identical.

On this foundation he will later show, in the second half of the article, that all analyses must be interpreted. The physical meaning of a stress and the extent to which chance factors may change the amount of the stress, have much to do with the safety of what the engineer builds. — EDITOR.

Evidence of increasing interest in the theory of structural analysis, if needed, is given by the number of articles appearing in this field. A review of the *Transactions* of the American Society of Civil Engineers shows that about five times as many such articles were published in the third decade of the century as in the first decade. Articles are appearing today which could not have found publication twenty years ago.

This represents a condition of interesting and healthy activity, but with many it produces a feeling of confusion, of uncertainty as to standard practices, and a vague unhappiness for fear of overlooking too many important elements in the problems of design. Practical men find difficulty in digesting and evaluating the large volume of new theoretical developments, and judicious engineers decline to use theoretical formulas whose derivation they have no time to unravel.

With the traditional conservatism of engineers the writer finds himself in heartiest sympathy; a designer of engineering structures upon which the integrity of property values and the safety of human life depend has no right to accept theoretical results unless he finds for them some support in experience or in common sense.

REASONS FOR INTEREST IN THEORY

The intense expansion of structural theory in recent years is in part a result of economic conditions and in part a phase of the passion for research which has dominated all fields of effort since the beginning of the century. It has paralleled the development of new structural types, and indeed has been partly inspired by it. An excellent illustration is found in the type of structure known in this country as the rigid-frame bridge, originated by motives partly economic and largely esthetic.

There are many cases in which standard structural forms fail to satisfy functional and esthetic requirements. In the past there has been strong discouragement of the development of new types, but this attitude is passing. In some cases the rise of new structural types has produced a group of protagonists who find in them all of the virtues and none of the faults of more standard forms. It is always to be remembered that a special advantage enjoyed by a new type of construction is the lack of restricting precedent; age-old experience fails to warn, and we dare cut the margin of safety to a point which later experience may indicate to be injudicious.

There is no argument against the use of the new type; we want new types, new solutions. We are entering into a period when the art of the structural designer will have more freedom from restrictions of precent; this benefits both the type of construction and the standing of the profession. But it is clearly important that we correlate our experience with standard forms to the theory to be used in designing the new type.

OBJECT OF STRUCTURAL ANALYSIS

We may distinguish (a) analytical procedures which are intended as tools of research, and (b) procedures which are intended as tools of design. In research, again, we may distinguish analytic research from experimental research. A complicated and erudite method of analysis may be quite useful as a method of studying certain phenomena in detail as a preliminary to devising a simple procedure for purposes of design. An obvious example is the value of Westergaard's classical work on slabs as a preliminary to current adaptations of it to design.

Research Analysis — Prof. Eddington is quoted as saying recently that "No experiment is worthy of credence unless supported by an adequate theory." With this paradoxical statement the writer agrees. Further, not only is the adequate theory necessary after laboratory experimentation for illuminating the data, but it is very much needed before experiments are begun, in order to plan the tests properly. Many procedures have their greatest value in the field of research, and it is necessary that the practical man understand that much material which seems so useless to him is not intended for his immediate use. Designers have often been too quick, rather than too slow, to incorporate directly the results of research, either analytical or experimental, in their design procedure. Sometimes they do not wait to determine whether the work has passed beyond the preliminary stage before accepting it as a basis for final conclusions.

The laboratory man is coming to demand more of the illumination of theory in planning his experiments, and it is safe to say that the period of indiscriminate testing, which was conspicuous years ago, will find less favor in the future.

Analysis for Use in Design — Theoretical developments may be intended to be applied to design only after these theories are supplemented by careful laboratory data and are further clarified and interpreted in terminology of design. Clearly, however, unless theoretical knowledge leads ultimately to an understanding of structural action and unless this understanding can be interpreted in terms of structural design, we have achieved only futility. The work of the structural analyst is valuable, then, only as it is ultimately useful to the structural designer.

The designer is accustomed to picture the possible deformations in a structural part, to weigh quickly but effectively the elements of chance involved in that picture, and to judge of the method of failure. Many do this with a quickness and accuracy which seems intuitive; others think they can do it, do it poorly and are dangerous. By adding definiteness of outline to his vague pictures, by familiarity with the simple relations of modern analysis, the man of structural vision learns to draw accurately pictures of more complicated structural action.

By making some definite analysis, by putting down some figures, the designer whose structural vision is myopic escapes many pitfalls and may finally improve his vision.

If the tools of analysis introduce too many new technical terms, too many unfamiliar procedures, if the glasses do not fit the patient, the designers with a God-given structural vision may go blind and the astigmatism of those designers whose structural vision is blurred may be accentuated. If structural analysis does not finally hitch up with structural sense, structural engineering is going backward.

DESIRABLE QUALITIES OF ANALYSIS

We may identify certain desirable characteristics of methods of analysis:

1. The method should be easy to learn and easy to remember. It should introduce as few new technical terms as possible, and such technical terms as are used should be quite familiar to those who are to use the method.

2. The method should not only not introduce new technical terms but should by preference introduce no radically new *concepts*. The type of concept which is presented should be familiar to the sort of person who will use the method. For designers, this means that the method should be easily correlated with the accumulated experience of structural engineers. When a theoretical investigation departs so radically from the concepts with which designers have been familiar that the designer either has to abandon previous concepts completely — throw away his accumulated experience — or else disregard the theoretical investigation, the writer has little doubt that the designer will wisely cling to his experience.

Thus, it is quite possible to find bending moments in one loaded span of a continuous frame by finding the equivalent elastic areas of all members beyond the loaded span and then analyzing this span by the column analogy. But this is a far-fetched concept, though the writer could cite cases where for purposes of research it has considerable value; designers do not see column analogies in the field, but they are accustomed to visualize the effect of joint rotations.

3. One of the most desirable characteristics of an analytical procedure to be used in design is that it shall enable us to see the approximate answer from the beginning. The first estimate furnished may be considerably in error, but the method should indicate at once the general order of magnitude of the quantity with which we are dealing. It seems very desirable that subsequent operations should revise rather than reconstruct the original picture.

To take a very simple case, suppose we wish to compute stresses, for some condition of loading, in a continuous truss. A traditional application of Maxwell's procedure would be to remove the center reaction, compute the deflection there and then compute the value of this reaction to bring the center support back to its original level. A procedure often better than this, however, is to guess at the center reaction as well as we can, then compute the deflection and find the additional reaction required to bring the supports level — the error in our guess. The advantage is that our guess, if it is at all good — and it can scarcely be very bad in this case — tells us at once about what stresses we are dealing with; and our revision of this guess helps us to guess better next time — so that we are developing analytical judgment.

If a student wishes to become familiar with the theory of arches, the writer thinks that the best way is for him to draw by eye pressure lines for various conditions of loading that "hug" the arch axis as closely as possible; then compute the correction to the reactions. The original guess usually cannot be very bad; the corrections are — or should be — small; we see at once about what the moments are, and after a little experience we can draw the original pressure line very well and learn to see from the beginning how variations in the design are likely to affect the result.

FLEXIBILITY IS IMPORTANT

4. Finally, it is desirable — one would feel tempted to say that it is *necessary*, if we were not so far from realizing it — that the method of analysis shall be flexible. This means that it shall without modification take account of any and all variations that occur in the material, that the effect of cracks, of soft spots and local irregularities may be readily estimated.

In most cases we are very far from this ideal at present. No one should expect that structural designers will adopt theoretical procedures that are incapable of even estimating the effect of such variations. In many procedures that have been presented one finds the prohibitive limitation that it is necessary to modify the structure hopelessly to fit the method of analysis, and it seems quite impossible to fit even approximately the method of analysis to the actual structure.

A series of parallel beams sharing a load on the same span cannot work together effectively if of slightly different depths — if Hooke's Law holds! Really they are quite effective if the difference of depth is not great — we must think beyond Hooke's Law. The analysis of slabs of reinforced concrete is quite unsatisfactory because we cannot conveniently include the effect of cracking. Analyses indicate certain distributions of reinforcing steel, whereas often quite different distributions are just about as effective. It may be added that no one has pointed this out more clearly than has Westergaard.

NOVELTY AND SPEED VERSUS SIMPLICITY

It will be noted that among the desired characteristics enumerated, novelty is not included. The field of structural analysis is one in which new ideas have frequently been presented because of their apparent novelty alone. Of course, if the method differs in no way from previous methods, it should not be published. But there is nothing new to be said in regard to the laws of statics and dynamics, or in regard to geometry. The facts are very simple, and they are true for a very long time. New properties may in some cases be brought out with regard to materials. What is needed at present is a clearer, more definite, more flexible restatement and correlation of fundamental procedures.

Many would emphasize that the method should be rapid. This depends on how often it is to be used, for what purpose — routine design or special design — it is to be used, and who is to use it. Professors and graduate students working on theses and other academicians who work in offices seem inclined to overestimate the importance of saving a few minutes in a design problem which comes up once a month or once in a professional career. *Simplicity is more important than speed.*

TYPE OF THOUGHT USED IN ANALYSIS

What type of thought is used in the analysis of structures?

In a certain sense the answer can be stated very simply. The structural analyst attempts to find the stress distribution in a given structure under a given loading which does three things: First, the stresses must satisfy the law of statics; they must be in statical (or, in certain cases, in dynamical) balance throughout the structure. Second, the strains produced by the stresses must satisfy geometry; they must not produce any discontinuity or break in the structure unless it is known that such discontinuity actually occurs. Finally, the relation of stress and strain must be in accordance with the known properties of the structural material with which we are dealing.

It is to be noted that the first two matters are in no way open to argument or discussion. Geometrical principles are not a proper subject for testing, statics is not a proper subject for testing. Where the relations, geometrical and statical, are perfectly clear and the properties of the material relating the statics to the geometry are perfectly definite, testing may have illustrative value but can scarcely have value as scientific demonstration. Where the geometrical and statical relations are not perfectly clear, tests may help our understanding of the problem, though ultimately these relations must be made clear by analysis. But where the properties of the material are uncertain and variable, tests may furnish valuable statistical data bearing on the effect of chance.

It is very desirable that the solution of a problem in stress analysis be so stated that anyone familiar with the subject may see whether the forces balance throughout the structure and whether the deformations are consistent with continuity in the structure. Thus, a pressure line for a fixed-end arch has the virtue that anyone can see, at least approximately, whether it fits the axis.

THE PICTURE-PUZZLE ANALOGY

Omitting for the present any consideration of variations in the properties of the material, we return to the question of how we are to find a solution that will satisfy the three conditions: (1) that stress must balance, (2) that the strain must be continuous, and (3) that the relation of the stress to the strain must agree with the actual physical properties of the material.

Finding such a solution is very much like solving an ordinary picture puzzle. To solve such a puzzle: (a) Make the pieces fit together — geometry — so that (b) the colors harmonize — statics — but (c) do this without using parts of different puzzles, without attributing to one material, such as concrete, properties that are true only for another material, such as steel. When a picture puzzle has been solved, there is no question whether the solution is correct. In order to find out whether it is correct, one does not ask by what system the pieces were put together.

One of the most powerful methods of analysis is, in a sense, no method at all — namely, to guess at a solution and then see if it satisfies statics and continuity. *The faculty of guessing at solutions is capable of great development. One of the chief values of formal analyses is to aid in its development.*

Sometimes we find a clue to a puzzle from the fact that we have solved similar puzzles, and we suspect that the gray color represents clouds at the top of the picture or that the brown earth goes at the bottom. This may mean that we suspect that a certain type of function may furnish a solution of our differential equation.

GEOMETRICAL AND ENERGY METHODS

We sometimes hear a vague statement that the methods of analysis based on the principle of the conservation of energy and usually referred to as "methods of work" achieve in some way an elegance and precision not characteristic of methods based immediately on geometrical conceptions. Such ideas, of course, have no foundation; the statement of problems in terms of geometry and the statement in terms of energy are identical statements.

We need not go here into a general discussion of the interrelation of the principles of statics, the principles of geometry and the principles of energy conservation. It may, however, be worth while to point out the identity of the relations in a simple case.

Suppose we have a weight suspended by two wires of different physical characteristics. Statics tells us that the whole weight P is taken by the two wires, and we can write

$$P_1 + P_2 = P \tag{1}$$

The stretch of each wire is proportional to the load that it carries, multiplied by a constant representing the physical characteristics of the wire. Call this constant C. The stretch is the same in the two wires, and we write

$$P_1 C_1 = P_2 C_2 \tag{2}$$

By formal algebra we can now deduce the values of P_1 and P_2, or in a less formal way we may see at once that the weight P is distributed between the two wires in inverse ratio to their C values.

If in Eq. (2), which is plain geometry, we substitute $P_2 = P - P_1$ from Eq. (1), which is pure statics, we have the equation of the condition of minimum internal work in the system. But it does not appear that thereby we have achieved any particular elegance, and it is clear that we have not added any elements not already contained in the problem.

GEOMETRICAL METHODS ARE CLEARER

Geometry is almost certainly the more familiar tool of thought to the structural engineer. The use of the energy relations may, it is true, sometimes avoid certain difficulties in setting up the formal statement; but what the engineer ultimately wants is a picture of the action of the structure, and this, at least for problems of statics, will be in terms of geometry.

The writer finds the geometrical picture clearer and more convincing even in problems in dynamics, but in such problems consideration of the energy involved has obvious advantages.

II — To be safe in application, the results of stress analysis must be interpreted in the light of service conditions — Many factors of chance to be considered — Finally, the physical meaning of stress in a member as related to the action of the structure as a whole should be studied

It is worthwhile here to remark, in connection with the problem of the load supported by two wires discussed in the first part of this article, that under either method of analysis the statics and the geometry are interrelated through the constants which define the physical characteristics of the bars. The procedure does not depend upon the assumption of proportionality of stress to strain nor upon any obscure assumption as to the action of the bar under load. It does, however, depend on our knowing the ratio of pull to deformation for the amount of pull which actually exists; apparently this relation can be got only from data of actual tests.

ANALYTICAL RESULTS MUST BE INTERPRETED

It is also important to note that the solution of even this simple problem, by any method whatever, calls for a good deal of interpretation before it can be applied to design. If the properties — especially the stress-strain relation — of this wire are definite and are definitely known, we may trace out exactly the relation of stress intensity to total load. The procedure is simple; compute the stress in each wire for values of C based on Hooke's Law; revise the values of C for the stresses thus found; recompute, and so proceed to any degree of approximation.

It will, of course, be found that after the yield point of the stiffer wire is passed, this wire "takes load less rapidly" than before. This conclusion is indicated by "common sense" (qualitative thinking about the matter) and is not indicated by what some would call "academic theory" (inadequate theory) based on Hooke's Law. If, however, after the yield point the stress in the stiffer wire is uncomfortably near to rupture, or if its action is decidedly erratic, we will not dare to depend upon the phenomena beyond the yield as an element in design.

The important point just here is that a solution of "the problem" — that is, the stresses in these wires — based on Hooke's Law is, alone, a very inadequate study of the problem, because:

(a) It fails to take account of the facts about the material (the limitations of Hooke's Law).

(b) It fails to take account of the chance elements involved (the possible erratic nature of the elastic relation after yield).

(c) It fails to interpret these elements in terms of probability of rupture (fails to throw light on the elements in factor of safety).

The elementary analysis fails because it lacks *flexibility;* it does not adapt itself to all elements in the problem. In this case the modification of method to attain such flexibility is fairly obvious. In complicated cases such modification is not obvious. But the fact remains that the usefulness of the information obtained is limited very much unless the method to be employed is flexible.

We might go farther and criticize even the modified solution here, because it takes no account of how this load is applied, whether rapidly or slowly. Dynamics then enters into the problem. We will need not only a method of solution of the problem in dynamics which can conveniently take account of the actual properties of the material, but we will need accurate knowledge from the laboratory as to those properties, especially as to the effect of time in modifying the properties. In this field the analytical procedures and the data from the laboratories are both unsatisfactory today.

DETAILS OF ANALYSIS

The purely geometrical relations of the movements in the structure — if this piece elongates or rotates so much, this point will move so far in this direction — may be deduced by various devices. We may note:

(a) The principle of virtual work, which includes Fraenkel's equation as a special case.

(b) Plain graphics. We draw the deformed structure and scale the movements. In a Williot diagram we draw the deformations but leave out the structure. There are all sorts of variations of this idea.

(c) Direct geometrical computations, preferably in the form of sketching a Williot diagram or one of its variations and then computing values in this diagram instead of scaling them.

Many tools may be used to facilitate the actual computations. Logarithms and the familiar slide-rule are examples. Today computing machines of various kinds are often convenient. Very convenient in many cases is the device of laying off distances on paper and effecting the computations by a graphical procedure.

Most graphics is merely a short cut in arithmetic having no inherent connection with mechanics at all. This is well illustrated in the analysis of arches, where the sums of various terms of the form abc, where a and b and c are definite quantities, are involved. These multiplications and summations may be performed graphically, but to do so has usually no special structural significance. Whether or not one cares to use it depends on convenience, on the precision desired and very much on personal choice. To discuss whether it is in all cases the best method is obviously futile.

Certain devices in analysis are almost entirely mnemonic. Thus, the use of area-moments translates a problem in geometry which the mathematician finds, because of his usual mode of thought, most convenient in its mathematical form, into a problem in the computation of shears, moments and reactions, which is familiar ground to the engineer. The same may be said of the column analogy. What convenience there is in the procedure is inherent not in the method itself but in the mode of thought of the engineer who is to use it.

METHOD MAY BE VARIED

It is not necessary that all quantities in an analysis be found by the same general procedure. Thus some quantities may be computed, either by arithmetic or in the case of continuous functions by the use of the calculus; some may be found graphically and some by the use of models, and the results combined. Often this is clearly a convenient procedure, often it leads to inaccuracy and sometimes to confusion; each case, or at least each type of problem, must be decided on its own merits.

When we consider that there are many special devices for simplifying and solving equations, it is seen that it is possible to produce many combinations of such devices. These do not constitute new methods or different methods. Novelty of arrangement alone is no virtue in this field, since the possibilities for such novelty are almost unlimited. If it gives the computer less work, if it is simple in its steps, then it is valuable.

There are a great many ways of writing and of solving the equations. All sorts of special tricks and devices are available — graphics, analogies, standard terms, tabulated values. The equations may be combined in different orders of arrangement, as where the moments are stated in terms of rotations in using the slope-deflection method, or the rotations are stated in terms of the moments in using the theorem of three moments. These equations may be solved in several different ways — by ordinary algebraic manipulations, by the use of determinants, by successive approximation, by successive convergence, sometimes by graphical methods, sometimes by use of standard solutions.

IRREGULARITIES IN PHYSICAL PROPERTIES

It is well to emphasize that many analyses are quite inadequate for two reasons: first, they fail to take proper account of variation in property of material; second — and this is in a sense the same thing — they fail to carry the analysis on to failure of the material.

We may divide the life history of a broken structural specimen into four parts. In the early stages of loading, initial irregularities are being eliminated; this stage is commonly of little interest to the designer. The next stage is that of working stresses; in this stage the specimen acts in a regular way, and conventional analysis is usually a pretty good guide to its performance. Later, the performance of the specimen becomes irregular, as the yield point is passed in steel or as such phenomena as bond slip begin in concrete; this danger zone precedes the fatal event, failure.

In a strongly paradoxical sense we may say that the engineer is often not especially interested in what does happen in the structure. We may plan an analysis to tell us what *does* happen in a particular case; such an analytical investigation is usually for the purpose of interpreting a test or for the purpose of investigating a failure. More often we plan an analysis to investigate what *may* happen in a structure.

Particularly we may wish to investigate *the probability* of such things happening, for engineers must always ask what rate of insurance they are willing to pay against failure. This whole field of probability of occurrence is inadequately treated in any formal way in present literature. It is, however, a question which must have some investigation in all cases where analysis is to be used as a basis for design. It is at the root of all factor-of-safety determinations.

THE ELEMENT OF CHANCE

To throw some further light on this phase of the subject, it may be said that there enters here, in the solution of any problem in structural analysis, a large element of chance, and we can scarcely say that we have analyzed the stress conditions until we have taken account of this element. In many cases it is possible by a purely analytical procedure to show that such variations as are possible in the physical properties of the material can produce only small effects on the final solution. In other cases it can be shown that the uncertainties in the physical properties change the answer very much, and hence that the action of the structure is, within a wide range, a matter of chance.

When we recognize such facts, we cover them by adjusting the factor of safety; the stale joke "factor of ignorance" has been overworked in this connection. But structural analysis is incomplete and may be quite dangerous, which fails to weigh this element of chance. No formal mathematical procedure seems available for doing so, but we can use the crude statistical procedure of varying the constants, to see what effect such variation has on the answer.

The writer tried to do this some years ago in studying the effect of erratic variations of the modulus of elasticity of concrete upon the moments in an arch ring. Various combinations of moduli in different parts of the ring were assumed, analyses made for these combinations, and the resulting data were studied statistically. Much work of this kind remains to be done.

Such studies must cover a pretty wide range of variation to be serviceable. One is tempted to ask how wide this range must be. The problem of maxima and minima where there are many variables is one which the engineer encounters daily. In many such cases the range puts the problem entirely outside the possibility of definite answer by a laboratory, and the too-familiar phrase *"Tests clearly show"* often needs to be considerably modified.

INTERPRETATION OF ANALYSES

There is with some a persistent feeling that all stresses are equally important, that every case of overstress indicates danger and every case of understress inefficient design. Yet the fact is that computed stresses have quite different significance in different structures and in different parts of the same structure.

In some indeterminate structures each member or part has its own work to do independently in carrying the load. It may be interfered with by the action of other members — secondary stresses; the objective of the designer is to reduce such interference below a value which experience has shown to be permissible. Beyond this he is not interested in the exact values. All structures that nominally are statically determinate belong in this group.

In a second group of indeterminate structures each part is assisted in its main work of carrying the load by the action of the other parts, but moderate variations in the proportions of one part do not seriously affect the assistance which it gives to another part. Most of the standard forms of indeterminate structures belong to this class. Thus, in a continuous steel truss, small change in the relative size of the members is not very important in determining the maximum stress in any member. In an arch rib of reinforced concrete a change in springing thickness produces only a small effect on the maximum crown moment. Structures of this type can be designed efficiently and economically.

In a third type the members participate in carrying the load, but any change in the load-carrying capacity of one relieves the other immediately of some burden. Sometimes the two parts work together with perfect (or almost perfect) efficiency; elementary examples are parallel beams of the same material and equal depths, double diagonals in truss panels with parallel chords under full-span loading. But in other cases the participating parts cannot work together efficiently; if one part carries more load, the other is not proportionately relieved.

TWO SCHOOLS OF THOUGHT

This sort of differentiation of structural type may serve to clarify, if not to reconcile, two conflicting viewpoints that have always run through the literature of structural analysis in America. One group of thinkers, of the older school, claims that the indeterminate structure is always inefficient, that the different parts interfere with each other. The other holds that indeterminacy always has special virtues, of which economy is one. The older school seems to have erred in grouping all indeterminacy under the inefficient group indicated in the third heading above, but the other school errs equally in neglecting this important classification entirely.

Enthusiastic stress analysts often seem inclined to undiscriminating determination of all possible stress conditions, and there seems a lack of consideration of the relative importance of stress conditions found. It is very important to distinguish between primary and secondary stresses, however these terms may be defined. To the writer it seems most useful to define primary stress as the stress which is depended upon to carry the load, or in other words the stress that is ordinarily computed as an element in the design. The secondary stress, then, is the additional stress resulting from an incident to the deformation produced by the primary stress, but not depended upon to carry the load.

The important difference here is that in steel the primary stress will in general increase in direct proportion to the load intensity up to rupture. The secondary stress will not increase in direct proportion to loading after the yield point of material is passed. The same distinction in part can be applied — but with less clearness — to structures of reinforced concrete.

The importance of properly interpreting results of stress analysis is clearly indicated in the case of the Vierendeel girder. Claims of economy for this type of structure suggest that the Vierendeel girder has been designed for a total stress equal to the primary stress plus the secondary stress usually allowed in designing riveted trusses. This means that this type has been designed for a primary stress of perhaps 23,000 lb. per sq. in. because triangulated trusses are allowed a principal stress of 18,000 plus a secondary stress of 5,000 lb. per. sq. in. The load-carrying capacities of the two structures are presumably not at all the same.

It is important also, as nearly all structural engineers understand, to interpret stress analysis in terms of method of failure. It is immaterial in some cases to the structural designer that a computed stress exceeds a certain prescribed value if there is no conceivable way in which the failure of the material could actually occur. *The interpretation of stress analysis makes absolutely necessary a clear idea of the action of the structural part up to the stage at which rupture is conceivable.*

PROBABLE FUTURE DEVELOPMENTS

Let no one imagine that all of the important work has been done in the analytical field. It would seem more probable that we are just beginning our work. The methods of analysis for internal and localized stress, methods of analysis for slabs, and the treatment of the problem of dynamics of structures are still unsatisfactory.

If one may venture to predict, a great future lies in the development of more flexible tools of analysis, so that we may try to take account of the variations in material and so come to study the whole field, not alone of stress conditions that would exist in ideal material but of stress conditions that might exist in the materials which we actually have.

Again, we are coming slowly but definitely to recognize that many of the most important phenomena connected with structural action are dynamic, and that static pictures are often quite inadequate. The present status of the field of structural dynamics is far from satisfactory. The mathematical theory is perfect except that it works very awkwardly in practical cases. The voice of experience in the field is beginning to be quite emphatic in its statements but continues to be very vague in its terminology; it speaks glibly of rigidity but fails to identify which of several possible meanings of the word is intended.

Here, as elsewhere, popular terminology crudely synthesizes experience, while scientific terminology underlies specialized thinking; the one has breadth, the other definiteness. Such terms as "wobble" or "shudder" represent types of motion, but we are far from correlating them with the definite terminology of mathematical analysis.

We need in this field to know a good deal better what quantities we want to compute, we need more data from laboratory and field as to physical constants to be used in our computations, we need more convenient methods of computation, and we shall need to know what the figures mean after we get them.

Specifically, in the case of buildings, we need to know when and to what extent amplitude of vibration is important and when regularity is important; what allowance should be made for inelastic distortions and for damping. We must know what movements are objectionable, and we need simpler analytical procedures, convenient to use, in terminology that we all can understand. Eventually we are sure to get all this, but the road will be long and the byways many.

6

WHY CONTINUOUS FRAMES?

INTRODUCTION

THE problem of continuity was obvious from the earliest days of construction in reinforced concrete. In recent years it has increased in prominence and in importance. Constantly today some new form of continuous construction challenges the ingenuity of the analyst or offers new possibilities to the architect and structural designer. Many would like to know why the new types are being developed, what are their possibilities and what future developments may be expected in this field. It is difficult to answer all of these questions, but it may be profitable to look at certain phases of the subject.

Some structures are almost necessarily continuous and some structures become continuous by will of the designer. I wish to discuss chiefly the latter type but I shall refer somewhat to the former type also.

Let us recognize in the first place that continuity is not a new element in structural design nor is it peculiar to structures of reinforced concrete. The Baths of. Caracalla in Rome are quite definitely continuous structures. Most construction in stone is continuous; Gothic cathedrals, the Renaissance stairways of France. You may ask how we can have flexural continuity in a structure built of stone without any tensile strength in the material. The answer is quite clearly that tensile resistance is developed in the material by adding weight; it is essentially a negative compression resistance, but acts quite as effectively as does reinforcement in a concrete structure. Buttresses supporting Gothic vaults, then, are quite definitely columns subjected to flexure.

Reinforced concrete as a material of construction started out with two obvious handicaps. In the first place, it is, like stone, much heavier in comparison with its strength than is timber or steel. Its weight eats up its strength in long-span construction. Moreover

*Presented at the 31st Annual Convention, American Concrete Institute, New York, Feb. 19-21, 1935.

unless designed with skill, it looks heavy, has an awkward appearance, in long spans.   If you doubt it, look at any of the through concrete girder bridges built twenty years ago on our highways.

CONTINUITY

Reinforced concrete is almost necessarily continuous.   Continuity in construction is not by any means an unmixed blessing.   We often go to considerable expense to avoid continuity in steel construction and we shall hear today from Mr. Moreell of expedients in the form of hinges devised to avoid continuity in structures of reinforced concrete.   As many of you know, Prof. Wilson has recently completed at the University of Illinois extensive experiments to study the objectionable features of continuity between deck and superstructure in concrete arches.   This continuity is by some designers carefully avoided by the use of joints. As we all know, continuity is a prolific source of cracking in many structures, in the walls of houses, in brick piers, in concrete floors, in the decks, gutters and handrails of bridges.

On the other hand, I need scarcely plead before this audience that concrete has many virtues.   From the point of view of the architect, its leading virtue is plasticity; it can be molded.   We can have any form we like, any shape, any curve.   Note here that another older material of construction has now also gone plastic, for today we burn and weld steel into forms which could not have been considered some years ago.

Continuity may be a considerable nuisance to the designer but artfully handled it not only ceases to be a source of danger but in most cases points the way to overcoming the handicap of dead weight and massive appearance and lends itself to the full utilization of the plasticity of concrete by the development of more graceful forms of construction.   Careful study, then, of this necessary nuisance will point the way to full realization of the full possibilities of reinforced concrete as an architectural material.

These possible advantages from continuity in structures of reinforced concrete are in many ways quite different from those in structures of steel.   These two materials have aped each other too much.   In structures of reinforced concrete, dead load commonly predominates as a source of stress much more than in structures of steel.   We are consequently enabled to design concrete structures primarily for a single condition of loading and only incidentally for moving live loads.   Too little attention seems to have been paid in structural literature to the great importance of the relative values of the source of stress in comparing structural types or in comparing different structures of the same type but built of different materials.

STUDY OF A RIGID FRAME

I should like now to point out certain characteristics of a familiar structural type the design of which is commonly a routine matter and the analysis of which is often a professor's plaything. This is a simple, two-legged bent carrying vertical loads.

Assume that the girder has been designed as a beam simply supported. We wish to study the effect of flexure of the beam on the column stresses and of column flexure on the beam stresses, as the column depth varies. Assume for the present that the column width is constant and neglect for the present the effect of column reinforcement.

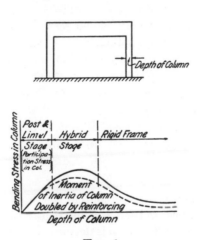

Fig. 1

We can distinguish clearly three quite different stages of action of this structure. Fig. 1 shows the curve of flexural stress in the column as the depth of column varies. You will note that if the column is very slender the flexural stress in it varies almost directly as the depth. The column here does not have to take a certain stress, it has to take a certain deformation, it has to bend through a certain angle. All we ask of it is that it shall bend through this angle without its main function as a compression member being impaired. It must, then, act as a hinge to the girder; of course the thinner this hinge, the less dangerous it is. Strength in flexure has little or nothing to do with it; if we add reinforcement we increase its capacity as a column but we do not decrease appreciably its fibre strain as a hinge.

We are constantly calling upon concrete members—and steel and timber members too, for that matter—to act as hinges. They do it very satisfactorily. Usually we do not worry about it. But if the hinge is too thick—too stiff in the common loose sense of the word—we do need to worry. I shall return to this subject of hinges.

I like to call this stage of this simple problem the stage of Post and Lintel Construction. The columns here are subjected to participation stress—more accurately, to participation strain.

As the column depth increases a stage is reached where the flexural stress is uncertain. Increase in column depth may either increase the stress or decrease it. Approximately, however, at this stage the stress is independent of the depth. Clearly the column may no longer be considered as a hinge and it may be dangerous as a column; moreover, it is not helping the girder appreciably. I call this the Hybrid stage of action. If the stresses here are too high, it is difficult to relieve the situation without changing the general proportions of the structure; an increase of 100 per cent in moment of inertia secured by adding steel may reduce the stresses only 25 per cent.

Beyond this stage we have what may well be called a Rigid Frame. The moment carried by the column is now more and more nearly equal to the fixed-end moment in the girder. We can now directly proportion the member for a definite or nearly definite moment.

The structure is now a rigid frame, but it is a very poor rigid frame. We do not need all that concrete in the center of the span. It produces high dead load stresses to little purpose. So we core out the soffit of our girder as shown in Fig. 2, save material, reduce dead load and add to the gracefulness of the structure. We are now coming to the usual type of rigid-frame bridge and continuity is here pointing the way to economy of material and to improved appearance.

This Concrete Omitted

Fig. 2

How far can we go in reducing this center depth? Further than is customary in the design of rigid frame bridges if we wish to do so. As we continue to decrease the depth of this center portion of the girder, this portion becomes also a hinge.

If we go further and hinge the bases of the columns, the structure is a three-hinged arch and, except for the center hinge—quasi-hinge, if you prefer— the moments are very definite, they are determined by statics; we may design for them at once. So we have passed from one type of articulated or hinged structure, the forces in which are determined by statics—a beam simply supported by columns which act as hinges—to another type of hinged structure—a three-hinged arch. Just so architecture passed from post and lintel in the Parthenon to Gothic vaults with buttresses at Chartres.

QUASI-HINGES

Nowhere in this construction need we insert definite articulations, actual hinges. We may do so if we like but we do not need them if our quasi-hinges are properly designed. We may have if we prefer— and I often do very much prefer— essentially action of a hinged or discontinuous type in a structure which is everywhere continuous in its material.

It is not necessary to define with precision the degree of flexibility for which a thin section may be considered a quasi-hinge. The important concepts are (1) that by inserting in our structures sections that are relatively flexible we may make these structures act very nearly as statically determinate, articulated, structures, (2) that the angular deformation occurring at such quasi-hinges is, over a considerable range, nearly independent of the flexural resistance of the hinge. The second characteristic might lead to a specific definition, for example that doubling the section modulus of the quasi-hinge shall not reduce the angular deformation at the hinge by more than ten per cent, though in any given structure this would depend somewhat on the loading condition or source of deformation. The hinge action is a matter of relative flexibility of the hinge in a given structure and not one of absolute flexibility or definite thickness.

There is an important difference between subjecting a structural part to a load and subjecting it to a deformation. Many phenomena which tend to bring on failure in the former case tend to inhibit failure in the latter case. Specifically, cracking of a concrete beam tends to bring on failure due to applied moment but tends to delay failure due to an imposed angular rotation.

It may be well to caution against undiscriminating substitution of the viewpoint here presented for the more classical analytical viewpoint. We shall still need the analyses but this viewpoint helps in interpreting them. We must also be cautious against a too ready acceptance of time flow in relieving the hinge because time flow, while it increases the flexibility of the hinge, also increases the angular deformation to which it is subjected as an effect of loads. Departure from Hooke's Law is, however, a very dependable source of relief in any case and time flow is a dependable source of relief for deformations not due to loads.

But we need to know more about these quasi-hinges. Laboratory experimentation in the past has concentrated its attention on the strength of concrete members. We need from the laboratories more information on the permissible deformations of members of reinforced concrete. Such studies have recently been published in steel; Professor Parcel has shown us that the hinge action—secondary stresses—of the members of a steel truss need not in many cases be a matter of serious concern. We know that often concrete columns are subject to considerable deformation without serious damage. But we need more definite information as to desirable type of reinforcement, shape of hinge, manner of disintegration for large deformations, strength against direct and shearing forces after some disintegration has occured as a result of large angular deformations.

The quasi-hinge at the center of the rigid frame is a very different hinge from that at the ends of the simple girder. For the columns supporting the simple girder we may see that for a given angle change in a given length, the strain in the outer fiber is proportional to the depth of the member. But the hinge at the center of the rigid frame is a tapered hinge; the greater its center depth the greater the length brought into bending. In this hinge, then, we find that the strain in the outer fiber for a given angular rotation is more nearly independent of the depth at the center.

DEFORMATION STRAINS

All of these frames—post and lintel type, hybrid type, rectangular rigid frame type, rigid frame with curved soffit—are, of course, subject to what I like to call deformation strains—strains produced by shrinkage, by abutment movements, by changes of temperature. These strains may be insignificant or they may be serious. In many cases they are a source of much concern to engineers. If the structure is of a statically determinate type—post and lintel or three-hinged arch—we need concern ourselves only with the action of the quasi-hinges. These quasi-hinges are subject to a fixed deformation and the unit fiber strain will depend on the amount of angular rotation and on the shape and depth of the hinge. But here again as we approach the discontinuous hinged type, the action of the main structural frame is pretty definitely determined.

RIGID-FRAME BUILDINGS

We may consider another very similar type of rigid frame which has large possibilities, practical and aesthetic. This is the rigid frame building, Fig. 3. This structure is designed essentially for gravity loads; in general, wind loads do not affect the design and there are either no moving loads or they are small.

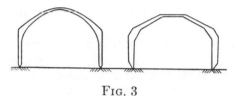

FIG. 3

The question at once forms, How does such a structure act? A more significant question is, How do you want it to act? It may be anything between a post and curved lintel—simple beam—construction and a three-hinged arch as the designer chooses. We may within these limits draw any curve of moments we wish consistent with the loads and then so proportion the structure that this will be the true curve of moments. We may do this by varying the moment of inertia along the frame.

What do we want here? Since the chief function of the material in the frame is to carry dead load, we may expect maximum economy by reducing and re-arranging this dead load. It is most economically carried to the footings by direct compression in the columns, not by bending in the roof girder. Hence the three-hinged arch construction is indicated as the desirable form, the shape approaching as nearly as architectural requirements permit to a pressure line for the dead load of the structure itself.

ECONOMY FROM REDISTRIBUTING DEAD LOAD

The economy to be realized by re-arrangement of dead load may be suggested by study of a beam fixed at ends. It is true that there is no such thing as a beam absolutely fixed at ends but we do approach such a condition in the case of the ordinary rigid-frame bridge. Suppose that the beam is to be designed for fixed maximum fiber stress and is to carry only its own dead weight.

Two designs are compared in Fig. 4. In one the beam is of constant section throughout. In the other, the soffit tapers as a parabola to a very small depth at the center. Neglect any slight arching effects. The amount of material required in the second case is only 1/12 of that in the first case, and the amount of reinforcement is of the order of ¼ as much. The conclusion here is not to be taken too seriously for there is no live load involved but the values at least challenge attention.

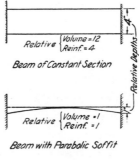

Relative {Volume = 12 / Reinf. = 4}

Beam of Constant Section

Relative {Volume = 1 / Reinf. = 1}

Beam with Parabolic Soffit

Fɪɢ. 4

ORDINARY BUILDING FRAMES

Ordinary building frames are necessarily continuous; continuity is essential to their stability under the action of horizontal forces. We have found it most convenient here to use members of constant section. Much of the dead load is in the slabs and haunching to redistribute the dead load presents less attraction than in the case referred to above. An important problem now before the profession is whether or not we shall depend upon the column flexure to relieve the moment in the girders as we did in the rigid frame bridge just discussed. You will remember that the First Joint Committee did not permit this but that our present code permits it in a somewhat arbitrary fashion in certain cases. Some now wish to do it in all cases and in a systematic way rather than in an arbitrary way. I may say here that I strongly favor this movement not because I see that it will lead immediately to any great improvement in our buildings so long as we stick to present forms, with beams and columns of constant section, but rather because I have a profound faith in the ingenuity of structural designers when they are permitted to exercise their ingenuity.

Some uncertainties are inevitably involved in this procedure. It is of interest to go back to our simple bent. The flexural stresses in a column may be written in a very familiar form as

$$M \frac{c}{\Sigma aI}, \text{ where}$$

M is the fixed-end moment at the joint.

c has the usual meaning in flexure formulas, distance from neutral axis to outer fiber.

ΣaI is the sum of the adjusted moment of inertia of all members meeting at the joint, the factor a depending on the conditions of restraint, upon the relative length of the members, and upon the condition of loading.

The value of f thus computed may be further modified to allow for reduction of moment to the bottom of the girder and for the cracking of the section. This, however, is not important for our present purpose. The important relation brought out is that the moments of inertia of both column and girder are involved and that extreme precision in the computation of one is futile unless we can secure precision in the computation of the other. But, as we all know, there is considerable uncertainty as to the moments of inertia of the girders.

As nearly as I can determine, the flexural stresses indicated in the wall columns of ordinary buildings may be of the order of 300 to 400 p.s.i. In general the frames are in the hybrid stage of construction indicated above for the rigid frame and neither increase in column diameter nor added reinforcement affects very much the flexural stresses. Reduction must be made then for these stresses in determining the stresses available to carry direct load.

In ordinary building frames continuity of girders with adjacent girders is an obvious factor for which we have always made some provision in our designs. Continuity of girders with columns is something of a nuisance to the designer but he can get from it some benefit if he clearly recognizes it and allows for it in his design. Haunching promises some economy in these structures but has often serious architectural disadvantages.

In other types of concrete construction, building frames and bridges of long span, continuity points the way to a discontinuous structure with redistribution of dead load and consequently to economy and added gracefulness. (By study of the possible discontinuous types the concrete designer may realize the full possibilities of the remarkably plastic material with which he has to deal.)

CONCLUSION

Reinforced concrete has entered upon a new phase. At first, so many detailed problems of research crowded on our attention that it was difficult for us to realize the full possibilities of this type of construction.   Many and probably most of the more pressing problems of research have been solved, at least tentatively.   In the past, the designer has often found himself restricted to standard structural types, fearing to depart from them because of the maze of uncertainties constantly raised by the questioning attitude of the research man.

But concrete today has passed out of leading strings.   It is a plastic material, a material for an artist.   We can build with it as we wish, of new forms, with new proportions and to new spans.   We must encourage the designer to do so.   We must encourage him by liberalizing our codes and specifications and by developing a different point of view in our texts.

7

DESIGN OF REINFORCED CONCRETE COLUMNS SUBJECT TO FLEXURE

Columns of reinforced-concrete are nearly always subject to flexure and often to heavy flexure. Sometimes the flexure is a result of bracket loads but more frequently it is due to bending of connecting girders or to shrinkage or temperature changes.

The theory of stress analysis on the usual assumptions—which are not very accurate—is treated in meticulous detail in the literature, but the resulting formulas are so awkward as to be useless in design. The designer then resorts to tables, but these are necessarily very limited in their scope.

But stress analysis is only a small part of the problem. The magnitude of the moments involved is uncertain; the allowable stresses are more uncertain even for known forces. Is not a simpler design procedure which takes account of more elements in the problem to be preferred?

The object of this paper by Professor Cross is to encourage discussion as a whole of an important subject which has heretofore been treated only in a few individual aspects.—EDITOR

NEARLY all columns of reinforced concrete are at some time subjected to a combination of direct stress and bending; most of them receive their greatest stress under such a combination; many of them receive their critical design stress under combined stress. It is the purpose of this paper to point out certain peculiar conditions which result from these combined stresses where columns are designed according to usual practice in such cases.

Our code specifies certain basic stresses for columns axially loaded, to be applied on the transformed section. Where columns are subjected to bending these stresses may be increased in tied columns by one-third and in spiralled columns by 15% fc′.

It is specified that "moments shall be computed and provided for." The beam theory $f = \frac{P}{A} + \frac{Mc}{I}$ is used in computing stresses, the effective section being the transformed section with concrete in tension omitted.

In only one case is the method of computation of column moments indicated. It is specified that wall columns in flat slab construction shall be designed for a total moment of $\frac{WL}{35}$ which is to be distributed between the two columns in the ratio of the values $\frac{I}{h}$. This is apparently an oversight, since the stiffness of a column is affected both by the value of E and of I; the distribution should therefore be in the ratio of $\frac{EI}{h}$ or, what comes to the same thing, of $\frac{fc'I}{h}$. There is some question as to whether I should be computed for the gross or for the net section of columns spirally reinforced. It seems more logical to use the gross section, because the deformation, except at the point of failure in case failure occurs, is determined by the gross section. The steel may be neglected in computing the moment of inertia as a measure of stiffness.

SOURCES OF FLEXURE

Concrete columns are often subjected to moments which vary greatly with the stiffness (EI value) of the column; occasionally they are subjected to moments which do not vary appreciably with the column stiffness. The moments may be due to loads eccentrically applied along the column, to flexure of girders connected to the column, to temperature or shrinkage of connecting girders, to wind or other transverse forces.

In practically every case in actual construction, so far as the writer can see, the amount of moment carried by the column depends to some extent on the column stiffness. In the case of eccentric loads and of transverse loads, such as wind, however, the variation with column stiffness is so small that for present purposes it may be neglected. Also in the case of moments due to flexure of connecting members, if the columns are very stiff compared with the other members at the joint, as in the case of columns in flat slab construction, the total moment carried by the columns is little affected by their stiffness, though the distribution of the moment between the columns is considerably affected by their relative stiffness.

In the cases where slender columns are bent by flexure of heavy girders or by changes in length in the girders, the moments are very much affected by the stiffness of the column itself.

Problems in the design of columns subject to flexure may, then, be divided into two classes depending on whether the amount of moment to be carried does or does not vary much with the column stiffness.

BENDING MOMENTS IN COLUMNS NOT INTEGRAL WITH GIRDERS

It is assumed by some designers that if the girder is poured separately on top of the column without dowels, eccentricity in the column is thus avoided. Unless rocker bearings are used, it should be evident that up to the point where tension occurs it makes no difference whether the column is continuous with the girder or not. If tension is indicated, then the center of pressure lies somewhere between the kern point and the column edge; in this case the maximum stress intensity is twice the average on that part of the column section which is not in tension.

DESIGN METHODS

The usual method of design is to determine first the size of column for direct stress and then test this for combined stress. If the computed compressive stress is too high, several possibilities suggest themselves. We may add more steel or enlarge the column all along the axis or we may flare the column where the high moments exist or we may use stronger concrete. These methods may be effective or not depending on conditions. A study of these conditions is one of the objects of this paper.

Rectangular homogeneous columns subject to flexure about one major axis would be designed by the formula

$$f = \frac{P}{A}\left(1 + 6\frac{e}{d}\right)$$

This suggests the use of a similar formula in designing columns of reinforced concrete

$$f_c = \frac{P}{A_t}\,(1 + 6\,e/d)c$$

Where A_t is the area of the total transformed section

$$A_c + (n—1) A_s$$

c is a correction constant whose value depends on
  (a) the percentage of reinforcement
  (b) the eccentricity
  (c) the distribution of the reinforcement between ends and
      sides
  (d) symmetry of reinforcement
  (e) embedment of reinforcement

The constant c for ordinary cases varies within rather narrow limits, from about 0.8 to 1.2. For $f_c' = 2000$ and p = 0.03 it varies from about 0.9 to 1.1. It is not practicable to completely tabulate the values even for all common cases. In the case of rectangular columns we have to deal with both end steel and side steel and hence have, even in symmetrical cases, three parameters for our tables, $\frac{d'}{d}$, n, and the ratio of side steel to end steel; there is always side steel. Irregular and unsymmetrical cases, though common enough, cannot be tabulated at all, nor can the very common case of flexure about two major axes.

This constant c is, in a rough way, a measure of the efficiency of the section as a column. The larger the value of c, the more deeply is the column cracked and hence only a small part of it is effective in carrying the load. We expect deep cracking where the eccentricity is large or the steel percentage is small or where n is small.

DESIGNING FOR INVARIABLE MOMENTS

Where the bending moment on the column is a fixed quantity relief of overstress can be had by increasing the column size or by increasing the amount of longitudinal reinforcement and also by increasing the strength of the concrete..

Increasing the strength of the concrete, however, is surprisingly ineffective. In the first place, for the same size of column and amount of steel, A_t decreases and c increases. In addition, the allowable stress as given by the code for spiralled columns decreases less rapidly than the strength of the concrete.

In the case of tied columns the following relative values of

A_t and of c are found for various concrete strengths when compared with 2000 pounds concrete.

$$e/d = 1 \qquad p = 0.02$$

	Relative A_t	Relative c.	Relative Strength
$f'_c = 2000$	100	100	$100 \times 1.0 = 1.00$
3000	92.1	120	$77 \times 1.5 = 1.15$
4000	88.5	132	$67 \times 2 = 1.34$

For spiralled columns we must also take account of the relatively low stresses permitted for concrete with high strength. Thus, for combined stresses the code permits for $p = 0.02$.

			Relative
for $f_c' = 2000$	f_c allowable =	960	100
3000		1290	134
4000		1620	169

If we take $e/d = \frac{1}{2}$, compute the values of A_t/c and multiply by the ratio of these allowable stresses

			Relative Strength
for $f_c' = 2000$	100×100	=	100
3000	84×134	=	112
4000	71×169	=	119

In spiralled columns, then, there is almost no increase in column strength due to the use of increased concrete strength where there is very much bending. Even for axial load only, the relative strength of the spiralled column increases very slowly as the relative strength of the concrete increases.

VARIABLE MOMENT

Where the moment in the column is a result of deformation rather than of load, the moment in the column is itself a function of the size of the column and of the elastic modulus, or, what comes to about the same thing, of the strength of the concrete of which it ·is made. Where a girder is connected to a column, the top of the column must rotate through the same angle as the end of the girder. If the girder is very stiff compared with the column, this angle is affected only slightly by the size or stiffness of the column. The column, then, is subject to a fixed deformation and must be designed for the deformation and not for any particular moment. The process of computing the moment from the deformation and then computing the stress from the moment is a rather awkward device, justified by our greater familiarity with this process.

If the strength of the concrete is increased, the same deformation takes place. Now there is a difference between concrete and steel which is very important in this connection. Steel fails at a given stress dependent on its strength whereas concrete fails at a given strain which is practically independent of its strength. Evidently, then, there is no advantage in increasing the strength of concrete which is subject to a fixed deformation.

Evidently for a given rotation in the column, the outer fibre will be stretched in proportion to its distance from the column axis; in other words, the bending stress varies directly with the column diameter.

If the stiffness of the column is increased further, the resistance of the column restrains somewhat the bending of the connecting girder and the column stress due to bending increases less rapidly than the column diameter. If the column becomes very stiff relative to the girder, a point is finally reached where the bending stress decreased as the column diameter increases.

For stresses due to temperature change or shrinkage of the connecting girder, also, there is no advantage in using stronger concrete and there is a disadvantage in increasing the column diameter.

HIGH STRENGTH CONCRETE

In reference to the use of high strength concrete we have seen above that increased concrete strength increases the column strength very little even where the moment is fixed. In the case where the moment varies with the column stiffness, the use of high strength concrete may, if we follow the code, actually weaken the column, so that a larger column is needed the greater the concrete strength.

To take a very simple case, assume a single spiralled column connected to one end of a girder, the other end of the girder being rigidly fixed. Assume that $\frac{I}{L}$ for the girder is five times $\frac{I}{L}$ for the column when $f_c' = 2000$. Then for other concrete strengths, the column dimensions being otherwise the same, the value of c/d will be increased because of the increased stiffness of the column. The relative factor of safety can now be computed for the column having stronger concrete. We find,

Value c/d for $f_c' = 2000$	Factor of Safety Relative to a Column in which $f_c' = 2000$ of Columns in Which $f'_c =$		
	2000 lb. $\#D''$	3000 lb. $\#D''$	4000 lb. $\#D'$
¼	100%	90%	85%
½	100%	82%	73%
1	100%	79%	69%

The figures here given are based on compressive stress. Some of these columns would be overstressed in tension also.

The point illustrated is that the common practice of using in the same frame work members in which the concrete is of different strengths may be dangerous if we accept the rulings of the code.

VARIATION OF COLUMN DIAMETER

Under existing theories of column design, solutions of the problem of combined stress are so complicated that precise generalizations are hardly possible. The following statements, however, give some idea of the effect on the bending stress of variation in column diameter where the bending stress is a result of the flexure of connecting members.

If both dimensions of the column are varied, so that the column remains square or round, then when the stiffness of the column is about one-fifth the sum of the stiffness of all members at the joint, increasing the column diameter does not affect the bending stress very much. If the column is relatively stiffer than this, the stress decreases as the column size increases, slowly at first and then more rapidly until when the column stiffness approaches one-half the total joint stiffness, the bending stress is decreasing about as rapidly as the diameter increases. If the column is relatively less stiff than one-fifth of the total joint stiffness, the bending stress will increase with increase in the column diameter. It will usually be more economical to widen the column than to make it deeper.

Columns are usually designed first for axial load, the bending in them is computed and then they are tested for compressive stress. If the stress in the concrete is found to be larger than allowable, the column size may be increased. This reduces the axial stress and may increase the bending stress or may not affect it or it may decrease it. If the bending stress is high and the column relatively slender, then the column diameter must be greatly increased. Of course if the column diameter is increased sufficiently, then the bending stress as well as the axial stress will eventually fall off, but we have now changed the construction from girder and column to a rigid frame in which the column functions chiefly to resist moment.

If the stresses due to expansion of connection girders are fairly high in the original column, they may increase so much as the diameter is increased as to make a design in which the girder is continuous with the column entirely impossible if the column is to remain square or circular and of uniform section. This is common in the design of continuous viaducts of reinforced concrete.

TENSILE REINFORCEMENT

Tensile reinforcement in columns presents what is called reversed stress. Cases of reversed stress are common; the most familiar is that of counter braces in steel trusses.

Assume that in a certain column the stress in the tensile steel due to dead load has an intensity of 10,000 lbs. per sq. in. compression and that the stress is changed by certain live load conditions to 10,000 lbs. per sq. in. tension. If the live load is doubled, the stress will be about 30,000 lbs. per sq. in. tension, or three times as much as before.

If the bending is large there seems to be less chance of any great increase in its value due to change in load conditions or to erroneous assumptions in its computation than if the moment is small. This question of factor of safety should be automatically taken care of in the method used for computing the tensile stress. How much adjustment should be made is, however, a matter of judgment. It should be recognized that overstressing the tensile steel, while objectionable, does not threaten immediate failure.

Even an accidental increase in concrete strength may seriously overstress the tensile steel. Where the moment varies rapidly with the diameter of column, increase in the size of column without change in the amount of steel may result in overstress in the steel.

The amount of steel required for a given moment could be found simply by taking moments about the centroid of compression if we knew its position. The writer recommends that the required area of tensile steel be computed by assuming the centroid of compression at a distance 3/4d from the tensile steel and by using the usual stress in the steel.

In circular columns one-fourth of the peripheral steel is to be considered as tensile steel.

This will give designs somewhat more conservative than will an exact solution using the present code. It should be realized, however, that if the eccentricity is small, the extra amount of steel is not very important; if the eccentricity is large, an unsymmetrical design is indicated and an exact solution is rather tedious. Additional steel adds very little to the cost of the column.

In nearly all cases maximum tension in the reinforcement occurs under an entirely different condition of loading from maximum compression. Usually the maximum tension in the reinforcement is very much greater than the tension which accompanies maximum compression. Whether high unit stresses in the steel are dangerous and to what extent they are really objectionable in such cases depends on circumstances. Evidently tensile stresses exceeding the elastic limit would tend to destroy the bond but this would occur for only a short distance.

FLARED COLUMN HEADS

Where a slender column is overstressed by flexure of connecting members the economical treatment is to increase the column diameter in the region of high moment near the top of the column. This increases somewhat the moment in the column but increases greatly the resistance to such moment. It will be found that the moment increases less rapidly than the diameter of the flared head while the stress decreases about as the square of this diameter. A very good method of design is to increase the diameter at the top in proportion to the overstress and continue the flared head down to the point where it is no longer needed for overstress.

ALLOWABLE STRESSES

On the subject of allowable stress our data are very limited. Most concrete columns receive their greatest stress from a combination of flexure and direct load and it is not improbable that they would fail under such a combination; it is unquestionable that many would fail in this way, yet test data on the strength under such conditions are almost absent from the literature.* It seems that information as to strength under combined axial load and flexure is more immediately needed than further information as to strength under axial load.

Data on the strength of columns eccentrically loaded might lead to a more dependable value of the axial strength as a limiting condition. To the writer this seems a promising line of investigation.

Consideration of the permissible stress involves the following topics:

(a) allowable axial stress with and without spirals
(b) effect of shrinkage and time flow
(c) effect of spirals in cases of combined stress
(d) general theory of flexure in cases of combined stress
(e) effect of localization of high stress on any cross section and also along the axis of the column.

It is obviously not possible to make definite statements on these points in view of the present status of the experimental data.

Where high bending stresses exist it seems doubtful whether spiralling justifies such high stresses as are permitted (1280 lbs. per sq. in. on 2000-lb. concrete with 6% of logitudinal reinforcement) even if high stresses are permissible in such columns where the stress is uniform over the section.

---

*For a brief review of each data see "A Study of Bending Moments in Columns," F. E. Richart, Am. Concrete Inst. *Proceedings*, Vol. 20, p. 495, 1924.

On the other hand there is considerable reason to doubt whether the theory of the cracked section gives a valid basis for computing compressive stresses in reinforced concrete columns subject to combined stresses. In these columns the shear and bond stresses are small and there is not much cracking. The theory of the cracked section implies an improbable variation in the stress conditions on the compressive face where a crack occurs on the tensile face.

DESIGN METHODS

The problem of rational design here involves, as indicated above, problems of method of analysis, of allowable stress, of factor of safety, of methods of reducing overstress. The problem is complicated in all its phases. For rational and expeditious design we need a simpler procedure than that now specified.

After considerable study of the problem, the writer suggests the following procedure as approximately satisfactory in the light of our present knowledge.

Determine the required section from

$$A_t = \frac{P}{f_a} \text{ or } \frac{1P}{2f_a} + \frac{P'}{f_b}$$

P is the axial load.

A_t is the required area of transformed section $= A_c + (n{-}1) A_s$

P' is the equivalent flexural load $= \dfrac{6M}{d}$

f_a is the allowable axial stress

f_b is the allowable bending stress

The amount of tensile steel required is to be determined by taking moments about the centroid of compression, assuming jd = 0.75. For spiral columns, one fourth of the peripheral steel may be counted as tensile steel; for square columns with the same reinforcement in all sides this value may be taken as one-third and for rectangular columns with all steel in the ends as one-half.

SUMMARY AND CONCLUSIONS

(a) The problem of rational design of reinforced-concrete columns in flexure is unusually complicated.

(b) There are almost no test data from which to determine

working stresses. In the absence of such data, it seems best to provide for flexure on the basis of the allowable bending stress and for axial load on the basis of the allowable axial stress. In order to allow for the small eccentricities which are already provided for by the low stresses permitted for axial loads,* the axial load may be reduced one-half where combined stresses are to be provided for.

(c) A high factor of safety should be provided for the tensile steel, as in all cases of reversed stress, especially where the bending is small. It is to be noted that additional tensile steel adds very little to the total steel required in the section.

(d) The standard method of stress analysis using the transformed section has little rational and no experimental basis. It is almost impossible to apply it in cases of unsymmetrical flexure involving tension. It can be tabulated for only a very limited number of cases. For these reasons it furnishes a most unsatisfactory basis of design.

(e) Practically all reinforced concrete columns are subject to flexure, most of them receive their highest stress under combined stress, many of them would undoubtedly fail under combined stress. Too much attention seems to have been given to the stress analysis as compared with the lack of attention to determination of the moments or of the allowable stresses.

(f) Bending stresses are commonly a result of flexure of connecting members. There is, and always will be, a good deal of uncertainty about the relative stiffness of concrete members. All that we can hope to do is to provide consistently for all elements in the problem. Great precision is futile.

(g) Where overstress is indicated due to bending or expansion of connecting members in a column the size of which has been determined by axial stress only, different procedures are indicated depending on the relative amount of bending stress and relative column stiffness. If the column is flexible, increasing the diameter will increase the bending stress; if the column is stiff, increasing the diameter will decrease the bending stress. If the bending stress is very high in a flexible column, the diameter must be increased until the column is very stiff if a column of uniform

---

*The writer is not sure that such allowance was made in fixing allowable axial stresses. Information on this point would be valuable.

section is desired; in such a case, the most economical procedure is to increase the column diameter only in the region of high moments.

(h) The tensile steel may be designed by taking moments about the center of compression, assuming jd = 0.75 and using the usual stress in steel.

(i) The total area of transformed section required may be designed by the formula

$$A_t = \frac{P}{f_a} \text{ or } \frac{1}{2}\frac{P}{f_a} + \frac{6M/d}{f_b}.$$

(j) Where double flexure occurs, add the effect of moments about the two axes.

(k) High strength concrete offers little advantage where there is much flexural stress in the column. Where a flexible column has high bending stress due to flexure of connecting members the use of high strength concrete in the column alone is definitely harmful.   Similarly, abrupt changes in concrete strength in columns on successive floors is harmful.

8

DEPENDABILITY OF THE THEORY
OF CONCRETE ARCHES

I. INTRODUCTION

1. *Purpose of Investigation.*—There has been a revival of interest in recent years in the whole theory of analysis of concrete arches. Much of this has been directed to investigations of the effect of temperature changes and of the interaction of rib and superstructure. Considerable attention has, however, been directed to the theory of the action of the bare rib either on unyielding abutments or on elastic piers.

Some of the problems involved are clearly problems of physical fact to be determined by measurements in the laboratory or the field. Some are entirely of a mathematical nature, and hence not proper subjects for empirical study.

Some of the problems of arch analysis, however, apparently cannot be solved by either rational or empirical methods alone. They are problems in probability in which the range of uncertainty of certain fundamental variables is a matter for observation, but the probable uncertainty in the results consequent upon accidental combinations of these variables can scarcely be determined by experiments.

If the distortions in arches resulting from known forces on different parts of the arch can be determined, the analysis of the arch is a definite problem in geometry. But these distortions cannot be predetermined with definiteness. The purpose of the bulletin is to study the effect on the moments and thrusts resulting from this uncertainty as to the physical action under load of different parts of the arch. It isolates the assumption implied in elastic analyses and throws some light on the limit of uncertainty involved in these assumptions. The investigation is restricted to the bare arch rib and involves no questions of interaction between arch rib and deck.

2. *Acknowledgments.*—The work was conducted as a part of the work of the Engineering Experiment Station of the University of Illinois, of which DEAN M. S. KETCHUM is the director, and of the Department of Civil Engineering, of which PROF. W. C. HUNTINGTON is the head. The detail computations were made by M. F. LINDEMAN, Graduate Research Assistant.

II. Description of the Investigation

3. *Sources of Stress in an Arch.*—In any investigation of methods of analysis in structural engineering it is well to keep in mind the possible relations of such analysis to the art of design. In order to get some scale on the stresses—more or less arbitrarily separated—which enter into the design of an arch, consider the following approximate figures for computed stress in a typical open-spandrel arch of about 100-ft. span.

Dead load stress—

Due to thrust......................................	300 lb. per sq. in.
Due to moment.................................	80 lb. per sq. in.
Due to rib shortening...........................	50 lb. per sq. in.
Total......................................	430 lb. per sq. in.

Maximum live load stress—

Due to thrust......................................	50 lb. per sq. in.
Due to moment.................................	200 lb. per sq. in.
Due to rib shortening...........................	10 lb. per sq. in.
Total......................................	260 lb. per sq. in.

Maximum temperature stress—

Due to thrust......................................	10 lb. per sq. in.
Due to moment.................................	100 lb. per sq. in.
Due to rib shortening...........................	....
Total......................................	110 lb. per sq. in.
Grand total...........................	800 lb. per sq. in.

These will be subject to considerable variation in different arches, but may be taken as in a rough way representative. There will also in many cases be additional stresses due to foundation distortions, but these certainly cannot be predetermined with any accuracy in the light of facts yet known, and the chance of their occurrence would perhaps be covered by arbitrarily reducing the total working stress.

It will be noted that nearly half of the total stress is due to dead load thrust. For given dead loads this stress is a perfectly definite quantity practically independent of any assumptions whatever. This will be shown later.

The term "temperature stress" really includes also stresses due to shrinkage and to changes in moisture content of the concrete. These are universally recognized as subject to considerable uncertainty from reasons independent of uncertainties in the method of analysis.

In a rough general way, then, it may be said that about one-half of the total stress is as definite as in any statically determinate structure, about one-fourth is subject to considerable uncertainty from causes in no way dependent on the method of analysis used, leaving about one-fourth of the total stress dependent on the validity of the method of analysis used in designing the arch. This last amount may in some cases reach as much as one-third of the total stress. It will in general be a smaller per cent of the total the longer the span or the lighter the live load.

It becomes evident, then, that the method of analysis used may be subject to a considerable number of discrepancies without very seriously affecting the design. Nevertheless, it becomes important to investigate what discrepancies in the theoretical analysis are possible, and what range of variation in results is possible and probable. It is important, however, to realize that such variations have only a small relative importance, and that uncertainty in the results amounting to twenty per cent represents less than ten per cent variation in the total computed maximum stresses, provided the method of stress analysis—the beam formula $f = \dfrac{P}{A} \pm \dfrac{Mc}{I}$—is correct. Any uncertainty on the latter score is in no way peculiar to arches, but is common to all concrete structures, although the range of uncertainty from this source is perhaps less in the case of arches, because of the smaller variation of stress over the section and the smaller amount of cracking.

4. *Theory of Arch Analysis.*—The procedure commonly used in the analysis of arches is usually referred to as the theory of elasticity. The analysis deals chiefly with the bending effects in the arch ring. The effect of shearing distortions is small in most beams and in ordinary arches is negligible because the shearing stresses are very small. The effect of linear distortion in the arch ring is also small; any errors in the theory used in computing it can scarcely be very serious.

Attention then may be focused on the effects of bending in the arch. There are two conditions to be satisfied by the external loads and abutment reactions: first, the laws of statical equilibrium must be satisfied; second, the arch ring, unless rupture occurs, must remain a continuous structure.

Structural engineers do not consider the laws of statics open to question. The fact of continuity is also not open to discussion, but the laws by which the arch reactions are related to this fact are a proper subject for review.

Flexure on any segment of the arch ring produces a relative rotation of normal planes at the ends of the segment; this is only a repetition of terms, for this is what we mean by flexure. These rotations are very small. Hence the displacement in any given direction of any point connected to one end of the segment with reference to the other end equals the rotation times the normal distance from the center of rotation to the axis of displacement. This corresponds to the most elementary geometrical conception of a rotation.

Now the abutment reactions must have values determined by the fact that the rotations take place so as to maintain continuity. Stated in other words, the rotations must bear to each other such a relation that at any point on the arch ring there will be no relative rotation and no relative displacement horizontally or vertically across any imaginary section. In mathematical "short hand"

$$\Sigma\phi = 0, \ \Sigma\phi x = 0, \ \Sigma\phi y = 0$$

where ϕ is any rotation within a segment having coördinates x and y from any origin. Thus far there is nothing to investigate or debate.

Let $\dfrac{\phi}{M} = a$, where M is the bending moment at any section. In order to determine the abutment reactions from the three equations just stated it is necessary to assume (a) that the center of rotation is known for each section, and (b) that the value of $a = \dfrac{\phi}{M}$ is known for each section. Shearing and linear distortions are neglected, as already explained.

Both of these assumptions are incorrect. We do not know exactly either the amount of rotation or the center of rotation for a given moment. But it seems very important to recognize that the assumption that we do know them is the only assumption involved in the analysis of arches if the effects of linear distortions (shear and rib shortening) are neglected.

5. *The Study.*—

(a) Assumptions

While we do not know the exact centers of rotation due to moment, we do know that they lie well within the arch ring, for statics requires that one side of the ring be in compression and the other side in tension for pure flexure. It is scarcely conceivable that these rotation centers can depart far from the center of the arch ring until rupture is far advanced. This assumption can, then, scarcely be seriously in error.

There remains, then, only one thing to investigate, and that is the accuracy of our knowledge of the values $a = \dfrac{\phi}{M}$ and the importance of the uncertainty which exists as to these values. These values are usually computed as $\dfrac{1}{EI}$ times the length of the segment, where I is computed as usual and E is taken as a predetermined constant for the concrete of which the arch is constructed.

Now it is at once recognized that this is not exact, because

(a) The moment of inertia is not a correct measure of flexure in concrete, because the beam formula applies imperfectly to concrete beams.

(b) The ratio of the stress to the deformation of concrete is not a constant for any given concrete, but varies with the magnitude and duration of the stress.

(c) This ratio, which we call E, cannot be exactly predetermined; it varies with many factors.

The value a, then, for any given segment cannot be predetermined, nor is it a constant for that segment. It is not, however, necessarily assumed that it is a constant, but merely that its value for that segment, and for the bending moment which happens to exist in that segment, is known. The mathematical procedure usually referred to as the "theory of elasticity" does not necessarily assume elasticity at all; it would be better called the "geometrical theory." It becomes useless, however, unless laboratory data can enable us to predetermine values of a within limits. Given, then, the limits within which the values of a for the different segments are known to lie, it is theoretically possible to determine the limits within which the values of the reactions, moments, and shears may vary. If such an analysis were made, the limits within which the moments lie, for given limits of variation for the value a, could be stated with mathematical certainty. But the true moments could not be predetermined, because they are a matter of chance, though it might be possible to throw some light on their most probable value.

This latter problem would not be merely a problem in the mathematical theory of probability, because the probable combination of variations depends on conditions in the field. It is not probable that the properties of two sections poured at the same time from the same batch will vary nearly as much as those of two sections poured on different days under different weather conditions.

(b) Method of Investigation

The investigation here recorded represents an effort to study the relation between the range of variation of the values of $a = \dfrac{\phi}{M}$ and the consequent range of variation of the bending moments. Because the chief source of variation in the value of a is the value of E, the data are presented in terms of the variation of E.

The arch studied is supposed to be made of six voussoirs or blocks of concrete, and the values of E for each of these blocks are supposed to be subject to independent variation. All moments are first computed on the assumption that the moment of inertia is constant in all sections. This is taken as the normal case. The values of E are then increased or decreased a given amount ($+$ 50 per cent or $-$ 33⅓ per cent) in certain selected segments, and in these arches certain bending moments have been recomputed.

The fundamental arch chosen for study has a parabolic axis and the section is assumed to vary in such a way that the moment of inertia varies as the length of axis for a given horizontal projection. The span, rise, and crown thickness are immaterial, since the relations deduced would have been the same no matter what these values. This arch has the advantage that its properties and those of the arches derived from it are readily determined by integration, and also that, for load uniformly distributed over the entire span, the moments at all points on the axis are zero.

It seems unnecessary to discuss the method of analysis used. Except for the treatment of rib shortening, all methods of arch analysis by the elastic theory are exactly identical in their fundamental equations, though the identity may not be apparent. The only theory now used in arch analysis which is not always classed with the elastic theory is the pressure line theory. But the theorem that the pressure line for the loads is that string polygon which lies nearest to the arch axis is based on the elastic theory. In the case here investigated the theorem will, if accurately applied, give exactly the same result as the elastic theory. It is, however, less convenient to apply with accuracy. Methods of analysis by the theory of elasticity differ somewhat in precision, those using integration being mathematically exact, while those using summations are less precise, especially if $\dfrac{\Delta s}{I}$ be made constant. Rib-shortening may be included in the original analysis, or it may be corrected for. Shearing distortions have an inappreciable effect.

In all of the comparisons here shown, the effect of rib-shortening has been omitted. Integration was used in determining the properties, but the moments were computed with a 10-in. slide rule.

In cases of **moments** due to loads, only the variations in elastic properties are **important**, but moments due to temperature or to abutment movements are affected both by the variations in relative properties and by the general stiffening of the arch. In order to eliminate the second factor, which is irrelevant in determining the effect of variations, the moments have also been computed on the assumption that $\int \dfrac{ds}{EI}$ is the same for all arches. This is nearly the same as assuming that the average value of EI is the same in all arches.

We have here, then, the record of what may be called an analytical experiment. It involves in all over one thousand moment determinations on about one hundred and fifty arches. It is true that because of symmetry and of the geometrical properties of the arch chosen corresponding values for different arches are not all independent. But the interrelation of the values is involved in the theory of analysis of which the sensitiveness to variations in assumptions is being tested. Hence it seems that they may be considered as independent evidence in the case.

(c) Scope of Investigation

It must be emphasized that the investigation here conducted is suggestive only; it is neither exhaustive nor conclusive. The probable variation in shear, moment, and thrust at any section in a concrete arch for any given loading or deformation will depend on

(a) The total magnitude of variation in elastic properties
(b) The rate of such variation, whether by sudden jumps or gradual change
(c) The location of such variations relative to the section being investigated.

The probable variation in the value of the shear or moment is also a function of the location of the section and of the type of loading or deformation. Probably to a small extent it is a function also of relatively small changes which in ordinary arches occur in the shape of the axis and of the rib.

For six voussoirs there are sixty-three different combinations of voussoirs which may be varied, but for ten voussoirs there are one thousand and twenty-three possible combinations. The range of variation in moments for a given range of variations of E depends on the number of voussoirs chosen. The data presented then are to be taken merely as evidence in the case, to be treated as empirical data with all the reservations which should accompany the interpretation of such data.

It seems probable that a large arch will be subject to a greater number of possible combinations of varying properties than a small arch, and it seems almost certain that an arch poured under field conditions will be subject to a greater range of variation than one poured in a laboratory.

The effects of variation of individual voussoirs are not additive nor are they even approximately so. The relation of reactions to individual elastic properties is not even approximately linear.

With so many variables any exact mathematical generalization could be made only with great difficulty. It seems important, however, to realize it is theoretically possible, and also to realize that even if it were made, it is not clear that it would be very useful to the engineer in his designs.

It is also important to caution against extending the data to other types of structures even in a qualitative way. They should not, for example, be extended to bents or to continuous girders.

After all, the interest of the designer is in what may possibly happen and in what will probably happen in his structure. He tries to adjust the factor of safety in a rough way to the probability. He is, therefore, interested in what "actually happens" in any particular structure only as he can estimate from it the probability of occurrence in other structures.

These data tell without any question what actually happens in certain structures of definite properties. They may, then, be used as a guide to probability just as any other empirical data would be used. The "normal" case of constant E has been used as a basis of comparison, not because it is "true" or "right" but simply because it is convenient; and it should be used in design for the same reason.

6. *Dead Load Thrusts.*—The loads may be either concentrated, as in an arch with open spandrels, or distributed, as in an arch with filled spandrels. In the former case it is never possible to make the string polygon for loads exactly fit the arch axis, because the axis is curved while the polygon has vertices at the panel points. If the load is distributed, however, it is always possible to choose a loading for which a string polygon may be made to fit the arch axis. This loading may be the dead load or the dead load plus some live load.

Now it is certain that in any given case there is only one set of values that will satisfy both the equations of statics and the equations of continuity. Since there will be no bending moment, there will be no bending if a string polygon for loads follows the arch axis. This, then, is a true pressure line satisfying the required conditions if rib-shortening is neglected and this is true whatever the elastic properties of the sections may be.

In the arch with open spandrels a string polygon cannot be drawn exactly fitting the arch axis, but unless the curvature of the axis is very sharp, or the panel unusually long, a polygon may be drawn for which the moments and ϕ values are so small that variations in the values $a = \dfrac{\phi}{M}$ will have very little effect on the shape of the polygon even though they may affect considerably the small moment values.

It will be seen, then, that for a large part of the loading on an arch the reactions are either entirely or practically independent of any assumptions involved in the analysis. This justifies the statement already made that any assumptions in the theory can affect only a part of the total stress.

7. *Relief of Weak Concrete.*—It has sometimes been argued that weak concrete is not so much a source of danger in arches because at a weak section the stresses will be automatically decreased. This is true to only a small extent even if the elastic modulus varies with the strength. In the first place, a large part of the stress on any arch section is due to thrust; this is one very important difference between ordinary beams and arches. The total thrust for loads at any section will be affected very slightly by any variation in elastic properties. The data here presented also show that, for variation in the elastic properties of any one of the relatively large sections here shown, the moment is in general affected much less than the strength; if the sections were shorter, the effect would be even less. Moreover, if several sections vary in elastic properties simultaneously, the moment at a weak section may be even larger than is expected. Any dependable relief of a weak section before failure begins is, then, too improbable to be considered in design.

III. Summary

8. *Data.*—The results of the analyses are recorded in Tables 1 to 6 and in Figs. 1 to 11.

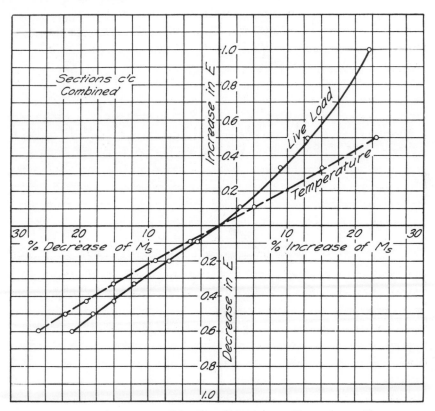

FIG. 1. RELATION OF MOMENT VARIATION TO VARIATION IN E

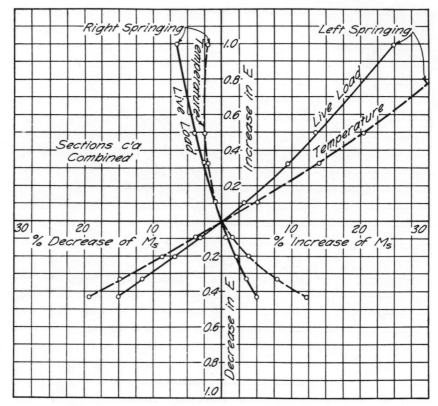

FIG. 2. RELATION OF MOMENT VARIATION TO VARIATION IN E

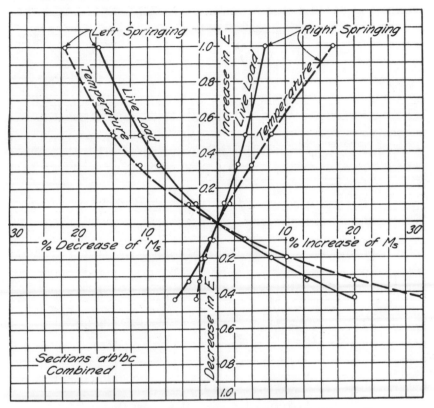

FIG. 3. RELATION OF MOMENT VARIATION TO VARIATION IN E

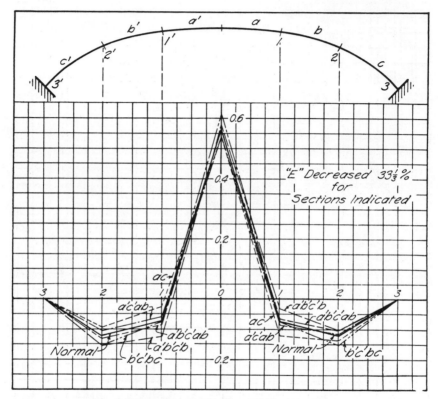

FIG. 4. INFLUENCE LINES FOR MOMENT AT CROWN

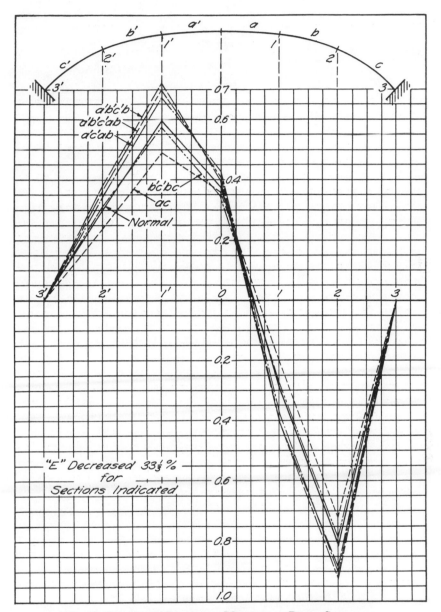

FIG. 5. INFLUENCE LINES FOR MOMENT AT RIGHT SPRINGING

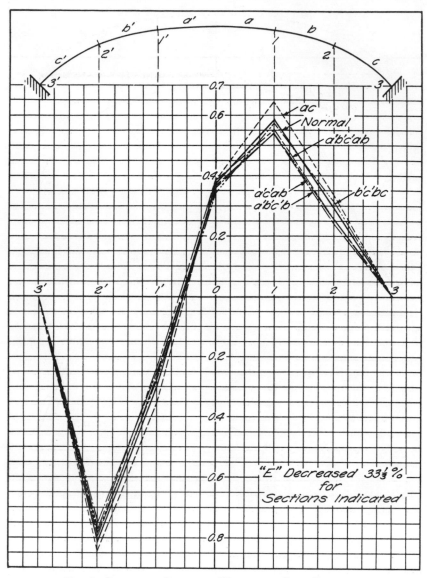

FIG. 6. INFLUENCE LINES FOR MOMENT AT LEFT SPRINGING

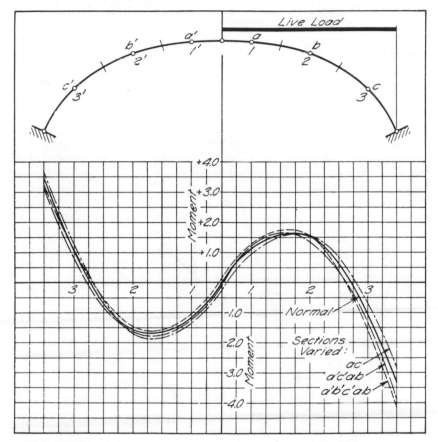

FIG. 7. MOMENT CURVES SHOWING VARIATION OF MOMENT ALONG ARCH AXIS

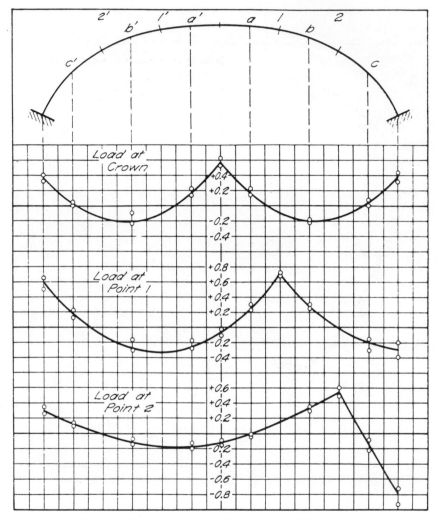

FIG. 8. MOMENT CURVES SHOWING MAXIMUM AND MINIMUM VARIATION
FROM NORMAL

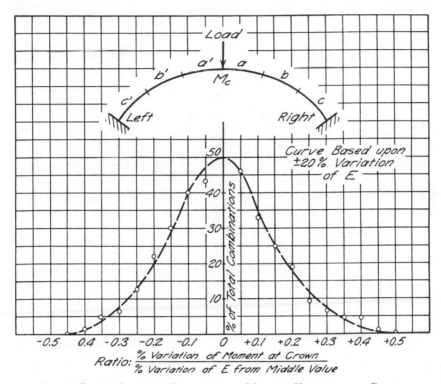

FIG. 9. CURVES SHOWING FREQUENCY OF MOMENT VARIATIONS AT CROWN

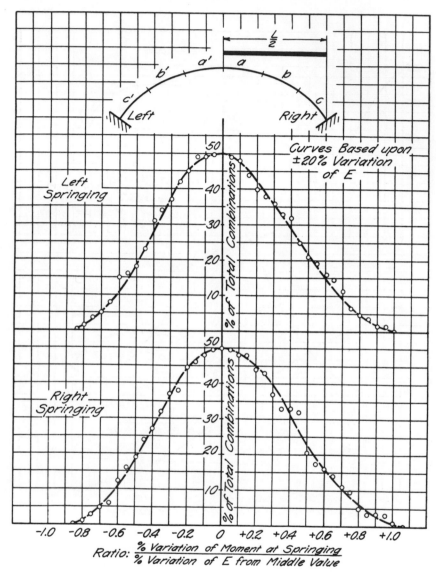

FIG. 10. CURVES SHOWING FREQUENCY OF MOMENT VARIATIONS AT SPRINGING

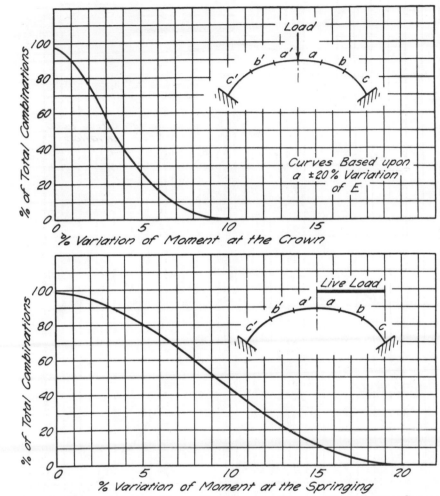

FIG. 11. CURVES SHOWING AVERAGE FREQUENCY OF MOMENT VARIATIONS AT CROWN
AND SPRINGING

TABLE 1
MOMENTS AT CROWN AND AT SPRINGINGS PRODUCED BY LOAD
Percentage variations due to indicated variations of the modulus of elasticity of sections indicated

50% Increase	33⅓% Decrease	Combinations of Sections	Left		Right	
			50% Increase	33⅓% Decrease	33⅓% Decrease	50% Increase
+9	−8	a'a	−3	+3	+3	−3
−8	+9	b'c'bc	+3	−3	−3	+3
−6	+6	b'b	−9	+9	+9	−9
+6	−6	a'c'ac	+9	−9	−9	+9
−3	+2	c'c	+13	−12	−12	+13
+2	−3	a'b'ab	−12	+13	+13	−12
0	0	a'b'c'abc	0	0	0	0
−4	+2	a'b'c'b	+11	−9	+20	−16
+2	−4	ac	−9	+11	−16	+20
−4	+2	b'abc	−17	+19	−10	+9
+2	−4	a'c'	+19	−17	+9	−10
−3	+3	a'b'bc	−11	+16	−4	+5
+3	−3	c'a	+16	−11	+5	−4
−3	+3	b'c'ab	+2	−5	+14	−11
+3	−3	a'c	−5	+2	−11	+14
−2	+1	b'c'ac	+2	−3	−8	+11
+1	−2	a'b	−3	+2	+11	−8
−2	+1	a'c'bc	+11	−8	−2	+3
+1	−2	b'a	−8	+11	+3	−2
0	0	a'c'b	+15	−14	+16	−14
0	0	b'ac	−14	+15	−14	+16
+8	−7	a'c'a	+14	−13	+9	−8
−7	+8	b'bc	−13	+14	−8	+9
+8	−7	a'ac	−8	+8	−12	+15
−7	+8	b'c'b	+8	−8	+15	−12
+4	−4	a'b'c'a	+9	−8	+12	−11
−4	+4	bc	−8	+9	−11	+12
+4	−4	a'abc	−12	+12	−9	+9
−4	+4	b'c'	+12	−12	+9	−9
−5	+4	b'c'abc	−1	+1	−4	+5
+4	−5	a'	+1	−1	+5	−4
−5	+4	a'b'c'bc	+5	−4	+1	−1
+4	−5	a	−4	+5	−1	+1
−4	+5	c'b	+14	−13	+10	−10
+5	−4	a'b'ac	−13	+14	−10	+10
−4	+5	b'c	−10	+10	−12	+15
+5	−4	a'c'ab	+10	−10	+15	−12
−5	+4	b'c'c	+6	−7	−7	+9
+4	−5	a'ab	−7	+6	+9	−7
−5	+4	c'bc	+9	−8	−7	+6
+4	−5	a'b'a	−8	+9	+6	−7
+1	−3	a'c'c	+14	−12	−6	+9
−3	+1	b'ab	−12	+14	+9	−6
+1	−3	c'ac	+8	−7	−12	+15
−3	+1	a'b'b	−7	+8	+15	−12
+3	−2	a'c'abc	+6	−6	−4	+5
−2	+3	b'	−6	+6	+5	−4
+3	−2	a'b'c'ac	+3	−4	−5	+5
−2	+3	b	−4	+3	+5	−5
+1	+1	b'c'a	+8	−6	+9	−6
+1	+1	a'bc	−6	+8	−6	+9
−2	+1	a'b'c'c	+7	−8	−4	+4
+1	−2	ab	−8	+7	+4	−4
−2	+1	c'abc	+3	−5	−7	+8
+1	−2	a'b'	−5	+3	+8	−7
+2	−1	a'b'c'ab	+4	−5	+19	−15
−1	+2	c	−5	+4	−15	+19
+2	−1	a'b'abc	−15	+17	−6	+6
−1	+2	c'	+17	−15	+6	−6
0	0	a'b'c'	+13	−12	+13	−13
0	0	abc	−12	+13	−13	+13
0	0	c'ab	+8	−9	+10	−9
0	0	a'b'c	−9	+8	−9	+10

TABLE 2

MOMENTS AT CROWN AND AT SPRINGINGS PRODUCED BY TEMPERATURE CHANGE

Percentage variations due to 33 ⅓ per cent decrease in modulus of elasticity of sections indicated

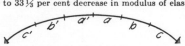

Total Stiffness $\int \frac{ds}{EI}$, Constant			Combination of Sections	Total Stiffness $\int \frac{ds}{EI}$, Variable; E for Unchanged Sections, Constant		
At Springings		At Crown		At Crown	At Springings	
Left	Right				Left	Right
+3	+6	−6	a	−13	−5	−3
+6	+3	−6	a′	−13	−3	−5
+7	+9	+6	b	−2	−2	0
+9	+7	+6	b′	−2	0	−2
+2	−16	+4	c	−5	−6	−23
−16	+2	+4	c′	−5	−23	−6
+9	+14	−1	ab	−15	−6	−3
+14	+9	−1	a′b′	−15	−3	−7
+4	−13	−4	ac	−18	−11	−26
−13	+4	−4	a′c′	−18	−26	−11
+8	−15	−3	a′c	−17	−8	−27
−15	+8	−3	c′a	−17	−27	−8
+13	+10	−1	a′b	−15	−4	−5
+10	+13	−1	b′a	−15	−5	−4
+10	−11	+9	b′c	−7	−6	−24
−11	+10	+9	c′b	−7	−24	−6
+9	+9	+1	a′a	−17	−7	−7
+16	+16	+10	b′b	−6	−1	−1
−15	−15	+7	c′c	−8	−27	−27
−9	+8	+7	b′c′	−8	−22	−8
+8	−9	+7	bc	−8	−8	−22
+10	−11	−8	a′ac	−27	−12	−29
−11	+10	−8	a′c′a	−27	−29	−12
−11	−8	+10	c′bc	−12	−29	−27
−8	−11	+10	b′c′c	−12	−27	−29
+11	−8	+1	b′ac	−19	−11	−26
−8	+11	+1	a′c′b	−19	−26	−11
+18	+21	+4	b′ab	−17	−6	−4
+21	+18	+4	a′b′b	−17	−4	−6
+16	+16	−6	a′ab	−25	−8	−7
+16	+16	−6	a′b′a	−25	−7	−8
+16	−4	+11	b′bc	−11	−8	−23
−4	+16	+11	b′c′b	−11	−23	−8
−6	+10	−1	a′b′c′	−20	−25	−12
+10	−6	−1	abc	−20	−12	−25
+14	−8	0	a′bc	−20	−9	−27
−8	+14	0	b′c′a	−20	−27	−9
−14	−12	−1	c′ac	−21	−32	−30
−12	−14	−1	a′c′c	−21	−30	−32
−10	+15	+2	c′ab	−18	−28	−8
+15	−10	+2	a′b′c	−18	−8	−28
+16	−5	−4	a′b′ac	−28	−13	−29
−5	+16	−4	a′c′ab	−28	−29	−13
+20	−3	+5	a′b′bc	−21	−10	−27
−3	+20	+5	b′c′ab	−21	−27	−10
−7	−8	+2	a′c′bc	−23	−31	−31
−8	−7	+2	b′c′ac	−23	−31	−31
+16	−4	−5	a′abc	−29	−13	−28
−4	+16	−5	a′b′c′a	−29	−28	−13
+17	0	+5	b′abc	−22	−13	−26
0	+17	+5	a′b′c′b	−22	−26	−13
−10	−5	+2	c′abc	−23	−33	−29
−5	−10	+2	a′b′c′c	−23	−29	−33
−11	−11	−6	a′c′ac	−30	−33	−33
+23	+23	−1	a′b′ab	−26	−8	−8
−4	−4	+13	b′c′bc	−15	−28	−28
+22	+1	−1	a′b′abc	−30	−14	−29
+1	+22	−1	a′b′c′ab	−30	−29	−14
−3	−1	+6	b′c′abc	−25	−32	−30
−1	−3	+6	a′b′c′bc	−25	−30	−32
−6	−4	−3	a′c′abc	−32	−34	−33
−4	−6	−3	a′b′c′ac	−32	−33	−34
0	0	0	a′b′c′abc	−33	−34	−34

TABLE 3
MOMENTS AT SPRINGINGS PRODUCED BY ABUTMENT ROTATIONS
Percentage variations due to 33 ⅓ per cent decrease in modulus of elasticity of sections indicated

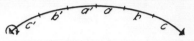

Total Stiffness $\int \frac{ds}{EI}$, Constant		Combination of Sections	Total Stiffness $\int \frac{ds}{EI}$, Variable E for Unchanged Sections, Constant	
Left	Right		Left	Right
+6	+6	a	−3	−3
+7	+6	a′	−1	−3
+7	+12	b	−1	+3
+4	+12	b′	−4	+3
+6	−12	c	−2	−19
−22	−12	c′	−28	−19
+13	+17	ab	−3	0
+11	+17	a′b′	−5	0
+12	−8	ac	−4	−22
−16	−8	a′c′	−28	−22
+13	−8	a′c	−3	−21
−17	−8	c′a	−29	−21
+14	+14	a′b	−3	−2
+8	+14	b′a	−8	−2
+10	−6	b′c	−6	−20
−16	−6	c′b	−28	−20
+13	+11	a′a	−3	−5
+10	+25	b′b	−5	−7
−17	−23	c′c	−29	−34
−17	−2	b′c′	−29	−16
+13	−2	bc	−3	−16
+19	−4	a′ac	−5	−23
−12	−4	a′c′a	−30	−23
−12	−15	c′bc	−30	−32
−13	−15	b′c′c	−31	−32
+14	+1	b′ac	−8	−19
−11	+1	a′c′b	−29	−19
+15	+31	b′ab	−8	+4
+17	+31	a′b′b	−6	+4
+20	+23	a′ab	−4	−2
+16	+23	a′b′a	−7	−2
+16	+9	b′bc	−7	−13
−13	+9	b′c′b	−30	−13
−13	+1	a′b′c′	−30	−19
+18	+1	abc	−5	−19
+20	+2	a′bc	−4	−18
−14	+2	b′c′a	−31	−18
−13	−21	c′ac	−30	−36
−12	−21	a′c′c	−29	−36
−13	+1	c′ab	−30	−19
+16	+1	a′b′c	−7	−19
+21	+6	a′b′ac	−9	−21
−7	+6	a′c′ab	−30	−21
+22	+12	a′b′bc	−8	−16
−9	+12	b′c′ab	−32	−16
−7	−12	a′c′bc	−30	−34
−10	−12	b′c′ac	−33	−34
+26	+6	a′abc	−5	−20
−9	+6	a′b′c′a	−32	−20
+20	+12	b′abc	−10	−16
−8	+12	a′b′c′b	−31	−16
−8	−13	c′abc	−31	−34
−8	−13	a′b′c′c	−31	−34
−8	−18	a′c′ac	−31	−38
+22	+36	a′b′ab	−8	+2
−9	−6	b′c′bc	−31	−29
+28	+17	a′b′abc	−10	−17
−4	+16	a′b′c′ab	−32	−18
−5	−3	b′c′abc	−33	−31
−4	−3	a′b′c′bc	−32	−31
−3	−9	a′c′abc	−31	−36
−5	−9	a′b′c′ac	−33	−36
0	0	a′b′c′abc	−34	−33

TABLE 4

AVERAGE AND MAXIMUM VARIATIONS OF MOMENTS AT SELECTED SECTIONS

Percentage variations due to 33⅓ per cent decrease in the modulus of elasticity of the sections

Loads

	Crown		Springing			
			Left		Right	
	+	−	+	−	+	−
Av............	3.1	3.6	8.7	8.2	9.2	8.1
Max..........	9.0	8.0	19.0	17.0	20.0	16.0

Temperature, $\int \frac{ds}{EI}$ Constant

	Crown		Springing			
			Left		Right	
	+	−	+	−	+	−
Av............	5.5	3.2	11.8	8.1	11.7	7.9
Max..........	13.0	8.0	23.0	16.0	23.0	16.0

Abutment Rotation, $\int \frac{ds}{EI}$ Constant

	Springing			
	Left		Right	
	+	−	+	−
Av....................	14.3	10.5	11.5	9.7
Max....................	28.0	22.0	36.0	23.0

TABLE 5

VARIATION OF MAXIMUM MOMENTS AS DETERMINED FROM INFLUENCE LINES FOR SIX PANELS

Percentage variations due to 33⅓ per cent decrease in the modulus of elasticity of sections indicated. See Figs. 4, 5, and 6.

Sections	Left Springing		Crown		Right Springing	
	Pos.	Neg.	Pos.	Neg.	Pos.	Neg.
a'b'c'b........	−6	−8	0	+8	+20	+19
a'b'c'ab.......	−3	−5	−1	−8	+15	+23
a'c'ab.........	−6	−10	−6	−8	+14	+19
b'c'bc.........	−3	−5	+9	+17	−5	−1
ac............	+9	+5	−7	−5	−19	−13

TABLE 6
COMPARATIVE MOMENTS ALONG ARCH AXIS FOR VARIOUS LOAD POINTS WITH *E* VARIED FOR SECTIONS INDICATED

Moments at Centroid of Sections for 3 Load Points

Point	a'b'ab	a'c'ab	b'c	ac	a'b'c'b	a'b'c'ab	c	a'a	Normal	Sections Varied ('E' Increased for Shaded Sections)
Crown	+0.32	+0.44	+0.36	+0.37	+0.39	+0.41	+0.39	+0.33	+0.38	
Pt.1	+0.50	+0.69	+0.54	+0.49	+0.65	+0.71	+0.55	+0.55	+0.59	
Pt.2	+0.27	+0.35	+0.25	+0.24	+0.34	+0.37	+0.26	+0.28	+0.30	
Crown	+0.01	+0.08	+0.02	+0.03	+0.04	+0.07	+0.04	+0.03	+0.04	
Pt.1	+0.12	+0.27	+0.16	+0.13	+0.22	+0.29	+0.17	+0.17	+0.19	
Pt.2	+0.09	+0.16	+0.09	+0.08	+0.13	+0.17	+0.09	+0.10	+0.12	
Crown	-0.20	-0.20	-0.24	-0.22	-0.21	-0.20	-0.21	-0.18	-0.21	
Pt.1	-0.31	-0.23	-0.29	-0.27	-0.30	-0.24	-0.28	-0.29	-0.27	
Pt.2	-0.15	-0.10	-0.12	-0.12	-0.12	-0.10	-0.11	-0.15	-0.12	
Crown	+0.18	+0.15	+0.14	+0.15	+0.16	+0.16	+0.16	+0.22	+0.17	
Pt.1	-0.25	-0.23	-0.26	-0.21	-0.29	-0.25	-0.25	-0.25	-0.25	
Pt.2	-0.19	-0.15	-0.16	-0.14	-0.18	-0.17	-0.15	-0.20	-0.16	
Crown	+0.58	+0.53	+0.53	+0.55	+0.55	+0.56	+0.56	+0.62	+0.56	
Pt.1	-0.07	-0.06	-0.09	-0.03	-0.11	-0.08	-0.06	-0.07	-0.07	
Pt.2	-0.14	-0.10	-0.12	-0.09	-0.14	-0.13	-0.11	-0.15	-0.12	
Crown	+0.18	+0.14	+0.15	+0.16	+0.15	+0.16	+0.16	+0.22	+0.17	
Pt.1	+0.29	+0.28	+0.25	+0.32	+0.23	+0.26	+0.26	+0.27	+0.27	
Pt.2	-0.03	+0.01	-0.02	+0.01	-0.02	-0.03	-0.01	-0.04	-0.01	
Crown	-0.20	-0.24	-0.20	-0.21	-0.22	-0.21	-0.20	-0.18	-0.21	
Pt.1	+0.31	+0.30	+0.25	+0.30	+0.28	+0.27	+0.25	+0.29	+0.28	
Pt.2	+0.35	+0.36	+0.30	+0.33	+0.34	+0.32	+0.30	+0.31	+0.34	
Crown	+0.01	+0.02	+0.08	+0.04	+0.03	+0.04	+0.07	+0.03	+0.04	
Pt.1	-0.18	-0.19	-0.27	-0.24	-0.15	-0.20	-0.30	-0.21	-0.21	
Pt.2	-0.09	-0.09	-0.21	-0.16	-0.08	-0.13	-0.22	-0.14	-0.14	
Crown	+0.32	+0.36	+0.44	+0.39	+0.37	+0.39	+0.41	+0.33	+0.38	
Pt.1	-0.26	-0.26	-0.38	-0.36	-0.20	-0.26	-0.40	-0.29	-0.29	
Pt.2	-0.75	-0.74	-0.90	-0.85	-0.72	-0.79	-0.92	-0.80	-0.80	

In Tables 1 to 4 are shown the variations in moments at crown and springings due to variations in the values of E in certain selected voussoirs for temperature changes, abutment rotations, and for certain conditions of loading.   Table 5 shows variations of maximum moments.   Table 6 shows comparative values of the moments at various points along the arch axis due to concentrated loads at the panel points for several combinations of variations in the elastic properties of the voussoirs.

Figures 1 to 3 show the relation of moment variation to variation in elastic properties in certain cases.   Figures 4 to 6 show influence lines for bending moment at different points along the arch axis for several combinations of variations in elastic properties.   Figures 7 and 8 show range of variation in the moment curves for different conditions of loading and give at a glance some idea of the range of variation in bending moments.   Figures 9 to 11 show the probable relations between the range of variations in elastic properties and the range of variations in moments at crown and at springing for a particular range of variation in elastic properties.

9. *Results.*—Tables 1, 2, and 3 give the percentage variations from the normal value, due to the loadings or distortions indicated, of the moments at the designated points for the stated variations in E for the sections shown.

In Table 1 the third row shows what portions of the arch axis have been varied in stiffness.   For a unit load at the crown, if the value of E for sections a' and a is increased 50 per cent ,the crown moment is increased 9 per cent; if the value of E for these sections is decreased $33\frac{1}{3}$ per cent, the crown moment is decreased 8 per cent.   In the same way are shown the percentage changes in moment at left and right springings for live load over one-half of the arch.

In Table 2 are shown the percentage changes in moments at crown and at each springing produced by a given temperature change.   On the left of this table the moment has in each case been computed for the same value of $\int \frac{ds}{EI}$ in all arches.   This is nearly equivalent to assuming the same average value of E in all arches.   The adjustment is made in order to isolate the effect of the variations in the value of E within the arch as distinguished from the variation in the average value of E in different arches.

The figures on the right of Table 2 are like those on the left, except that it has not been assumed that $\int \frac{ds}{EI}$ is the same in all arches. Here the moment is affected both by the variation in E within the arch ring and also by the change in the average value of E. A comparison of the figures on the right and on the left shows the effect of these two factors.

Thus the table shows that if the value of E for section a is one-third less than that for the other sections in an arch, the average value of E being the same as if all sections had the same value of E, then, due to a given temperature change, the moment at the crown would be decreased 6 per cent, that at the left springing would be increased 3 per cent, and that at the right springing increased 6 per cent.

If, however, the change in E for section a were not accompanied by any corresponding change in E at the other sections, then the moment at the crown would be decreased 13 per cent, the moment at the left springing would be decreased 5 per cent and that at the right springing 3 per cent.

Table 3 is like Table 2 except that it shows the effect on the moments at the springings of variations of E when the abutment is rotated a given amount.

Table 4 summarizes the data given in Table 1 and on the left sides of Tables 2 and 3. It shows the average and the maximum increase and the average and the maximum decrease in moment at crown and springings for loads as indicated, and for temperature change and rotation of abutment, as shown in Tables 1, 2, and 3. These are average and maximum values for all possible combinations of voussoirs in an arch having six voussoirs with E varying $33\frac{1}{3}$ per cent from its maximum value but always having the same average value of E. This table shows that the moment may vary almost as much as does the value of E.

In Table 5 variation in maximum moments is shown for certain selected cases. These cases were chosen more or less at random, but in general they are cases which showed large variations in the previous tables. The variations shown are about as large as in Table 4. Thus if the elastic modulus of all voussoirs except that next to the right springing (a′ b′ c′ ab) were two million pounds per square inch, and that of the remaining voussoir (c) were three million pounds per square inch, the maximum positive moment at the right springing due to live load would be increased 15 per cent and the maximum negative moment due to live load would be increased 23 per cent.

Table 6 shows comparative bending moments at various points along the arch axis for loads at various points. The modulus of elasticity of some sections—indicated by heavy lines—has been increased by 20 per cent and of others—indicated by light lines—has been decreased by 20 per cent from an assumed normal value.   The chief value of this record is in showing that the moments at a weak section—a section of small E value—are decreased only slightly, if at all.

Figures 1, 2, and 3 show the ratio of the variation in moment to the variation in E when the variation in E is restricted to the sections indicated—(c'c) in Fig. 1, (c'a) in Fig. 2, (a'b'bc) in Fig. 3.   These curves suggest that, for reasonable variations in the value of E, the relation of change in moment to change in E is approximately linear. The values given are for moments at the springing due to temperature change and to live load over the right half of the arch.   The moments due to change of temperature are for arches of constant value of average E.

The influence lines shown in Figs. 4, 5, and 6 show the effect of a decrease of one-third in the values of E for the sections shown.   These have been plotted from the data contained in Table 6.   They indicate a rather wide zone within which influence ordinates may lie.

It is of interest to note that since the values of E vary with the magnitude of the moment on a section these influence lines would not be determined by an actual moving unit load.   Influence lines cannot in any accurate sense be determined experimentally unless Hooke's Law applies.

Figure 7 shows moment curves for the live load shown for a decrease of one-third in the value of E for the sections indicated, and also the normal moment curve for constant E.

Figure 8 is plotted from the data of Table 6.   It shows normal curves of moments for three load positions, and also the maximum and minimum values of moments as shown in the table.   It does not therefore represent maxima and minima for all possible combinations of the six segments.   It does, however, give some idea of the uncertainty involved in such moment curves.

Figures 9, 10, and 11 summarize the data bearing on the main point investigated, the relation of the variation in moment to the variation in elastic properties.

In Fig. 9 the ordinates represent the percentage of the total number of values of crown moment for load at the crown which exceed a certain value of the abscissas.   The abscissas represent the ratios of the percentage variation of moment to percentage variation of E from its middle value.   In this investigation the variation of E from its middle value is ± 20 per cent, which is the same as a 50 per cent increase of the larger value over the smaller value, or a decrease of $33\frac{1}{3}$ per cent of the smaller value from the larger value.

Figure 10 is like Fig. 9 except that it is for moments at the springings with live load over the right half of the span.

The irregularity of the individual points plotted seems to have no special significance; it depends on the interval of the abscissa values.

Figure 11 summarizes Figs. 9 and 10 without reference to sign. The abscissas here, however, are actual—not relative—percentages of moment variation. The curves give some idea of the probability of a given variation in moment. They show, for instance, that in this investigation where E varies ± 20 per cent, for crown moment with load at the crown half the values lie at least ± 3 per cent from the value computed by the usual theory, and for the springing moments for half span loading half the values lie at least ± 9 per cent from the value usually computed. The variation at the crown, however, may reach ± 10 per cent, and that at the springing ± 20 per cent, but these values are highly improbable. The "normal" value with constant E, however, is also very improbable.

10. *Conclusions.*—The investigations here recorded indicate:

(1) that for a large part (over one-half) of the stresses in an arch there can be practically no uncertainty arising from assumptions involved in the method of analysis used.

(2) that for the flexural stresses due to live load the true stresses cannot be predicted with absolute precision, because the stresses are a matter of chance.

(3) that the departure of the stresses existing in any arch from the values given by the usual methods of analysis can scarcely be greater than the variations in the quality of the concrete, and will most probably be very much less.

Beyond this it does not seem wise or profitable to draw conclusions, though others are apparently indicated by the data. The important fact is that any wide departure from the predicted values of the moments and thrusts in a concrete arch is not possible unless the variation in the properties of concrete is much greater than is commonly supposed. Within a narrow zone of uncertainty, then, the maximum moments and thrusts due to loads in a concrete arch are given without possible question by the "geometrical" (elastic) analysis. The zone of such uncertainty here seems to have a width of about ± 10 per cent; the zone of probable uncertainty seems to have a width of about ± 5 per cent. The terms "true value" and "real value," however, are meaningless except as applied to a given arch under a given condition of loading and a given atmospheric condition; otherwise the reactions are a matter of chance.

The geometrical theory of analysis for arch reactions appears more dependable than the theory of flexure used to compute the fibre stresses produced by these reactions, and much more dependable than the concrete itself.   It is not exact or precise, but it is a safe and convenient guide in design.

9

THE COLUMN ANALOGY

I. Introduction

1. *Purpose of the Monograph.*—The object of this bulletin is to present some theorems dealing with the elastic analysis of continuous frames. In ordinary cases these theorems are identical in form with the theorems, with which every structural engineer is familiar, for finding internal stresses in beams and struts.

The subject of structural mechanics is now experiencing demands for greater precision by the very accurate analyses demanded in the design of airplanes. In any case it is of the greatest importance to isolate definitely those matters which are sources of uncertainty from those which are certain and hence not proper fields of experiment.

Problems dealing with the analysis of restrained flexural members—straight beams, bents, arches—occupy a large space in structural literature. The treatment often presented involves complicated equations; in nearly all cases the method of solution is hard to remember.

If the elastic properties of the different portions of the structure are definitely known, the analysis of restrained members is essentially a problem in geometry, because the member must bend in such a way as to satisfy the conditions of restraint. The geometrical relations involved are identical in algebraic form with the general formula for determining fiber stress in a member which is bent.

Since the analysis of problems in flexure is a familiar procedure to structural engineers, it is advantageous to state the relations involved in the analysis of fixed-end beams, bents, and arches in terms of the beam formula. The advantages for structural engineers are similar to those which result from using the theorems of area-moments in finding slopes and deflections of beams; in some respects the concepts involved are identical, and the use of the beam formula in the analysis of restrained members may be thought of as an extension of the principles of area-moments. The general conception referred to in this monograph as the "column analogy" includes the principles of area-moments and also the conception of the conjugate beam.*

In this bulletin it is shown that bending moments in arches, haunched beams, and framed bents may be computed by a procedure

*See H. M. Westergaard, "Deflection of Beams by the Conjugate Beam Method," Journal of Western Society of Engineers, December, 1921.

analogous to the computation of fiber stresses in short columns subject to bending, and that slopes and deflections in these structures may be computed as shears and bending moments, respectively, on longitudinal sections through such columns.

The theorem makes available for the analysis of plane elastic structures the literature of beam analysis, dealing with the kern, the circle of inertia, the ellipse of inertia, graphical computations of moments and products of inertia, and conjugate axes of inertia.

Certain terms are defined in such a way that the method is extended to include the effect of deformations due to longitudinal stress and to shear in ribbed members, and to include trussed members.

The conceptions used in arch analysis by these methods make possible a general statement of the relations of joint displacements to joint forces, of which the familiar equation of slope-deflection* is a special case, and hence make possible the convenient extension of the method of slope-deflection, or of the theorem of three moments, to include curved members and members of varying moment of inertia.

The method here presented has application in the fields both of design and of research. In the field of design we use certain physical properties of the materials, which are necessarily assumed. In research we may either resort to the laboratory and study by empirical methods the properties of the structure as a whole, or we may study only the physical properties of the materials themselves, and depend on the geometrical relations to determine the properties of the structure. It seems obvious that the geometrical relations are not themselves a proper subject for experimental research.

The relations pointed out in this bulletin have at first been carefully restricted to geometry, and the assumptions which are necessary to apply this geometry to the design of structures are developed later in the discussion.

2. *Validity of Analyses by the Theory of Elasticity.*—The mathematical identity of the expressions for moment in an elastic ring and for fiber stress in a column section has some value in considering in a qualitative way the general validity of analyses based on the elastic theory.

It appears at times that engineers are not altogether discriminating in considering the value of elastic analyses, and seem to hold that one must either accept as precise the results of such analyses or reject entirely their conclusions.

---

*"Analysis of Statically Indeterminate Structures by the Slope-Deflection Method," Univ. of Ill. Eng. Exp. Sta. Bul. 108, 1918.

Now no one but a novice accepts without discrimination the results of the beam formula. It is open to many important objections, such as lack of homogeneity of the material, effect of initial deformations, and other defects; and yet it is difficult to conceive of modern structural design existing without the beam formula, nor is anyone seriously disturbed because lack of homogeneity modifies somewhat the properties of the section, or by the fact that imperfect elasticity in the material makes invalid the superposition of stresses determined by the beam formula for different conditions of loading. Moreover the beam formula becomes a most inaccurate guide to the maximum stress in any section near the point of failure; and yet it is still true that one can scarcely conceive of modern structural design without the guidance of the beam formula.

Similarly we say that in an elastic structure the value of E may vary from section to section, that imperfect elasticity makes superposition of stresses not quite correct, and that near failure the method has only limited application. The normal process of structural design is to determine moments and shears, and from these fiber stresses. Whatever procedure is followed in the determination of the moments and shears, the beam formula is used for final determination of stress. There seem to be grounds for believing that the elastic analysis of an arch or bent with truly fixed or truly hinged ends has greater validity than does the method of analysis used later in design. The question of foundation distortion and of its effect involve engineering judgment. Elements involving judgment should be clearly isolated so that the limits of such judgment can be established.

3. *Acknowledgment.*—The bulletin was written as a part of the work of the Engineering Experiment Station of the University of Illinois, of which DEAN M. S. KETCHUM is the director, and of the Department of Civil Engineering, of which PROF. W. C. HUNTINGTON is the head. The computations were made by M. F. LINDEMAN, Research Graduate Assistant in Civil Engineering.

II.   ANALYSES FOR FLEXURAL STRESS

4. *General Equation of Flexural Stress.*—Equations for stress due to flexure are usually based on the assumption that the variation of stress over the cross-section may be represented by a linear equation. This assumption is based on the assumption that the beam axis is straight and also on the assumption, based chiefly on experimental

observations, of the conservation of plane right sections and of the proportionality of stress to strain.

It will be shown later that none of these assumptions is necessary, and that the same general form of equation may be used whatever the facts as to variation of stress intensity over the section, provided the facts as to the shape assumed by deformed sections and the stress-strain relations are definitely known. For the present, however, a linear equation of stress variation over the section will be assumed. The stress will then have the general equation $f = (a + bx + cy)$, in which the coefficients a, b, c, are to be determined from the statical conditions which state that the sum of the fiber resistances must equal the applied load and that the sum of the moments of these fiber resistances about any axis in the plane of the section must equal the moment of the applied loads about that axis.

Let x, y = coördinates of any point on the cross-section along any two mutually perpendicular axes X and Y through the centroid of the section.

$\quad f$ = intensity of normal stress at point x, y

$\quad A$ = area of section

$\quad I_x = \int x^2 dA$ = moment of inertia about axis Y (along the axis X)

$\quad I_y = \int y^2 dA$ = moment of inertia about axis X (along the axis Y)

$\quad I_{xy} = \int xy \, dA$ = product of inertia about axes X, Y

$\quad P$ = normal component of external forces

$\quad M_x$ = moment of external forces about axis Y

$\quad M_y$ = moment of external forces about axis X

Also write

$$M'_x = M_x - M_y \frac{I_{xy}}{I_y}$$

$$M'_y = M_y - M_x \frac{I_{xy}}{I_x}$$

$$I'_x = I_x - I_{xy} \frac{I_{xy}}{I_y}$$

$$I'_y = I_y - I_{xy} \frac{I_{xy}}{I_x}$$

All these terms are practically standard in the literature of flexure except the "skew" terms designated by primes.

Write: $f = a + bx + cy$

Then, from statics, $\Sigma V = 0$

whence: $P = \int f dA = a \int dA + b \int x dA + c \int y dA$

Since the axes are taken through the centroid, $\int x dA = 0$ and $\int y dA = 0$, by definition of centroid. Then $P = aA$, $a = \dfrac{P}{A}$.

The total moment about the axis of Y equals zero, whence
$$M_z = \int f x dA = a \int x dA + b \int x^2 dA + c \int xy dA$$
$$= bI_z + cI_{zy} \tag{1}$$

The total moment about the axis of X equals zero, whence
$$M_y = \int f y dA = a \int y dA + b \int xy dA + c \int y^2 dA$$
$$= bI_{zy} + cI_y \tag{2}$$

Multiplying (2) by $\dfrac{I_{zy}}{I_y}$, and subtracting from (1),

$$b = \frac{M_z - M_y \dfrac{I_{zy}}{I_y}}{I_z - I_{zy} \dfrac{I_{zy}}{I_y}} = \frac{M'_z}{I'_z}$$

Multiplying (1) by $\dfrac{I_{zy}}{I_z}$, and subtracting from (2),

$$c = \frac{M_y - M_z \dfrac{I_{zy}}{I_z}}{I_y - I_{zy} \dfrac{I_{zy}}{I_z}} = \frac{M'_y}{I'_y}$$

Hence
$$f = \frac{P}{A} + \frac{M'_z}{I'_z} x + \frac{M'_y}{I'_y} y \tag{3}$$

At the neutral axis $f = 0$. The equation of the neutral axis, then, is

$$\frac{P}{A} + \frac{M'_x}{I'_x}x + \frac{M'_y}{I'_y}y = 0$$

and the intercepts of the neutral axis are

$$x_1 = -\frac{\dfrac{P}{A}}{\dfrac{M'_x}{I'_x}} \qquad\qquad y_1 = -\frac{\dfrac{P}{A}}{\dfrac{M'_y}{I'_y}}$$

Equation 3 is a general equation of flexure for all cases if we assume linear variation of stress intensity. In order to apply it, it is first necessary to know the area and centroid of the section and I_x, I_y, I_{xy} for two mutually perpendicular axes through the centroid. The products of inertia should be computed first about the most convenient axes and then transferred to parallel axes through the centroid after this is located.

The foregoing brief statement of the formula contains all information necessary to its application. Like all mathematical relations, it is subject to unlimited variation of form. The general formula may be stated for principal axes, conjugate axes, neutral axis, kern axis; the S-polygon may be computed; the moments and products of inertia may be evaluated by summation, by integration, or graphically by use of the properties of string polygons; these moments and products of inertia may be combined to give the desired constants in the function for (f) by use of the circle of inertia or the ellipse of inertia, using in the latter case the polar properties of the ellipse. These are interesting lines of mathematical investigation; wherever they add appreciable convenience to the solution of the problem, any selected portions of the literature of flexure may be used.

It may sometimes be more convenient to concentrate all "prime" expressions in one term of the formula. Write

$$f = \frac{P}{A} + \frac{M'_x}{I'_x}x + \frac{M'_y}{I'_y}y = \frac{P}{A} + \frac{M_x}{I_x}x + \frac{M'_y}{I'_y}y - \left[\frac{M_x}{I_x} - \frac{M'_x}{I'_x}\right]x$$

the bracketed term reduces to

$$\frac{M_y - M_x\dfrac{I_{xy}}{I_x}}{I_y - I_{xy}\dfrac{I_{xy}}{I_x}} \cdot \frac{I_{xy}}{I_x} = \frac{M'_y}{I'_y} \cdot \frac{I_{xy}}{I_x}$$

We then write

$$f = \frac{P}{A} + \frac{M_z}{I_z}x + \frac{M'_y}{I'_y}y'$$

where

$$y' = y - x\frac{I_{zy}}{I_y}$$

This expression will, however, usually be found less convenient than that given in Equation (3).

Some special cases of the general equation are more familiar.

If $I_{zy} = 0$, as in a symmetrical section,

$$f = \frac{P}{A} + \frac{M_z}{I_z}x + \frac{M_y}{I_y}y \tag{3a}$$

If $P = 0$, and $I_{zy} = 0$,

$$f = \frac{M_z}{I_z}x + \frac{M_y}{I_y}y \tag{3b}$$

If one of the axes is normal to the plane of bending, $I_{zy} = 0$, and $P = 0$.

$$f = \frac{M_z}{I_z}x, \text{ the usual beam formula.} \tag{3c}$$

If there is no bending,

$$f = \frac{P}{A} \tag{3d}$$

The kern of a section may be defined as that portion of the section within which a normal compressive force must act if all of the section is to be in compression. It is sometimes useful where it can be conveniently found.

If flexure is about one principal axis of a symmetrical section, the stress at the outer fiber is

$$f = \frac{P}{A} + \frac{M_z}{I_z}x$$

where x is the distance from the centroidal axis of Y to the outer fiber.

The distance e_k to the edge of the kern for this fiber can be found from

$$\frac{P}{A} + \frac{Pe_k}{I_x} x_1 = 0$$

$$e_k = -\frac{I_x}{Ax_1} = -\frac{\rho_x{}^2}{x_1}$$

where ρ_x is the radius of gyration.

Let M_k be the moment about the edge of the kern,

$$M_k = M_x + P \frac{I_x}{Ax_1}$$

Then $\qquad f = \frac{P}{A} + \frac{M_x}{I_x} x = \frac{x}{I_x}\left(M_x + P \frac{I_x}{Ax_1}\right) = \frac{M_k}{I_x} x \qquad (6)$

In computing the stresses in frames it is often convenient to compute the moments about the kern points and apply formula (6) to obtain the stress directly.

5. *Form of Computation Recommended.*—The arrangement of computations in applying the general equation for flexural stress is important where the computations are involved. It is convenient to first compute the properties of the section and the bending moments with reference to some convenient pair of axes. These properties are later corrected for axes through the centroid of the section and then corrected for lack of symmetry of the section.

A few illustrations are given to indicate the arrangement recommended. This arrangement is emphasized here because of its use later in computations required in analyses of restrained beams.

Compressive fiber stresses are taken as positive and loads which produce compression as positive. Coördinates will be taken as positive when measured upward or to the right from the axes. Positive moment produces compression on the positive side (top or right-hand side) of the section.

Problem 1.—Unsymmetrical Section Unsymmetrically Loaded

It is desired to find the neutral axis and a measure of the fiber stress in the section shown in Fig. 1. The section is unsymmetrical, and the elements have widths so small that their moments of inertia about their longitudinal axes may be neglected. The section is loaded at point P, shown in the figure with a load of 10 000 lb.

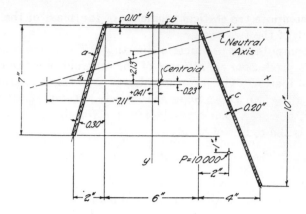

Member	Length	Width	x	y	Area a	Statical Moments ax	ay	Products of Inertia ax^2+i_x	ay^2+i_y	$axy+i_{xy}$	P	x	y	M_x	M_y
								Given — Properties of the Section / **Computed**			**Given** — Load			**Computed**	
a	7.29	0.30	-4	0	2.187	-8.748	0	35.0 / 0.7	0 / 8.9	0 / +2.6					
b	6.00	0.10	0	+3.5	0.600	0	+2.100	0 / 1.8	7.4 / 0	0 / 0					
c	10.79	0.20	+5	-1.5	2.158	+10.790	-3.237	54.0 / 2.9	4.9 / 18.0	-16.2 / -7.2					
Correct to Centroid			+0.41	-0.23	4.945	+2.042	-1.137	94.4 / 0.8	39.2 / 0.3	-20.8 / -0.5	+10000	+5	-4.5	+50000 / +4100	-45000 / -2300
Correct for Dissymmetry								93.6 / 10.6	38.9 / 4.4	-20.3				+45900 / +22300	-42700 / -10000
								83.0	34.5		+10000			+23600	-32700
Intercepts for N.A	-7.11	+2.13													

$$x_1 = -\frac{\frac{P}{A}}{\frac{M_x}{I_x}}, \quad y_1 = -\frac{\frac{P}{A}}{\frac{M_y}{I_y}}$$

Fiber Stress at any Point $= \frac{M_x}{I_x}$ x (Vertical Distance to Neutral Axis)

$\qquad\qquad = \frac{-32700}{34.5}$ x (Vertical Distance to Neutral Axis)

$\qquad$ or $= \frac{M_y}{I_y}$ x (Horizontal Distance to Neutral Axis)

$\qquad\qquad = \frac{23600}{83.0}$ x (Horizontal Distance to Neutral Axis)

FIG. 1. EXAMPLE OF AN UNSYMMETRICAL SECTION

Assume two convenient axes, in this case a horizontal axis X-X through the centroid of the portion of the section marked a and a vertical axis Y-Y through the centroid of the portion of the section marked b.

Tabulate first the known properties of the section and of the load. These are a description or key letter for each member, the length, the width, the coördinates x and y to the centroid of each member, the load, the coördinates of the load, or the moments about each of the two axes.

Now compute the statical moments of the areas of the members about each of the two axes.

Also compute the products of inertia.* These are computed as area times product of coördinates of the centroid plus the centroidal product of inertia. The latter equals $\frac{1}{12}$ area times product of projections on the two axes. Signs are entirely automatic. It should be remarked, however, that a product of inertia about the centroid is positive when $\frac{dy}{dx}$ for the member is positive, that is, when the member slopes up to the right.

Add columns to get total area, total statical moments, total products of inertia. If there are several loads or moments, add these also for total load and total moments.

Correct to the centroid. Divide the statical moments by the area to give the coördinates, $\bar{x} = +0.41$, $\bar{y} = -0.23$, of the centroid. Compute $A\bar{x}^2 = 0.8$, $A\bar{y}^2 = 0.3$, $A\bar{x}\bar{y} = -0.5$. Also compute $P\bar{x} = +4100$, $P\bar{y} = -2300$.

The signs are still automatic. Subtract the corrections to give products of inertia and moments about the centroidal axes.

Correct for dissymmetry. Compute $I_{zy}\dfrac{I_{zy}}{I_y} = +10.6$, and $M_y\dfrac{I_{zy}}{I_y} = +22\,300$, $I_{zy}\dfrac{I_{zy}}{I_z} = +4.4$, and $M_z\dfrac{I_{zy}}{I_z} = -10\,000$.

The signs are automatic here also. Again subtract the corrections.

Now compute

$$x_1 = -\frac{\dfrac{P}{A}}{\dfrac{M'_z}{I'_z}} = -7.11, \quad y_1 = -\frac{\dfrac{P}{A}}{\dfrac{M'_y}{I'_y}} = +2.13$$

These are the intercepts of the neutral axis on axes through the centroid parallel to the original axes.

The fiber stress at any point may be found by multiplying the vertical distance from the neutral axis by $\dfrac{M'_y}{I'_y} = -\dfrac{32\,700}{34.5}$ or by

---

*A moment of inertia is merely a special case of product of inertia where the same axis is taken twice.

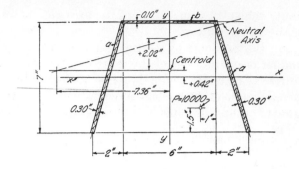

Properties of the Section											Load			
Given				Computed							Given		Computed	
Member	Length	Width	x	y	Area	Statical Moments		Products of Inertia			P	x	y	M_x	M_y
					a	ax	ay	ax^2+i_x	ay^2+i_y	$axy+i_{xy}$					
a	7.29	0.30	-4	0	2.187	-8.748	0	35.0 / 0.7	0 / 8.9						
b	6.00	0.10	0	+3.5	0.600	0	+2.100	0 / 1.8	7.4 / 0						
a	7.29	0.30	+4	0	2.187	+8.748	0	35.0 / 0.7	0 / 8.9						
Correct to Centroid			0	+0.42	4.974	0	+2.100	73.2 / 0	25.2 / 0.9		+10000	+2	-2	+20000 / 0	-20000 / +4200
								73.2	24.3					+20000	-24200

Intercepts for N.A. -7.36 $+2.02$ $x_i = -\dfrac{\frac{P}{A}}{\frac{M_i'}{I_x'}}$, $y_i = -\dfrac{\frac{P}{A}}{\frac{M_y'}{I_y'}}$

Fiber Stress at any Point $= \dfrac{M_y'}{I_y'} \times$ (Vertical distance to neutral axis)

$$= \dfrac{-24200}{24.3} \times \text{(Vertical distance to neutral axis)}$$

or $= \dfrac{M_x'}{I_x'} \times$ (Horizontal distance to neutral axis)

$$= \dfrac{+20000}{73.2} \times \text{(Horizontal distance to neutral axis)}$$

FIG. 2. EXAMPLE OF A SYMMETRICAL SECTION, UNSYMMETRICALLY LOADED

multiplying the horizontal distance of the point from the neutral axis

by $\dfrac{M'_x}{I'_x} = \dfrac{+23\,600}{83.0}$.

It will be observed that the sign of the stress is also automatic.

Since $\dfrac{M'_y}{I'_y}$ is negative, positive stress (compression) exists below the neutral axis.   Similarly, since $\dfrac{M'_x}{I'_x}$ is positive, compression exists to the right of the neutral axis.

Problem 2.—Symmetrical Section Unsymmetrically Loaded

If the section is symmetrical, the same order of procedure is followed, except that there is no product of inertia about the two axes and no correction for dissymmetry.

The problem just solved has been somewhat modified in Fig. 2 for a symmetrical section.   The computations follow the order of the previous problem.

Problem 3.—Symmetrical Section Symmetrically Loaded

If, further, the section is loaded symmetrically about the axis of symmetry, computations of the properties of the section about that axis may be omitted.   An illustration is shown in Fig. 3.

6. *Transformed Section.*—In deriving Equation (3) for fiber stress due to flexure it has been assumed that f is a linear function of x, y. The same type of expression may also be derived if fn is a linear function of x, y where n varies for different points on the section. In this case the equations of statics are satisfied if in place of dA we write $\dfrac{dA}{n}$ so that $fn\,\dfrac{dA}{n} = f dA$.   The differential areas dA are then to be divided by the values of n.

Let
$$A_t = \int \frac{dA}{n} \qquad\qquad I_{y_t} = \int \frac{dA}{n}\, y^2$$
$$I_{x_t} = \int \frac{dA}{n}\, x^2 \qquad I_{xy_t} = \int \frac{dA}{n}\, xy$$

where x and y are measured from the centroid of the section having differential areas $\dfrac{dA}{n}$.

The section thus defined, in which each area dA is replaced by an area $\dfrac{dA}{n}$, may be called the "transformed section."   For it we may derive, by the algebraic process used in deriving Equation (3),

$$nf = \frac{P}{A_t} + \frac{M'_x}{I'_{x_t}}\, x + \frac{M'_y}{I'_{y_t}}\, y \qquad\qquad (4)$$

the "skew" terms indicated by primes being defined in their relations

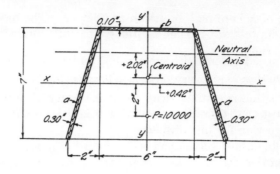

Properties of the Section										Load				
Given				Computed						Given			Computed	
Member	Length	Width	x	y	Area	Statical Moments		Products of Inertia			P	x	y	M_x	M_y
					a	ax	ay	ax^2+i_x	ay^2+i_y	$axy+i_{xy}$					
a	7.29	0.30	0		2.187		0		0 8.9						
b	6.00	0.10	+3.5		0.600		+2.100		7.4 0						
a	7.29	0.30	0		2.187		0		0 8.9						
Correct to Centroid					4.974		+2.100		25.2 0.9		+10000	0	-2	-20000 +4200	
			+0.42						24.3		+10000			-24200	
Intercepts of N.A.			+2.02	$y_1 = -\dfrac{\frac{P}{A}}{\frac{M_y}{I_y}}$											

$$\text{Fiber Stress at any Point} = \frac{M_y'}{I_y'} x\,(\text{Vertical distance to neutral axis})$$
$$= \frac{-24200}{24.3} x\,(\text{Vertical distance to neutral axis})$$

Fig. 3. Example of a Symmetrical Section, Symmetrically Loaded

to the other terms just as in **Equation (3)**. From the values of nf we may get $f = \dfrac{nf}{n}$.

This method has been used in analyzing beams of reinforced concrete on the usual assumptions as to the mechanics of such beams. In this case it is assumed that plane sections remain plane and hence that $\dfrac{f}{E}\,ds$ is a linear function of x, y. If the two sections between which deformation occurs are parallel, as in a straight beam, ds is constant across the section. Hence $\dfrac{f}{E}$ is a linear function of x, y.

The value of E here may be taken as relative. The modulus of concrete in compression is taken as unity, that of concrete in tension as zero (unlimited strain without stress), and that of the steel as $\dfrac{E_s}{E_c}$. The section then is transformed by multiplying the area of the steel by $\dfrac{E_s}{E_c}$, and that of the concrete in tension by zero. Finally, the apparent stress found in the concrete in tension is multiplied by zero, and that in the steel by $\dfrac{E_s}{E_c}$.

This method has been traced out in detail in this elementary case because it has broader usefulness. If the stress-strain diagram is known for any material it is a simple matter to deduce stresses for given loads on a section if we accept the assumption that plane sections remain plane. In such a case we would first analyze on the assumption of Hooke's Law, then transform the section by multiplying each differential area by the relative value of E corresponding to the stress just deduced. This transformed section is then analyzed and the deduced stresses multiplied by the relative value of E. Successive revisions will furnish any desired precision.

Another important application occurs in the case of beams having sharp curvature. Here it is usual to assume that plane sections remain plane and also that Hooke's Law holds. Hence $\dfrac{fds}{E}$ is a linear function of x, y. The modulus E is constant, but ds varies across the section, since the two sides of the differential element are not parallel.

The value of ds varies as the distance of each fiber from the center of curvature of the beam (see Fig. 4). We may, then, transform the section by dividing the width at any point by the radius of curvature R at that point. The properties of this transformed section are then determined. It will be shown later that these may all be deduced from the known properties of the original section and the area of the transformed section.

The values Rf are then found from Equation (4). These values of Rf are then divided by the values of R to give the fiber stresses.

It should be noted here that the moment to be used in this case is the moment about the centroid of the transformed section and not about the centroid of the original section. The centroid of the original section has no special significance in this problem, and certain awkward characteristics of the so-called Winkler-Bach formula arise from neglect of this fact.

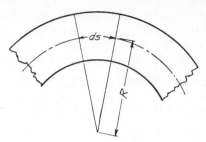

FIG. 4. SEGMENT OF A CURVED BEAM

In the usual treatment of curved beams the proportionality of stress to strain has been assumed. This, however, is not necessary. If Hooke's Law does not apply, but right sections plane before bending remain plane after bending, the value of $\dfrac{fds}{E}$ is a linear function of x, y and the section may be transformed by dividing the differential areas by $\dfrac{ds}{E}$. Hence sharply curved members of reinforced concrete, such as sometimes occur, may be analyzed by use of the transformed section. Brackets in rigid frames approximate this condition.

The transformed section could also be used either in combination with or without Hooke's Law to deal with cases in which plane sections do not remain plane in beams either straight or curved, provided we know anything or wish to assume anything as to the shape assumed by the plane after bending. In this case $\dfrac{fds}{E}$ is not a linear function of x, y but $\dfrac{fds}{rE}$ is such a function, where $r = \dfrac{\epsilon}{\epsilon'}$ defines the curvature of the deformed section, as shown in Fig. 5. The section

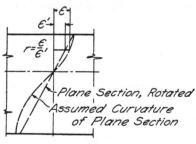

FIG. 5. RATIO, $r = \dfrac{\epsilon}{\epsilon'}$

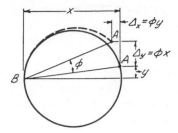

FIG. 6. CLOSED RING, CUT AND SUBJECTED TO AN ANGLE CHANGE

can then be transformed by multiplying each differential area by $\dfrac{Er}{ds}$.

A full understanding of the theory of the transformed section seems desirable in computing stresses in any case in which the stress distribution over the section is not linear. It has special advantage in such cases in dealing with problems involving continuity or deformations because in such cases if the transformed section is used the same methods are applicable in the analysis by the theory of elasticity as would be used where the stress distribution is linear. This will be explained in detail later.

III. THE COLUMN ANALOGY

7. *Formulas Similar to Flexure Formula.*—The flexure formula, then, is a solution not only of the problem to which it is usually applied of determining stresses where the variation of stress over the cross-section is linear and also, as shown in discussing the use of transformed sections, where this variation is not linear, but is a general type for the solution of certain algebraic problems. It will be shown that the problem of analyzing arches, bents, and beams with fixed ends in general is such a problem. The flexure formulas, at least for the special case of symmetrical flexure, are familiar tools to structural engineers, and therefore furnish a conveniently remembered routine in treating certain problems in elastic analysis.

8. *Geometry of Continuity.*—Consider any closed ring as shown in Fig. 6. Suppose this ring to be cut at A and that a certain rotation ϕ takes place at B.

At A there is now produced

    (a) A relative rotation of the two sides of the cut, $= \phi$

(b) A relative vertical displacement of the two sides of the cut, $= \phi x$

(c) A relative horizontal displacement of the two sides of the cut, $= \phi y$

If the ring is continuous there is actually no relative movement of the two sides of the cut. Distinguish the rotations which occur around the ring as those which would occur if the ring were cut and those which result from the continuity at A. Call the first ϕ_s—rotations due to the forces which are statically determined—and the latter ϕ_i—rotations due to forces which are statically indeterminate. Then, if continuity exists,

$$\Sigma \phi_s = \Sigma \phi_i$$
$$\Sigma \phi_s x = \Sigma \phi_i x$$
$$\Sigma \phi_s y = \Sigma \phi_i y$$

The rotations ϕ_i are due to equal and opposite forces on the two sides of the cut section at A. Any moments in the ring due to these forces will be a linear function of x, y. Call these moments m_i indeterminate moments. If for ϕ_i we write $m_i \dfrac{\phi_i}{m_i ds} ds$,

then

$$\int m_i \frac{\phi_i}{m_i ds} ds = \int \phi_s \tag{a}$$

$$\int m_i \frac{\phi_i}{m_i ds} x ds = \int \phi_s x \tag{b}$$

$$\int m_i \frac{\phi_i}{m_i ds} y ds = \int \phi_s y \tag{c}$$

where m_i is a linear function of x, y. $\qquad$ (d)

The values on the right-hand side of the equations are assumed to be known constants.

These relations are satisfied by an equation of which the equation of flexure is a type.

Thus we may write $m_i = a + bx + cy$ where a, b, and c are unknown coefficients to be determined from the three relations of continuity just given. Designate the physical constants $\dfrac{\phi_i}{m_i ds}$ —the rotations per unit of moment per unit of length—by the letter w (for width of the elastic section as defined later).

Then $\int m_i w ds = a \int w ds + b \int w ds x + c \int w ds y = \int \phi_s$

If the axes are taken through the centroid as defined by the equations $\int w ds x = 0$, and $\int w ds y = 0$, $a = \dfrac{\int \phi_s}{\int w ds}$

Also $\int m_i w ds x = a \int w ds x + b \int w ds x^2 + c \int w ds x y$

or $\qquad\qquad = b \int w ds x^2 + c \int w ds x y \qquad\qquad = \int \phi_s x$ (1)

and $\quad \int m_i w ds y = a \int w ds y + b \int w ds x y + c \int w ds y^2$

or $\qquad\qquad = b \int w ds x y + c \int w ds y^2 \qquad\qquad = \int \phi_s y$ (2)

Multiplying (2) by $\dfrac{\int w ds x y}{\int w ds y^2}$ and subtracting from (1)

$$b = \frac{\int \phi_s x - \int \phi_s y \dfrac{\int w ds x y}{\int w ds y^2}}{\int w ds x^2 - \int w ds x y \dfrac{\int w ds x y}{\int w ds y^2}}$$

Multiplying (1) by $\dfrac{\int w ds x y}{\int w ds x^2}$ and subtracting from (2)

$$c = \frac{\int \phi_s y - \int \phi_s x \dfrac{\int w ds x y}{\int w ds y^2}}{\int w ds y^2 - \int w ds x y \dfrac{\int w ds x y}{\int w ds y^2}}$$

Hence

$$m_i = \frac{\int \phi_s}{\int w ds} + \frac{\int \phi_s x - \int \phi_s y \dfrac{\int w ds x y}{\int w ds y^2}}{\int w ds x^2 - \int w ds x y \dfrac{\int w ds x y}{\int w ds y^2}} x$$

$$+ \frac{\int \phi_s y - \int \phi_s x \dfrac{\int w ds x y}{\int w ds x^2}}{\int w ds y^2 - \int w ds x y \dfrac{\int w ds x y}{\int w ds x^2}} y$$

If we conceive a narrow strip along the axis of the arch having a variable width $w = \dfrac{\phi_i}{m_i ds}$ then it is evident that $w ds$ corresponds to a differential area. If we treat this whole strip as an area A, we may conveniently write

$$\int w ds = A$$
$$\int w ds x^2 = I_x$$
$$\int w ds y^2 = I_y$$
$$\int w ds x y = I_{xy}$$
$$I_x - I_{xy} \frac{I_{xy}}{I_y} = I'_x$$
$$I_y - I_{xy} \frac{I_{xy}}{I_x} = I'_y$$

Also ϕ_s corresponds to a load. If we call these known rotations along the axis elastic loads, we may conveniently write

$$\int \phi_s = P$$
$$\int \phi_s x = M_x$$
$$\int \phi_s y = M_y$$

and

$$M_x - M_y \frac{I_{xy}}{I_y} = M'_x$$

$$M_y - M_x \frac{I_{xy}}{I_x} = M'_y$$

Hence

$$m_i = \frac{P}{A} + \frac{M'_x}{I'_x} x + \frac{M'_y}{I'_y} y$$

9. *The Analogy.*—If the effects of flexure only are taken into account there exists, then, an exact algebraic parallel between the indeterminate moments in an elastic ring and the fiber stresses on plane normal sections of a short column, as follows:

1. The stiffness $\dfrac{\phi}{m}$ of each short length of axis corresponds to a differential area a.

2. The indeterminate moments m_i correspond to stress intensities on the column section.

3. The known angle changes correspond to loads P on the column section. These angle changes may be due to external forces acting on the structure, or to other causes, such as rotations of abutments.

Consider any single-span plane structure, with axis either straight or curved, and with any variation in cross-section, subjected to known loads. Draw any curve of moments for these loads consistent with static equilibrium.

Picture a short length of column, a section of which has the same shape as the side elevation of the beam axis and a very small width varying along the axis as the elastic width defined above ($w = \dfrac{\phi}{mds}$, angle change for unit moment along a unit length).

Load this column with an intensity of load over these elastic areas equal to the bending moment given by the curve of moments just computed. The change in moment produced by restraint will now equal the fiber stresses which would exist on cross-sections of this column. The total moment at any point equals the net intensity of pressure—difference between load intensity at top and reaction

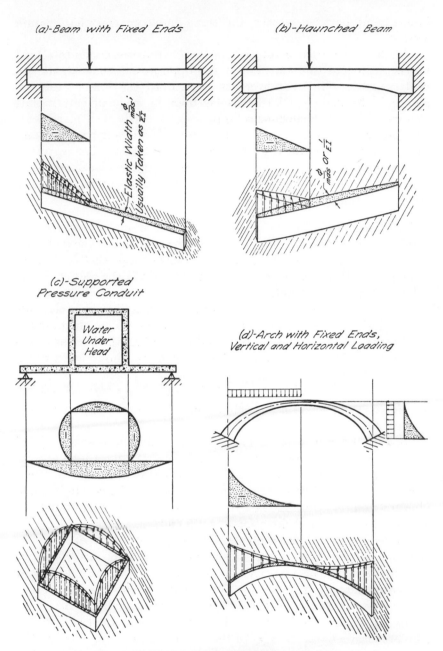

FIG. 7. TYPES OF ANALOGOUS COLUMN SECTIONS

intensity at bottom—at the corresponding point on this column section.

We have seen that a rotation in the beam corresponds to a load on the analogous column. Equal and opposite rotations about two centers produce linear movement normal to the line of centers. Hence, in the analogy, a linear displacement in the beam corresponds to a couple on the analogous column about the axis of displacement.

These rotations and displacements in the beam may be due to any cause whatever, abutment displacement, temperature change, forced distortion by jacking, or they may be imaginary displacements generating influence lines according to the principle of influence lines as stated by Müller-Breslau.

10. *The Elastic Column and Its Load.*—The analogy just stated furnishes a convenient mental picture of the relations of the moments in restrained members. In Fig. 7 are shown some sketches corresponding to these conceptions. The shaded area is the section of the column of any short length.

In Fig. 7a a straight beam of constant section and fixed at the ends is loaded with a single concentrated load. The most convenient curve of moments for such a load is obtained by treating the load as cantilevered from the nearer support. The analogous column has a width equal—or proportional—to the value $\dfrac{\phi}{mds}$ or $\dfrac{1}{EI}$ for the beam. The intensity of load on the column equals the moment curve just drawn.

In this case the average load intensity and the position of the resultant are known by inspection, and hence the total load and its moment are readily computed. Computations of the pressure intensity on the base of this short column will give the changes in bending moment resulting from the fact that the beam is not cantilevered but is fixed in position and direction at both ends.

In Fig. 7b the axis is assumed to be straight but the beam is not of constant section. The width of the column is, then, not constant, and the average load intensity and the position of the resultant load are not evident by inspection. The problem is conveniently solved by dividing the column section into a number of small lengths.

In Fig. 7a and 7b the elastic rings are closed by the earth, which has zero elastic area. In Fig. 7c the elastic ring is completed by the structure. The curve of moments due to the weight of water and to the pressure head is drawn on the assumption that the top and sides are simple beams—a stable condition. The elastic column and its load are as shown. Pressure intensities on the base of the column are changes in moment due to the fact that there are no hinges at the ends of the top and sides, but that there is really complete continuity at these points.

In Fig. 7d an arch is subjected to vertical loading on one side, and to horizontal loading on the other side. Moment curves are drawn independently for the two conditions of loading, the arch being assumed cantilevered from the left abutment for the vertical load, and from the right abutment for the horizontal load. Note that it is not necessary to assume the same statically determinate condition for the beam for all parts of the load.

11. *Signs in the Column Analogy.*—In flexural analyses it is convenient to consider compressive force and stress as positive and to measure coördinates as positive up and to the right from the centroid. Positive loads on columns, then, are downward, and positive couples are such as produce compression above and to the right of the centroid of the column section.

In applying the column analogy bending moments in the beam will be considered positive if they produce tension on the inside of the elastic ring. Shears are positive if they accompany positive rate of change of bending-moment, increase up or to the right.

Positive rotations are such as would accompany positive bending moments; positive displacements are such as would result from positive shearing forces. A clockwise abutment rotation at the left end of an arch, then, is positive; at the right end it is negative. An increase in arch span is a positive horizontal displacement. Settlement of the right abutment is a positive vertical displacement.

Note, however, that rotations and displacements which actually exist (abutment movements) are to be distinguished from those which are resisted (shrinkage or distortions due to temperature changes). In determining moments by the column analogy in the former case, the sign of the displacement may be conveniently reversed.

12. *Choice of Statically Determined Moments.*—The indeterminate forces are equal and opposite on two sides of any section, and hence satisfy the laws of statics whatever the determinate forces may be. Also the indeterminate forces are computed to have values such that continuity is preserved. Hence any set of determinate forces whatever which will support the loads may be chosen in the first place, since the conditions of both statics and continuity will be satisfied by the solution.

It is, of course, important to choose the most convenient curve of determinate moments. As a simple example, in the case of a fixed beam with a moment load, (upper part of Fig. 8) the four sets of determinate systems shown, among many, are available. In general the first or second moment curves will be more convenient.

The moment at x may be written directly by finding the indeterminate moment from the moment curve shown in (a) or in (b). Similarly the end moments may be written directly. To write M_b we use the moment curve in (a) and to write M_a we use the moment curve in (b).

In the lower part of Fig. 8 are shown three of the possible elastic loads on a rectangular bent carrying a single concentrated load. In the first case the curve of statically determinate moments is drawn as though the load were cantilevered from the left support, in the second as though the girder were simply supported on the columns, and in the third case as though the load were cantilevered from the right support. The indeterminate forces and moments will be different in the three cases, but the total moments will, of course, be the same. The second moment curve will probably be found most convenient.

13. *Components and Direction of Indeterminate Forces.*—The problem of analysis of rigid frames and arches is essentially that of finding the moments due to the indeterminate forces which are necessary to preserve continuity. These moments equal zero along the line of application of the indeterminate forces. This line of action, therefore, corresponds to the line of zero stress in the analogous column. This is the neutral axis for the given loading, and, as already found, it has intercepts on the axes through the centroid of $x_1 = -\dfrac{P/A}{\dfrac{M'_x}{I'_x}}$ and $y_1 = -\dfrac{P/A}{\dfrac{M'_y}{I'_y}}$.

The stress in a beam at unit horizontal distance from the neutral axis is $\dfrac{\delta f}{\delta x} = \dfrac{M'_x}{I'_x}$, and at unit vertical distance from the neutral axis is $\dfrac{\delta f}{\delta y} = \dfrac{M'_y}{I'_y}$.

The moment at unit vertical distance from the line of action of the indeterminate forces equals the horizontal component of the indeterminate force, and the moment at unit horizontal distance from the neutral axis equals the vertical component. Hence $h_i = \dfrac{M'_y}{I'_y}$

$$v_i = \dfrac{M'_x}{I'_x}.$$

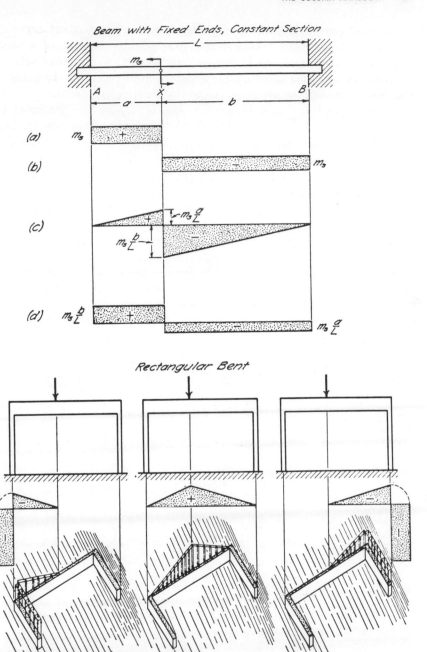

FIG. 8. POSSIBLE MOMENT LOADS FOR BEAM WITH FIXED ENDS
AND FOR RECTANGULAR BENT

A convenient basis for the computation of all indeterminate moments is to locate first the neutral axis of the analogous column and find one component along the axis.

The components of the indeterminate forces are changes in the reactions from those existing under the static conditions assumed. We may find the components of the reactions as $V = v_s - v_i$ $H = h_s - h_i$.

With the components of the reactions known it becomes a simple matter to draw the pressure line.

The pressure line for the structure may sometimes be drawn conveniently by superimposing the curve of statically determinate moments on the neutral axis to a vertical scale of $h_i = 1$ or to a horizontal scale of $v_i = 1$ according to whether the moment is laid off horizontally or vertically.

14. *Application to Simple Cases.*—The principle of the column analogy may be illustrated by application to a few simple cases. Let it be required to compute the end moments on the beam with fixed ends shown in Fig. 9a, assuming constant moment of inertia. Consider the moment curve shown, produced by the load P on a beam simply supported at its ends. Any static moment curve such as a cantilever over length (a) or (b) might equally well have been used. The centroid of a triangle using the notation of the figure may be shown to lie at a distance $\dfrac{L + a}{3}$ from one end.

In this case, then, the analogous column section is a narrow strip of length L and width $\dfrac{1}{EI}$. Both E and I, being assumed constant in this case, may be given a relative value of unity. The column section thus becomes simply L and the load $\dfrac{mL}{2}$. The outer fiber stresses in the column, analogous to the end moments, may be found by the usual column formula, or more conveniently in this case by taking moments about the kern points. Then, $f = \dfrac{M_k y}{I_o}$ where M_k is the moment about the opposite kern point, and I_o is the moment of inertia of the column section about its centroid.

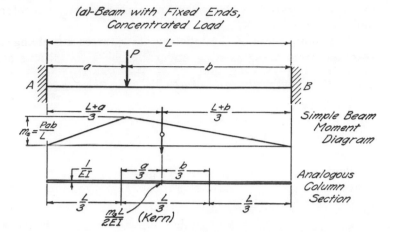

(a)-Beam with Fixed Ends, Concentrated Load

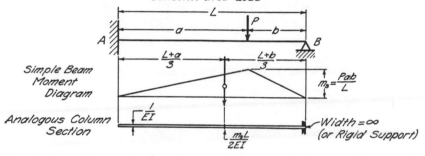

(b)-Beam Fixed at One End, Hinged at the Other End, Concentrated Load

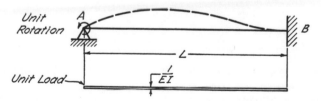

(c)-Beam with One End Fixed, Unit Rotation at the Other End

FIG. 9. APPLICATION OF THE PRINCIPLE OF COLUMN ANALOGY TO SIMPLE CASES

Further, for rectangular columns, $f = \dfrac{M_k y}{I_o} = \dfrac{M_k \dfrac{d}{2}}{\frac{1}{12}bd^3} = \dfrac{6M_k}{Ad}$

Then, at the left end, $f_a = M_a = \dfrac{6\dfrac{mL}{2} \cdot \dfrac{b}{3}}{L \cdot L} = m_s \dfrac{b}{L}.$

And, at the right end, $f_b = M_b = M_s \dfrac{a}{L}$ where m_s is the simple beam

moment, $m_s = \dfrac{Pab}{L}.$

For a beam of uniform section fixed at A and hinged at B, subject to a single concentrated load P, Fig. 9b, the hinge has an infinite elastic area (unlimited rotation due to a moment) and hence both the centroid and kern point of the infinite column section lie at the hinge.

Whence $M_a = \dfrac{M_k y}{I_o} = \dfrac{\dfrac{mL \cdot \dfrac{L+b}{3}}{2} \cdot L}{\dfrac{L \cdot L^2}{3}} = m_s \dfrac{L+b}{2L}$

Suppose the moment corresponding to unit rotation of the free end is required at each end of a supported beam which is fixed at one end, Fig. 9c.

The analogous column is a strip of width $\dfrac{1}{EI}$ and length L loaded with unit load at one end. Taking moments about kern points of A and B, write directly from the formula $f = \dfrac{6M_k}{Ad}$,

$$M_a = 6\dfrac{\frac{2}{3}L}{\dfrac{L}{EI}L} = 4\dfrac{EI}{L} \qquad M_b = -6\dfrac{L/3}{\dfrac{L}{EI}L} = -2\dfrac{EI}{L}$$

Suppose a beam with fixed ends subjected to unit relative displacement of the supports. Displacement in a beam corresponds to moment about the axis of displacement in the analogous column. For unit relative displacement of the supports, then, we write directly

$$M_a = M_b = \dfrac{6M_k}{Ad} = \dfrac{6}{\dfrac{L}{EI}L} = \dfrac{6EI}{L^2}$$

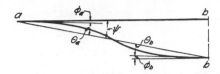

FIG. 10. ROTATION AND DISPLACEMENT OF THE ENDS OF A MEMBER

If the beam is subjected to loads and at the same time to rotations and displacements of the ends, we may write

$$M_a = M'_a + 4\phi_a \frac{EI}{L} + 2\phi_b \frac{EI}{L} - 6 \frac{\Delta EI}{L^2}$$

where M'_a is the fixed end moment at A due to the loads, ϕ_a and ϕ_b are rotations at A and B respectively, and Δ is the relative end displacement.

In place of $\dfrac{\Delta}{L}$ write ψ, the angle of tipping due to end displacement.

Also write $K = \dfrac{I}{L}$, and R_a instead of M'_a.

Then $M_a = 2EK(2\phi_a + \phi_b - 3\psi) + R_a$ which is the equation usually known in American literature as that of slope-deflection. The signs used for ϕ and ψ will depend on the convention of signs adopted.

For some purposes this may be more conveniently written as

$$M_a = 2EK(2\theta_a + \theta_b) + R_a$$

where ϕ and ψ are measured from the axis of the beam before flexure, and θ from the chord after flexure. This expression can be derived directly from the column analogy (see Fig. 10).

15. *Simple Numerical Examples.*—The column analogy is peculiarly fitted to the direct solution of numerical examples.

(a) Beam Fixed at Ends

The curve of moments will be drawn for a single concentrated load on a beam of constant section with fixed ends. Three curves of static moments will be used. The beam and its load are shown in Fig. 11. Of course for this case the formula $M = m_s \dfrac{a}{L}$ already derived is sufficient for finding the fixed-end moments.

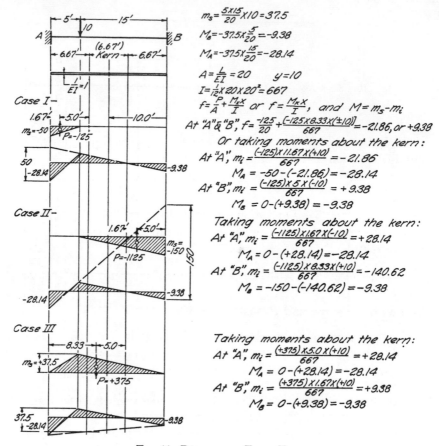

$$m_s = \frac{5 \times 15}{20} \times 10 = 37.5$$

$$M_B = -37.5 \times \frac{5}{20} = -9.38$$

$$M_A = -37.5 \times \frac{15}{20} = -28.14$$

$$A = \frac{L}{EI} = 20 \qquad y = 10$$

$$I = \frac{1}{12} \times 20 \times 20^2 = 667$$

$$f = \frac{P}{A} + \frac{M_K X}{I} \text{ or } f = \frac{M_K X}{I}, \text{ and } M = m_s - m_i$$

At "A" & "B", $f = \frac{-125}{20} + \frac{(-125 \times 8.33 \times (\pm 10)]}{667} = -21.86, \text{ or } +9.38$

Or taking moments about the kern:

At "A", $m_i = \frac{(-125) \times 11.67 \times (+10)}{667} = -21.86$

$$M_A = -50 - (-21.86) = -28.14$$

At "B", $m_i = \frac{(-125) \times 5 \times (-10)}{667} = +9.38$

$$M_B = 0 - (+9.38) = -9.38$$

Taking moments about the kern:

At "A", $m_i = \frac{(-1125) \times 1.67 \times (-10)}{667} = +28.14$

$$M_A = 0 - (+28.14) = -28.14$$

At "B", $m_i = \frac{(-1125) \times 8.33 \times (+10)}{667} = -140.62$

$$M_B = -150 - (-140.62) = -9.38$$

Taking moments about the kern:

At "A", $m_i = \frac{(+375) \times 5.0 \times (+10)}{667} = +28.14$

$$M_A = 0 - (+28.14) = -28.14$$

At "B", $m_i = \frac{(+375) \times 1.67 \times (+10)}{667} = +9.38$

$$M_B = 0 - (+9.38) = -9.38$$

FIG. 11. BEAM WITH FIXED ENDS

From this formula

$$m_s = \frac{5 \times 15}{20} \times 10 = 37.5 \qquad M_a = \frac{15}{20} \times 37.5 = -28.15$$

$$M_b = \frac{5}{20} \times 37.5 = -9.38$$

In case I the load is assumed cantilevered from A, in case II the load is assumed cantilevered from B, in case III the beam is treated as simply supported at A and B.

In case I, the end moment determined by statics is $-5 \times 10 = -50$, the average is $-\frac{50}{2} = -25$ acting over an area 5×1. Hence

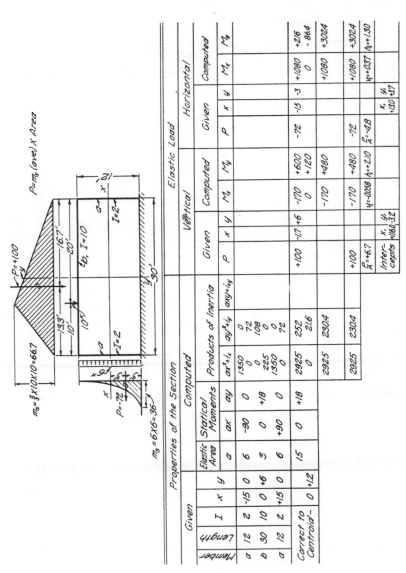

Fig. 12. Rectangular Bent

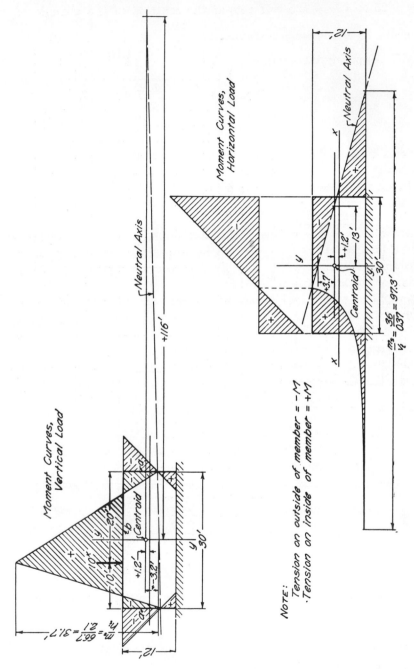

FIG. 12 (CONCLUDED). RECTANGULAR BENT

$P = -25 \times 5 = -125$. It acts at the centroid of the triangle of moments. For the column section $A = \dfrac{20}{1} = 20$, $I = \dfrac{1}{12} \times 20 \times 20^2$ = 667. Applying these values

$$f = \frac{P}{A} + \frac{M_z x}{I} = \frac{-125}{20} + \frac{(-125) \times 8.33 \times (\pm 10)}{667} =$$
$$-21.86 \text{ or } +9.38$$

Plot this moment curve, and on it as a base plot the original curve of moments.

The same procedure is shown for cases II and III.

(b) Simple Bents

Assume the rectangular bent shown in Fig. 12. Let the loads be a vertical load of $10k$ on the top and a horizontal load of $6k$ uniformly distributed along one side. It is desired to draw separate moment curves for the two cases of loading.

Assume as convenient axes a vertical through the center of b and a horizontal through the center of aa. Tabulate length L, moment of inertia I, horizontal coördinate of centroid x and vertical coördinate of centroid y for each of the members a, b, and a.

Also record the elastic loads and their centroids. For the load of $10k$, treating the girder as a simple beam, we have the moment curve shown, average moment $+\dfrac{66.7}{2}$, area loaded 3, and hence $P = +33.3 \times 3 = +100$. The centroid is as shown, and $x = -1.7$, $y = +6$. Whence $M_z = (-1.7) \times (+100) = -170.0$ and $M_y = (+6) \times (+100) = +600$.

For the horizontal load draw the curve of moments for the column as a cantilever. Average moment $-\dfrac{36}{3} = -12$; area loaded $= 6$. Hence $P = (-12) \times 6 = -72$. Also $x = -15$, $y = -3$. $M_z = (-15) \times (-72) = +1080$ and $M_y = (-3) \times (-72) = +216$.

Compute a, a_z, a_y, $ax^2 + i_z$, $ay^2 + i_y$ for each member. The centroidal moment of inertia (i_z and i_y) equals $\dfrac{1}{12} a \times (\text{projection along}$ the axis$)^2$. Find the totals.

Reducing to the centroid, $\bar{x} = 0$, $\bar{y} = +\dfrac{18}{15} = +1.2$. Find $A\bar{x}^2$, $A\bar{y}^2$, $P\bar{x}$, $P\bar{y}$, and subtract.

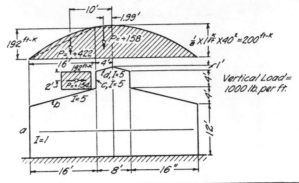

		Properties of Section					Elastic Load			
Member	Length	I	a	y	ay	ay^2+i_y	m_s, (av.)	P	y	M_y
a	12.0	1	12.0	0	0	0 / 144	0			
b	16.5	5	3.3	+8	+26.4	211 / 4	+128	+432	+8.5	+3585
c	4.0	5	0.8	+12	+9.6	115 / 1	+192	+154	+12	+1850
d	4.1	5	0.8	+14.5	+11.6	168 / 0	+197	+158	+14.5	+2290
			16.9		+47.6	643 / 134		+734		+7725 / +2070
Correct to Centroid				+2.82						
			16.9			509		+734		+5655
							$\frac{P}{A}=$	+43.4		
							$h_i=\frac{M_y}{I_y}=$			+11.1
							$y_i=-\frac{\frac{P}{A}}{h_i}=$		-3.92	

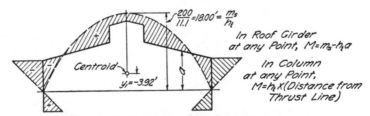

$\int \frac{200}{11.1} = 18.00' = \frac{m_s}{h_i}$

In Roof Girder
at any Point, $M = m_s - h_i a$

In Column
at any Point,
$M = h_i \times (Distance\ from\ Thrust\ Line)$

Centroid
$y_i = -3.92'$

FIG. 13. BENT WITH MONITOR

The intercepts of the neutral axis for the two conditions of loading are now found as $x_1 = -\dfrac{P/A}{M_x/I_x}$ and $y_1 = -\dfrac{P/A}{M_y/I_y}$. For the vertical load compute $h_i = \dfrac{M_y}{I_y} = +2.1$, and for the horizontal load compute $v_i = \dfrac{M_x}{I_x} = +0.37$. The neutral axes are then plotted, and on them the original curves of moments are drawn to the scale of distance.

Required:
Moment in Member a at Point O

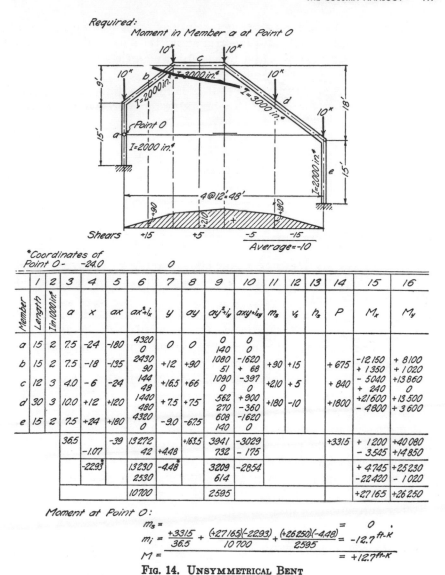

*Coordinates of Point O — −24.0   0

Member	$\ $	$\ $	a	x	ax	ax^2+i_x	y	ay	ay^2+i_y	$axy+i_{xy}$	m_s	v_s	h_s	P	M_x	M_y
(Member)	(Length)	(I in1000 in⁴)	1	2	3	4	5	6	7	8	9	10	11	12	13	14	15	16
a	15	2	7.5	−24	−180	4320 0	0	0	0 140	0 0					−12150 	+8100
b	15	2	7.5	−18	−135	2430 90	+12	+90	1080 51	−1620 +68	+90	+15		+675	+1350	+1020
c	12	3	4.0	−6	−24	144 48	+16.5	+66	1090 0	−397 0	+210	+5		+840	−5040 +240	+13860 0
d	30	3	10.0	+12	+120	1440 480	+7.5	+75	562 270	+900 −360	+180	−10		+1800	+21600 −4800	+13500 +3600
e	15	2	7.5	+24	+180	4320 0	−9.0	−67.5	608 140	−1620 0						
		36.5		−1.07	−39	13272 42	+4.48	+163.5	3941 732	−3029 −175				+3315	+1200 −3545	+40080 +14850
			−22.93*	−4.48*		13230 2530			3209 614	−2854					+4745 −22420	+25230 −1020
						10700			2595						+27165	+26250

Moment at Point O:

$$m_s = \frac{+3315}{36.5} + \frac{(+27165)(-22.93)}{10700} + \frac{(+26250)(-4.48)}{2595} = \; 0$$

$$m_i = \frac{+3315}{36.5} + \frac{(+27165)(-22.93)}{10700} + \frac{(+26250)(-4.48)}{2595} = -12.7 \text{ ft-k}$$

$$M = \qquad = +12.7 \text{ ft-k}$$

Fig. 14. Unsymmetrical Bent

For the vertical load plot for static moments $\dfrac{66.7}{2.1} = 31.7$ ft.; for the horizontal loads, $\dfrac{36}{0.369} = 97.3$ ft.

In Fig. 13 is shown a reinforced concrete bent having a monitor. The dead load on the roof is assumed uniform at 1000 lb. per horizontal foot.

In this case both load and structure are symmetrical, and there is no need to compute moment of inertia about the axis of Y. The axes are taken on the vertical center line and through the center of members aa.

The moment areas and their centroids for the different members have been computed separately by breaking them up into trapezoids and parabolas.

The same procedure is followed as in the preceding problem. The neutral axis, however, is horizontal. $h_i = \dfrac{M_y}{I_y} = +11.1$. Intercept of neutral axis $y_1 = -\dfrac{P/A}{M_y/I_y} = -3.92$. The rise of the pressure line is $\dfrac{200}{11.1} = 18.00$ ft.

The signs of the intercepts of the neutral axis can usually be found by inspection, since the neutral axis lies on the side of the centroid opposite to the load.

In Fig. 14 is shown an unsymmetrical bent subjected to vertical loads. The tabulation of elastic properties and of elastic loads follows the procedure already explained. The elastic moments may also be conveniently computed as previously explained. They have actually been computed as the sum of the moment of the elastic load acting at the centroid of the member plus the product of shear times elastic centroidal moment of inertia. The method is explained later as an extension of the analogy, but presents few advantages. The trial axes are taken as the vertical through the center of member c and the horizontal through the center of member a.

The correction to the centroid also follows the procedure already explained.

The correction for dissymmetry is made as follows:

for I_z in column (6) write $I_{zy} \cdot \dfrac{I_{zy}}{I_y} = (-2854)\left(\dfrac{-2854}{3209}\right) = 2530,$

for M_z in column (15), write $M_y \cdot \dfrac{I_{zy}}{I_y} = (+25\,230)\left(\dfrac{-2854}{3209}\right) = -22420$

for I_y in column (9), write $I_{zy} \cdot \dfrac{I_{zy}}{I_z} = (-2854)\left(\dfrac{-2854}{13230}\right) = 614$

for M_y in column (16), write $M_z \cdot \dfrac{I_{zy}}{I_z} = (+4745)\left(\dfrac{-2854}{13230}\right) = -1020.$

Subtract these corrections to get I'_z, M'_z, I'_y, and M'_y.

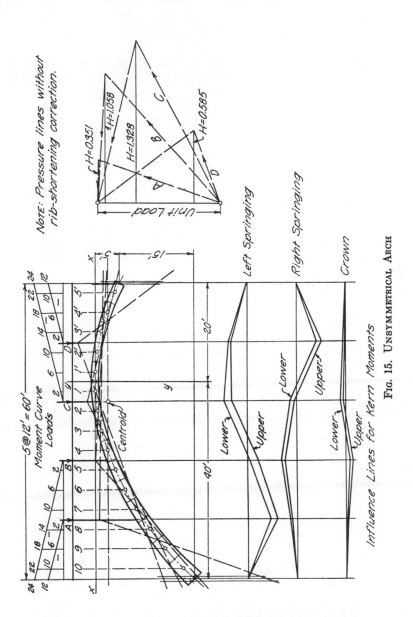

NOTE: Pressure lines without rib-shortening correction.

Influence Lines for Kern Moments

FIG. 15. UNSYMMETRICAL ARCH

| | | Properties of the Section | | | | | | | | | Elastic Loads — Unit Load at: | | | | | | | | | | | | | | | |
| | Given | | | | Derived | | | | | | A | | | | B | | | | C | | | | D | | | |
No.	L.ft	d.ft	x	y	a	ax	ay	ax²	ay²	axy	ms	P	Mx	My	ms	P	Mx	My	ms	P	Mx	My	ms	P	Mx	My
1	2	3	4	5	6	7	8	9	10	11	12	13	14	15	16	17	18	19	20	21	22	23	24	25	26	27
10	5.58	3.34	-38.0	-.1805	0.050	-.570	-271	217	490	+103.0	-10	-.50	+57.0	+27.1	-22	-3.30	+125.5	+59.5								
9	5.23	3.04	-34.0	-.1445	0.087	-.636	-270	216	390	+91.7	-6	-.12	+38.0	+16.2	-18	-3.36	+114.1	+48.6								
8	5.00	2.79	-30.0	-.1125	0.231	-.694	-260	208	293	+78.0	-2	-.046	+13.8	+5.2	-14	-3.24	+97.2	+36.4								
7	4.78	2.54	-26.0	-.0845	0.291	-.756	-246	197	208	+64.0					-10	-2.91	+75.6	+24.6								
6	4.55	2.33	-22.0	-.0605	0.361	-.793	-2.18	174	132	+48.0					-6	-2.17	+47.7	+13.1								
5	4.45	2.16	-18.0	-.0405	0.443	-.796	-1.79	143	7.3	+32.2					-2	-.89	+16.0	+3.6								
4	4.26	2.00	-14.0	-.0245	0.533	-.746	-1.31	104	3.2	+18.3																
3	4.17	1.83	-10.0	-.0125	0.684	-.684	-.085	68	1.1	+8.5																
2	4.05	1.67	-6.0	-.0045	0.874	-.525	-.039	32	0.2	+2.3																
1	4.01	1.54	-2.0	-.0005	1.02	-.221	-.006	4	0.0	+0.1									-2	-.221	+4.4	+0.1				
1'	4.01	1.54	+2.0	+.0005	1.02	+.221	-.006	4	0.0	-0.1									-6	-.661	-13.2	+0.3				
2'	4.05	1.67	+6.0	+.0045	0.874	+.525	-.039	32	0.2	-2.3									-10	-8.74	-52.4	+3.9				
3'	4.17	1.83	+10.0	+.0125	0.684	+.684	-.131	68	1.1	-8.5									-14	-9.57	-95.7	+12.0	-2	-.137	-13.7	+1.7
4'	4.26	2.00	+14.0	+.0245	0.533	+.746	-.131	104	3.2	-18.3									-18	-8.59	-134.2	+23.5	-6	-.320	-44.8	+7.8
5'	4.45	2.16	+18.0	+.0405	0.443	+.796	-1.79	143	7.3	-32.2									-20	-9.75	-175.2	+39.5	-10	-.443	-79.7	+17.9
Correct to Centroid			-4.06	-2.53	8492	-3449	-2145	1714	1749	+847		-.308	+108.8	+48.5		-1.587	+476.1	+185.8		-.4647	-466.3	+79.3		-.900	-138.2	+274
								140	543.5	+820			+12.5	+7.8			+64.4	+40.2			+188.5	+117.5			+36.5	+22.8
Correct for Dissymmetry								1574	1120.4	+297.7			+96.3	+40.7			+411.7	+145.6			-654.8	-382			-174.7	+4.6
								734	562.2				+100.4	+18.2			+359.2	+77.7			-942	-123.5			+11.4	-33.0
						8492		840	642			-.308	-4.1	+22.5		-1.587	+52.5	+67.9		-.4647	-560.6	+85.3		-.900	-185.1	+37.6
$\frac{P}{A} =$												-.363				-1.869				-5.475				-1.059		
$V_x = \frac{M_x'}{I_x}$												-.00049				+.0625				-.667				-.211		
$h_x = \frac{M_y'}{I_y}$												+.351				+1.058				+1.328				+.585		
$x_x = \frac{P}{A} / V_x$												-74.0				+29.9				-8.20				-5.03		

Computations are based on a rib-section 12 ft. wide, since $\frac{L}{I} = \frac{1}{12} bd^3$ taken equal to $\frac{2}{5}$.

Since all units are in feet, E should be taken in foot units in computing the effect of shrinkage, temperature change, or abutment movements.

Computations for temperature are for a free change in span of 100%.

Temperature, (Increase)
Correction for Dissymmetry

$M_x = -15$ $M_y = +60$
     $+148$ -28
$M_x' = -163$ $M_y' = +62.8$
$V = -0.016$ $H = +.0081$

Fig. 15 (concluded). Unsymmetrical Arch

The bending moment at any point, such as joint o, may now be found as $M = m_s - m_i$, as shown.

16. *Arch Analysis.*—The column analogy affords an unusually convenient means of analyzing reinforced concrete arches, because, once understood, it furnishes a familiar order of procedure. The actual computations are, of course, the same as presented by other writers.

In the case of unsymmetrical arches the equation given in this discussion seems to offer a much more convenient order of arranging the computations than is found elsewhere. For this reason it has seemed worth while to give in some detail the essential steps in the analysis of an unsymmetrical arch.

(a) Unsymmetrical Arch

The arch analyzed is shown in Fig. 15. It has a span of axis of 60 feet divided into five panels of 12 feet each. The total rise is 20 feet and the difference in level between abutments is 15 feet.

The arch axis is first divided into fifteen segments of equal horizontal projections.

Use as convenient trial axes horizontal and vertical lines through the highest point of the arch axis.

Tabulate first the known properties of the arch. These are the length of each segment L along the arch axis, the distances x and y to its centroid, the depth of the sections at their centers.

Now compute the elastic areas a, each equal to $\dfrac{L}{I} = 12\,\dfrac{L}{d^3}$; this is for unit width of rib. From these compute the statical moments ax and ay about the axes of x and y, the products of inertia about these axes ax^2, ay^2, axy.

Now tabulate the m_s values at centroids of sections for unit loads at each of the panel points, A, B, C, D. The statically determinate moments will be found for these loads cantilevered from the nearer end of the arch. The statically determinate moment on any segment between the load and the nearer abutment, then, equals the distance from the load to the centroid of that segment. We then compute the elastic load $P = m_s a$, the moment of the elastic load about the axis of Y, Px, and about the axis of X, Py. Note that for any segment these three quantities may be written by multiplying m_s by columns (6), (7), (8), successively.

Sum the columns for elastic area, statical moments, products of inertia, elastic loads, elastic moments.

Correct to the centroid. Compute $\bar{x} = \dfrac{\Sigma ax}{A}$ and $\bar{y} = \dfrac{\Sigma ay}{A}$ and the corrections for the products of inertia $\bar{x}^2 A$, $\bar{y}^2 A$, $\overline{xy}\,A$, and for the elastic moments $x\Sigma P$, $y\Sigma P$. Subtract the corrections.

Correct for dissymmetry. Write the value of $\dfrac{I_{xy}}{I_y}$. I_{xy} under I_x and of $\dfrac{I_{xy}}{I_y}$. M_y under M_x and write the value of $\dfrac{I_{xy}}{I_x}$. I_{xy} under I_y and of $\dfrac{I_{xy}}{I_x}$. M_x under M_y. Subtract the corrections.

Draw horizontal axis through the centroid. Now compute for a load at each panel point the values of the components of the more distant reaction $v_i = \dfrac{M'_x}{I'_x}$ and $h_i = \dfrac{M'_y}{I'_y}$ and the intercept on the X axis through the centroid, $x_1 = -\dfrac{P}{Av_i}$.

Rib-shortening has not been included in the computations. It may be corrected for by computing the average intensity of compression for any given condition of loading and from this the change of span which would take place if the arch were free to contract. This change of span may then be treated as if it were due to change of temperature, equivalent temperature change $= \dfrac{f_{av}}{E\,\epsilon}$.

The components and location of one reaction (at the more distant abutment) now being known, it is easy to draw the pressure lines. By scaling the ordinate from any pressure line to the kern point for any particular cross-section and multiplying by the H value for that pressure line, we can compute conveniently the moment about that kern point. Thus we can draw influence lines if we wish, by plotting kern point moments at various sections for different positions of the unit load. From the kern moments the stresses can be computed directly from the formula $f = \dfrac{M_k c}{I}$.

For temperature changes, the horizontal change in span if the arch were free to expand multiplied by E is $E\,\epsilon t \times 60$ ft. and the relative vertical movement of the abutments multiplied by E is $E\,\epsilon t \times 15$ ft. Omit the constant multiplier $E\,\epsilon t$ for the time being, and use it later as a multiplier for the temperature stresses. It has been shown that

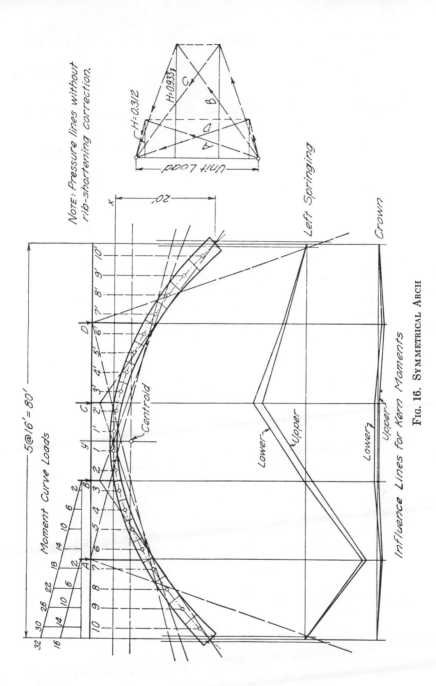

FIG. 16. SYMMETRICAL ARCH

Influence Lines for Kern Moments

	Properties of the Section										Elastic Loads – Unit Load at:																
	Given				Derived						A				B				C				D			
1	2	3	4	5	6	7	8	9	10	11	12	13	14	15	16	17	18	19	20	21	22	23	24	25	26	27
No.	L.ft	d.ft	x	y	a	ax	ay	ax²	ay²	axy	m_3	P	M_x	M_y	m_3	P	M_x	M_y	m_3	P	M_x	M_y	m_3	P	M_x	M_y
10	5.58	3.34	-38.0	-18.05	0.050	-5.70	-2.71	217	49.0		-14	-2.10	+79.7	+379	-30	-4.50	+171.0	+81.2								
9	5.23	3.04	-34.0	-14.45	0.087	-6.36	-2.70	216	39.0		-10	-1.87	+63.5	+270	-26	-4.86	+165.1	+70.2								
8	5.00	2.79	-30.0	-11.25	0.231	-6.94	-2.60	208	29.3	Due to Symmetry, axy Totals Zero	-6	-1.39	+41.7	+156	-22	-5.09	+153.0	+57.2			Same as Load at B				Same as Load at A	
7	4.78	2.54	-28.0	-8.45	0.291	-7.56	-2.46	197	20.8		-2	-0.58	+15.1	+4.9	-18	-5.24	+136.4	+44.3								
6	4.55	2.33	-22.0	-6.05	0.361	-7.93	-2.18	174	13.2						-14	-5.05	+111.0	+30.5		Due to Symmetry						
5	4.45	2.16	-18.0	-4.05	0.443	-7.96	-1.79	143	7.3						-10	-4.43	+79.6	+17.9								
4	4.26	2.00	-14.0	-2.45	0.533	-7.46	-1.31	104	3.2						-6	-3.20	+44.8	+7.8								
3	4.17	1.83	-10.0	-1.25	0.684	-6.84	-0.85	68	1.1						-2	-1.37	+13.7	+1.7								
2	4.05	1.67	-6.0	-0.45	0.874	-5.25	-0.39	32	0.2																	
1	4.01	1.54	-2.0	-0.05	1.102	-2.21	-0.06	4	0.0																	
Left Half					4.856	-6421	-1705	1363	163.1			-5.94	+200.0	+85.4		-33.74	+874.6	+310.8								
Right Half			0	-3.51	4.856	+6421	-1705	1363	163.1			-5.94	+200.0	+85.4		-33.74	+874.6	+310.8								
					9.712	0	-34.10	2726	3262	0			0	+20.8			0	+118.0								
							0	2726	119.5			-5.94	+200.0	+64.6	-3.47	-33.74	+874.6	+192.8								
					9.712		2726		2067																	

$\dfrac{P}{A} = -0.612$ ... +0.0734 ... +0.321

$V = \dfrac{M_x}{I_x} =$ ... +0.312 ... +0.933

$h = \dfrac{M_y}{I_y} =$

$x = \dfrac{A}{V} =$ ... +8.34 ... +10.8

Temperature (Increase)

Computations are based on a rib-section 12 ft. wide, since $I = \frac{1}{12}bd^3$ is taken equal to d^3.

Since all units are in feet, E should be taken in foot units in computing the effect of shrinkage, temperature change, or abutment movements.

Computations for temperature are for a tree change in span of 100%.

$M_y = +80$ $M_x = 0$
$H = +0.032$

Fig. 16 (concluded). Symmetrical Arch

a linear displacement is analogous to a moment about the axis of displacement. Hence we have on the analogous column elastic moments $M_x = \pm 15$ and $M_y = \mp 60$. That the signs of these moments are opposite is determined by the fact that the change of span is analogous to a moment about a line connecting the ends of the arch axis. Such a moment on the analogous column produces compression on the top and left or on the bottom and right of the section. After the line of action of the temperature thrust has been determined, the sign of the bending moment at any point is readily determined for a rise or for a fall of temperature by observing that a thrust is required to shorten the span, and a pull to lengthen it.

These moments $M_x = \pm 15$ and $M_y = \mp 60$ are now corrected for dissymmetry. The H and V components of the temperature thrust are then computed. The thrust, of course, passes through the elastic centroid, just as the neutral axis of a beam passes through the centroid for pure bending.

(b) Symmetrical Arch

If the arch is symmetrical, the procedure just given is shortened. It is now necessary to consider only one-half of the arch ring. By inspection the product of inertia is zero and there is no correction for dissymmetry.

In Fig. 16 is shown the analysis of an arch similar to the one just shown except that the span is 5 panels of 16 ft. = 80 ft.

17. *Haunched Beams.*—Because of the occasional importance of haunched beams in continuous frames, examples of the analysis of such beams have been included. The arrangement of the computations is the same as in the analysis of arches except that there are no y coördinates.

Attention is called to the computation of end moments resulting from unit rotation of one end. These values are constants needed in certain methods of analyzing continuous frames.* In order to compute these moments a unit load is applied at one end of the section of the analogous column and the outer fiber stresses in the column are determined.

A beam symmetrically haunched is shown in Fig. 17 and is analyzed for end moments due to a uniform load and also for end moments due to a rotation at one end.

---

*"Continuity as a Factor in Reinforced Concrete Design," Hardy Cross, Proceedings, A. C. I., Vol. 25, 1929.
"Simplified Rigid Frame Design," Report of Committee, 301, Hardy Cross, Author-Chairman, Journal, A. C. I., Dec., 1929.
"Analysis of Continuous Frames by Distributing Fixed-End Moments," Hardy Cross, Proceedings, A. S. C. E., May, 1930.

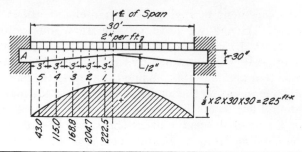

Section	Length in ft.	d in ft.	x	a	ax	$ax^2 + i_x$	m_s	P	
1	3	1.15	±1.5	1.97	±2.96	4.43 / 1.47	+222.5	+438	
2	3	1.45	±4.5	0.98	±4.40	19.80 / 0.73	+204.7	+200	$a=12\frac{L}{d^3}$
3	3	1.75	±7.5	0.56	±4.20	31.50 / 0.42	+168.8	+94	$a=\frac{L}{d^3}$, in this
4	3	2.04	±10.5	0.35	±3.68	38.65 / 0.26	+115.0	+40	computation.
5	3	2.35	±13.5	0.23	±3.10	41.90 / 0.17	+43.0	+10	Hence b=12 ft.
									$E=1$
				4.09	0	139.33		+782	

Multiplied by— $\dfrac{2}{8.18}$ ‖ $\dfrac{2}{278.7}$

$$m_{i_A} = m_{i_B} = \frac{+782}{4.09} = +191^{ft-k}$$
$$M_A = M_B = m_s - m_i = 0 - (+191) \doteq -191^{ft-k}$$

If support "A" rotates one unit.—
Find the moment necessary to give unit rotation by applying a unit load at "A" on the analogous column
$$\text{Then } m_{i_a} = \frac{1}{8.18} + \frac{(-15)(-15)}{278.7} = +0.929$$
$$m_{i_b} = \frac{1}{8.18} + \frac{(-15)(+15)}{278.7} = -0.687$$

m_a = *moment necessary to produce unit rotation at end "A".*

m_b = *moment at end "B", due to restraint, when end "A" is rotated one unit*
or, m_b for any given rotation at end "A", when "B" is fixed
$$\text{will be } = \frac{-0.687}{+0.929} \times m_a$$

FIG. 17. BEAM SYMMETRICALLY HAUNCHED

In Fig. 18 a beam unsymmetrically haunched is shown and this is analyzed for end moments due to rotations at the ends.

18. *Slopes and Deflections of Beams.—*

(a) Relation of the Column Analogy to Theorems of Area-Moments

The sum of the rotations, or change in slope, on the beam corresponds to shear on a section through the analogous column, because the product of moment by elastic area is rotation and the sum of load

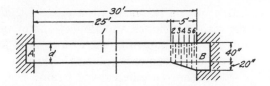

Section	Length in ft.	d in ft.	x	a	ax	$ax^2 + i_x$				
	25	3.33	-2.5	8.15	-20.4	51 / 425				$a=12\frac{L}{d^3}$
2	1	3.50	+10.5	0.23	+2.4	25 / 0				$E=1$
3	1	3.83	+11.5	0.21	+2.4	28 / 0				
4	1	4.16	+12.5	0.17	+2.1	27 / 0				
5	1	4.50	+13.5	0.13	+1.8	24 / 0				
6	1	4.83	+14.5	0.11	+1.6	23 / 0				
				9.00	-10.1	603 / 11				
			-1.12							
				9.00		592				

(a)—For Unit Rotation at "A" — apply unit load on analogous
column at "A";

then: $m_i = \frac{1}{9.00} + \frac{(-13.9)(-13.9)}{592} = +0.437$, moment necessary for unit
rotation at "A".

and $m_i = \frac{1}{9.00} + \frac{(-13.9)(+16.1)}{592} = -0.267$, moment at far end "B",
due to restraint.

(b)—For Unit Rotation at "B" — apply unit load on analogous
column at "B"

then: $m_i = \frac{1}{9.00} + \frac{(+16.1)(+16.1)}{592} = +0.549$, moment necessary for unit
rotation at "B"

$m_i = \frac{1}{9.00} + \frac{(+16.1)(-13.9)}{592} = -0.267$, moment at far end "A",
due to restraint.

In (a), then, for any given rotation or moment at end "A":
$$m_b = \frac{-0.267}{+0.437} \times m_a,$$ and

In (b), then, for any given rotation or moment at end "B":
$$m_a = \frac{-0.267}{+0.549} \times m_b$$

Fig. 18. Beam Unsymmetrically Haunched

intensity times area is shear. From the geometrical relations previously explained, it follows that the statical moment of the rotations about any section is the displacement at that section.

Slopes along the beam, then, correspond to shears on longitudinal sections through the analogous column and deflections of the beam correspond to bending moments on longitudinal sections through the analogous column parallel to the line along which the deflection is wanted.

The theorems of area-moments, then, are a part of the analogy. The theorems dealing with the slopes and deflections of beams are among the most useful and best known in the literature of structural analysis.   They deal with displacements relative either to a tangent to the curved beam or to a chord of the curved beam.

They may be conveniently stated as follows:

(1) (a) Slope at any point measured with reference to a tangent to the bent beam at another point may be found as area under the $\frac{M}{EI}$ curve between the two points; (b) deflections at any point measured with reference to a tangent to the bent beam at another point may be found as the statical moment about the first point of the area under the $\frac{M}{EI}$ curve between the two points.

(2) (a) Slope at any point measured with reference to any chord of the bent beam may be found as shear at that point due to the area under the $\frac{M}{EI}$ curve as a load on the chord acting as a beam simply supported at its ends; (b) deflection at any point measured with reference to any chord of the bent beam may be found as bending moment at that point due to the area under the $\frac{M}{EI}$ curve treated as a load on the chord acting as a beam simply supported at its ends.

All of these theorems are merely theorems of geometry stated in terms convenient to the structural engineer.   They neglect the effect of distortions other than rotations, and are applicable to any curved line where the angle changes are very small if we substitute "angle changes as loads" for "area under the $\frac{M}{EI}$ curve as a load" in the theorems.

In the column analogy the angle changes are treated as loads on the analogous column.   From the geometrical relations already pointed out it is evident that the conception involved in the column analogy is essentially that used in finding slopes and deflections.

If we use the column analogy in the extended form explained later in which the angle changes are represented as forces on the analogous column equal to moment times elastic area, and the linear distortions are represented as couples on the analogous column equal to shear times elastic centroidal moment of inertia, we may include at once the effect of both angular and linear distortions.   This is sometimes a useful theorem.   It is applied in the example of Fig. 14.

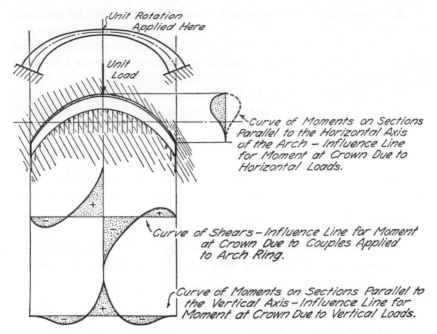

Unit Rotation
Applied Here

Unit
Load

Curve of Moments on Sections
Parallel to the Horizontal Axis
of the Arch – Influence Line
for Moment at Crown Due to
Horizontal Loads.

Curve of Shears – Influence Line for Moment
at Crown Due to Couples Applied
to Arch Ring.

Curve of Moments on Sections Parallel to
the Vertical Axis – Influence Line for
Moment at Crown Due to Vertical Loads.

Fig. 19. Influence Lines for Shear and Moment in an Arch
with Fixed Ends

(b) Influence Lines by the Column Analogy

The column analogy may be combined with Müller-Breslau's principle to compute influence ordinates. According to this principle, the influence ordinates equal the displacements of the load line which would result from a unit distortion corresponding to the stress function under investigation. For an influence line for moment, then, we would apply a unit rotation, for shear a unit displacement, and so on.

The application for crown moment in an arch is shown in Fig. 19. A unit rotation is applied at the crown and the displacements of points on the arch axis are determined. Vertical displacements along the arch axis are influence ordinates for crown moment due to vertical loads, horizontal displacements are influence ordinates for horizontal loads, rotations of the arch axis are influence ordinates for applied couples.

All of these may be found as shears and bending moments on sections through the analogous column when the column is loaded with a unit load at the crown, as shown in the figure.

Similarly for unit crown shear, apply to the column at the crown a unit couple about the vertical axis of the arch; for crown thrust, apply to the column at the crown a unit couple about the horizontal axis of the arch.

This procedure has great value in sketching influence lines. For numerical computation it is probably as rapid and convenient to compute the influence ordinates by the elementary procedure of applying unit loads at successive points on the arch axis.

19. *Supports of the Analogous Column.*—

(a) Types of Supports

The analogous column is supported on an elastic medium. The intensity of resistance offered by this medium is the indeterminate moment, resisting distortion, or the moment resulting from the restraint. The intensity times the area is the rotation produced by this resistance.

If there is a hinge in the beam, the rotation would be infinite if there were a constant moment at the hinge; the elastic area of the hinge is infinite. But it is inconvenient to represent an infinite area; instead we may choose a small area of infinite stiffness—a rigid point support. A hinge in the beam, then, may be represented by a rigid point support of the column.

A roller nest is equivalent to a rocker—two hinges on a line normal to the roller bed. Hence a roller nest or rocker may be represented by two point supports on a line normal to the roller bed.

A free end would be produced by three hinges not in line. Hence, it may be represented in the analogous column by three point supports not in line or by a fixed end.

It is interesting, though perhaps not very important, to note that if the beam is unstable, the column is statically indeterminate; if the beam is statically determinate, so also is the column; if the beam is statically indeterminate, the column would be unstable if it were not supported by the elastic medium.

In Fig. 20a is shown the analogous column and its load in the case of a beam simply supported. The area-moment relation is familiar.

Figure 20b shows a three-hinged arch and its analogous column. Note that in statically determinate structures only one stable curve of moments is possible and that there is no pressure on the elastic base—no indeterminate moment.

Figure 20c shows an arch having a crown hinge. In analyzing this case the rigid support is given an infinite area. The centroid, then, lies at the hinge and the total elastic area is infinite.

Figure 20d shows a cantilever beam. Note that the free end of the beam is rigidly fixed in the analogous column. The moment area

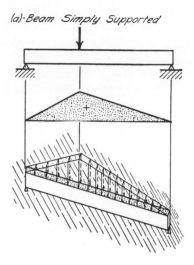

(a)-Beam Simply Supported

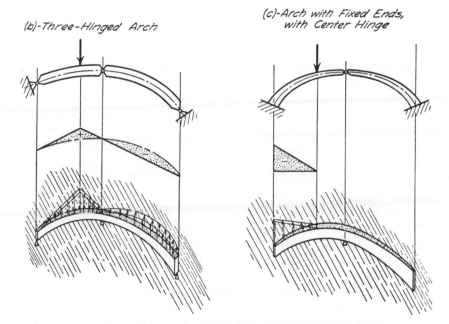

(b)-Three-Hinged Arch

(c)-Arch with Fixed Ends, with Center Hinge

FIG. 20. TYPES OF SUPPORTS FOR ANALOGOUS COLUMNS

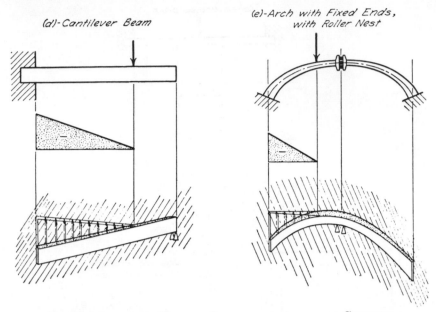

FIG. 20 (CONCLUDED). TYPES OF SUPPORTS FOR ANALOGOUS COLUMNS

relation is familiar to most students, as is also the conjugate beam relation.

In Fig. 20e is shown an arch having a roller nest equivalent to two hinges on a line normal to the roller bed. The elastic area is infinite and the elastic moment of inertia about the axis of the roller bed—the Y axis—is also infinite.

(b) Reciprocality of Hinges and Supports in Beam and Analogous Column

Just as hinges in the girder or arch may be represented by rigid supports in the analogous column, so rigid supports of the girder may be represented by hinges or combinations of hinges in the analogous column, since bending moment in the column corresponds to deflection in the beam. If the restraint is in two directions, the column at that point would contain two hinges at an angle with each other, which is equivalent to a universal joint.

These relations do not, however, seem to be very useful, since it is not convenient to analyze the stresses at the bases of such columns. The analogy, however, is illustrated in Figs. 21a and 21b. In Fig. 21b the analysis for moments in the beam is not affected by the hinge and joint in the analogous column, while analysis for slopes and deflections in the beam is facilitated by their use.

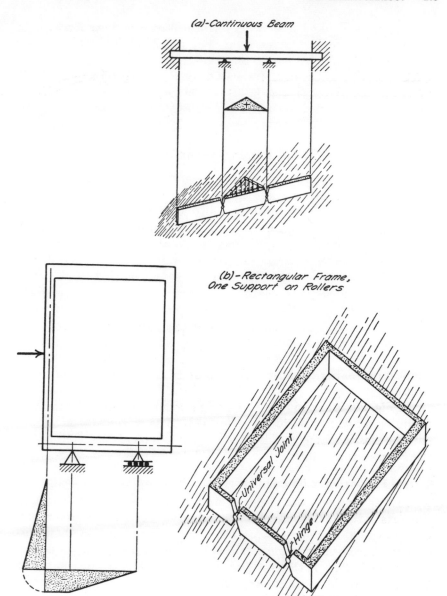

(a)-Continuous Beam

(b)-Rectangular Frame,
One Support on Rollers

Universal Joint

Hinge

FIG. 21. TYPES OF SUPPORTS FOR ANALOGOUS COLUMNS

(c) The Conjugate Beam

The term "conjugate beam" is due to Professor H. M. Westergaard. In an article entitled "Deflection of Beams by the Conjugate

Beam Method"* he has shown a reciprocal relation between straight loaded beams and certain imaginary beams which are subject to loads equal in intensity to the curves of moments on the original beams.

The conjugate beam as presented by Professor Westergaard will be seen to be the analogous column section. The conception, however, can be extended to curved as well as to straight beams.

IV.   Extension of the Analogy

20. *Introduction.*—The analogy between the computation of moments in beams, bents, and arches and the computation of fiber stresses on a section of an eccentrically loaded column as previously stated is simple and convenient. The analysis thus far explained, however, either neglects the effect of linear distortions within the structure or makes separate allowance for the effect of such distortions. In this section of the bulletin it is explained that by an extension of the analogy it is possible to include the effect of these linear distortions directly in the analysis. In doing this, however, the simplicity of the picture is marred. The extension here presented is, then, probably to be thought of as a very special tool to be used infrequently, if at all. The completeness of analysis furnished by this method of treatment justifies the inclusion of the material.

21. *Internal Distortions.*—The beam formula may be modified as follows: Moments may be separated into two parts, due to loads and due to couples and the products of inertia may be separated into two parts, due to the areas which make up the section and due to the centroidal products of inertia of those areas. The terms in the beam formula may then be redefined.

Write
$$P = \Sigma pa$$
$$A = \Sigma a$$
$$M_x = \Sigma pae_x + \Sigma M_x$$
$$M_y = \Sigma pae_y + \Sigma M_t$$
$$I_x = \Sigma ax^2 + \Sigma i_x$$
$$I_y = \Sigma ay^2 + \Sigma i_y$$
$$I_{xy} = \Sigma axy + \Sigma i_{xy}$$

Thus far in dealing with internal distortions only the angular rotations which take place about the centroids of the small sections into which the axis of the beam is divided have been considered.

---

*Loc. cit , page 7.

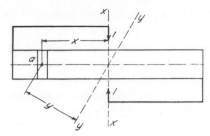

FIG. 22. TERMS USED FOR INTERNAL DISTORTIONS

Angular rotations have been treated as loads on the column section and an elastic body which will suffer angular distortion from moment has been treated as a part of the area of the column section. But a linear movement will result from two equal and opposite angular movements about different centers, and if these rotations are treated as loads, they will be parallel loads of opposite sense and will constitute a couple. Hence any linear distortion within the body corresponds to a moment load on the analogous column section.

The bending moment on any differential portion of a member due to unit forces through the elastic centroid of the member is x and the relative displacement of the ends along any axis Y due to this moment is axy (see Fig. 22). The total displacement then is Σaxy and is the product of inertia of the elastic areas about the elastic centroid. But it makes no difference whether this displacement is due to flexural or to shearing distortions. Whatever its cause, we can still treat it as if it were Σaxy and call it the centroidal product of inertia about the axes X and Y.

Just as any portion of a section may be represented for purposes of beam analysis by six quantities, namely, two coördinates of its centroid, its area, and its products of inertia about two centroidal axes, so the elastic properties of an elastic body may be completely represented by corresponding elastic quantities. And just as these six elementary properties of an area may be deduced from six other properties—namely, the statical moments about any three axes in the plane and the products of inertia about any three pairs of axes in the plane, so the elementary elastic properties of the section may be deduced if we have three displacements due to unit moment on the body and three displacements due to equal and opposite forces at the ends of the body.

This makes it possible to include automatically all types of stress distortion in beams directly in the analysis, if this seems desirable.

Moreover it is possible in members containing straight segments subject to constant shear to evaluate the bending effects by separating the effect of the total rotation and the relative displacement of the ends due to bending without finding the centroid of the moment curve.

The elastic area of a body, as the term is used here, is the total rotation produced in the body by opposite unit moments at its ends. The elastic centroid is the center about which the rotation occurs.

The total displacement of opposite ends of a member along one axis due to opposite unit terminal forces along any other axis is the elastic product of inertia of the body about these axes. If the axes are through the centroid, the displacement is an elastic centroidal product of inertia. If the axes are coincident through the centroid, the displacement is an elastic centroidal moment of inertia.

In computing the properties of a body as a whole, these centroidal products of inertia may be treated just as they are treated in the computation of the properties of beam sections. The elastic products of inertia of the analogous column, then, may be computed as the sum of the elastic areas times the products of their distances from the axes under consideration, plus the centroidal products of inertia of the elastic areas.

These centroidal products of inertia are useful also in computing the elastic moments on the analogous column, though the procedure has no simple analogue in beam analysis. It has been explained that known linear displacements may be treated as moment loads about the axis of displacement. Such displacements are produced by thrusts and shears on the portions of the elastic body. The displacement along any axis due to a force along any line equals the product of the force by the product of inertia of the body about the axis of displacement and the line of action of the force, as this product of inertia has been defined.

The elastic moments on the analogous column may be taken for each portion of the beam as equal to the moments at the elastic centroid of that portion times the elastic area plus a couple equal to the shear on that portion of the beam times the elastic centroidal moment of inertia. In this way the elastic moments have been computed in Fig. 14.

V. PHYSICAL CONSTANTS OF DEFORMATION FOR STRUCTURAL MEMBERS

22. *Nature of Physical Constants.*—Thus far consideration of the physical properties of the members has been restricted. No theory

has been propounded to predict the values of the elastic areas. If we are dealing only with distortions produced by external loads, it does not make any difference what are the absolute values of these elastic areas, or moduli of distortion; it is the relative values only that are wanted.

It seems somewhat unfortunate that the theory used in the analysis of continuous frames has come to be known as the theory of elasticity. In its simplest form it has nothing to do with elasticity in the ordinary sense of the word. The theory of elasticity merely states the geometrical conditions essential to continuity in terms of the physical properties of the structure. If these physical properties are known for the conditions of stress which actually exist, then the theory may be applied. It is thus possible to apply the theory of continuity in a perfectly definite way to plastic materials, such as concrete, taking account of the variation of the plastic distortions with both the intensity and the duration of the stress, provided the properties of the material are accurately and definitely known.

Thus, suppose an exact analysis of a concrete arch is desired and that the ratio of total stress to total deformation is known as a function of both intensity and duration of stress. We first assume a constant value of the ratio of stress to total deformation, which we will call E, throughout the arch rib, and find all stresses. Since the value of E is now a variable over each section, we transform the sections as explained previously. Using the transformed sections, the stresses are again found and the process is repeated to any desired degree of precision.

We now know accurately the stress conditions at the time of loading. After an interval all values of E will be changed and we can repeat the process just outlined. By successive repetitions we could trace out the complete stress history of the structure.

Whether we could ever know the physical properties of the material with enough accuracy to take account of their variations is a question of fact to be considered separately. Whether the structure is sensitive enough to such variations in properties to make the variation in results secured from any such analysis appreciable is also another matter. Of what importance such information would be in the safe and economical design of the structure is still another matter.

Qualitative thinking along these lines will disperse certain illusions which seem to be current as to mysterious results from plastic flow and from time yield of concrete. The subject will not be pursued here, since the monograph is restricted to geometrical relations. The important point just now is to clearly distinguish those facts which are purely geometrical from those which are necessarily a subject for laboratory equipment.*

23. *Method of Determining Physical Constants.*—Determination of the elastic constants themselves involves a knowledge of the properties of the material. In general they are to be determined as follows: (a) apply a unit moment at each end of the body and determine the magnitude of the rotation and the center of rotation (this gives the elastic area and its centroid); (b) apply unit forces along an axis Y at the ends of the member and through the elastic centroid and determine the relative linear displacements of the ends along and normal to axis Y. Similarly apply unit forces along an axis through the elastic centroid along axis X, normal to axis Y, and determine displacement along axis X (this gives I_x, I_{xy}, I_y).

The elastic properties of a body as just defined—the elastic area, elastic centroid, and elastic products of inertia—are true physical properties for the stress condition in the body. If they are known for each portion of the body, they can be computed for the whole. If certain assumptions are made we can predict the properties of the individual parts.

In the deductions which follow a constant value of E and the conservation in bending of plane right sections is assumed. In most cases these assumptions are very nearly correct. But these values cannot be predicted with absolute precision because of chance variations in the properties of the material.

The elastic properties of a body are defined for two ends at which alone forces are supposed to be applied to the body. For another pair of termini another set of elastic properties would be deduced.

The elastic properties for a given pair of termini may be determined experimentally as follows:

Hold one of the ends rigidly and apply through a bracket attached to the other end a vertical force and a horizontal force successively at each of two points. In each case measure the vertical displacement and the horizontal displacement of each of two points on the bracket (see Fig. 23).

We now have sixteen quantities from which to deduce the six quantities desired. If Hooke's Law holds for the material, only ten of these quantities will be different and only six will be needed. Many

*For a treatment of these matters, see "Neglected Factors in the Analysis of Stresses in Concrete Arches," by Lorenz G. Straub, presented as a thesis for the degree of Doctor of Philosophy at the University of Illinois in 1927 and later published in part as "Plastic Flow in Concrete Arches," Proc., A. S. C. E., Jan., 1930.

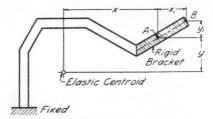

F<small>IG</small>. 23. E<small>XPERIMENTAL</small> D<small>ETERMINATION</small> <small>OF</small> P<small>HYSICAL</small> C<small>ONSTANTS</small>

different combinations of measurements may be used. The six quantities may all be deflections due to unit forces, as follows:

Vertical at A due to vertical force at $A = I_x + Ax^2$

Vertical at A due to vertical force at $B = I_x + Ax(x + x_1)$

Vertical at A due to horizontal force at $A = I_{xy} + Axy$

Vertical at B due to vertical force at $B = I_x + A(x + x_1)^2$

Horizontal at A due to horizontal force at $A = I_y + Ay^2$

Horizontal at B due to horizontal force at $B = I_y + A(y + y_1)$

From these the values of A, x, y, I_x, I_y, and I_{xy} may be deduced by simple algebra for known values of x_1, y_1.*

If Hooke's Law does not hold, different sets of measured displacements will not be consistent even though the measurements are made with absolute accuracy, because the body does not have any one set of elastic properties but has a different set for each different condition of stress.

24. *Computation of the Constants.*—Only a few of many possible illustrations of the computation of elastic constants is given here.

(a) Hinges and Roller Nests

Since forces acting on solid foundations produce no deformation, the elastic constants for the earth are taken as zero if we assume immovable abutments.

Eccentric forces acting on a frictionless hinge will produce no linear movement of the hinge but will produce unlimited rotation; hence the elastic area of a hinge is infinite, and its elastic centroidal products of inertia are zero.

Forces acting on a roller nest and inclined to its bed will produce no rotation, no displacement normal to the bed, and unlimited displacement along the bed; hence a roller nest has zero elastic area, zero

---

*A procedure which is simpler algebraically is as follows: Apply unit moment and measure rotation and horizontal and vertical displacement of one end. This gives the elastic area and locates the elastic centroid. The elastic centroidal products of inertia may then be measured directly as displacements along the centroidal axes due to unit loads through the centroid.

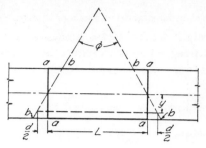

FIG. 24. FLEXURAL DISTORTION OF A BEAM

elastic centroidal moment of inertia about an axis normal to the bed, infinite elastic centroidal moment of inertia about an axis lying in the bed.

For a free end all elastic constants are infinite. The fact has no particular significance except that the theorem which states the column analogy is of perfectly general application to all plane beams, whether statically determinate or not, both simply supported and cantilevered.

(b) Flexural, Longitudinal, and Shearing Distortions in Straight Beams

The angle of flexure in a length of straight beam of constant section subjected to a given bending moment is readily computed by geometry if sections plane before bending remain plane after bending.

In Fig. 24 let a-a be given length L of the beam before bending and b-b after bending. The angle change ϕ equals the change in length of any fiber d divided by its distance from the neutral axis y.

Then $\phi = \dfrac{d}{y}$. From the definition of E, $d = \dfrac{fL}{E}$ where f is the fiber stress along any fiber. But $\dfrac{f}{E} = \dfrac{My}{I_t}$, where I_t is the moment of inertia of the transformed section obtained by dividing the areas of the original section by their values of E. Then $\phi = \dfrac{ML}{I_t}$ for straight beams.

Flexure of curved beams is discussed below.

Longitudinal distortion is computed as $\dfrac{PL}{A_t}$ for a force through the centroid of the transformed section.

The shearing distortion per unit of length of beam equals the shear divided by the continued product of area, the shearing modulus of elasticity and a factor depending on the shape of the section.

(c) Straight Homogeneous Beam of Uniform Section

Consider a straight segment of a homogeneous beam of uniform section. Let its properties be represented by length $= L$, area $= A$, moment of inertia $= I$, modulus of elasticity $= E$, radius of gyration $= \rho$.

Apply unit moment, unaccompanied by shear. Rotation is $\dfrac{L}{EI}$ and centroid of rotations is at the mid-point.

Apply unit transverse shear, otherwise unaccompanied by moment. Transverse displacement of end

(a) due to bending $= +\int x^2 da = \dfrac{1}{12}\dfrac{L}{EI}L^2$

(b) due to shearing distortions $= +\dfrac{L}{nAG}$, where n is the factor referred to above and G is the shearing modulus of elasticity. Normally, this displacement is unimportant. There is no longitudinal displacement due to transverse shear.

Apply unit longitudinal force. Longitudinal displacement $= +\dfrac{L}{AE} = +\rho^2\dfrac{L}{EI}$. No transverse displacement.

The elastic properties, then, are:

Elastic area $= \dfrac{L}{EI}$

Elastic centroidal moment of inertia about longitudinal axis

$$= \frac{1}{12}\frac{L}{EI}L^2 + \frac{L}{AGn}$$

Elastic centroidal moment of inertia along longitudinal axis $= \dfrac{L}{AE}$

Elastic centroidal product of inertia about two axes $= 0$

Elastic centroid on axis at mid-point.

These six quantities completely describe, on the ordinary assumptions of mechanics, the elastic properties of this body for terminal forces.

(d) Bars of Trusses

The strain of a bar in a truss produces a rotation at the moment center for that bar $\dfrac{\Delta}{r}$. If a unit moment acts at that center, $\phi = \dfrac{L}{AEr}$. This determines the elastic area.

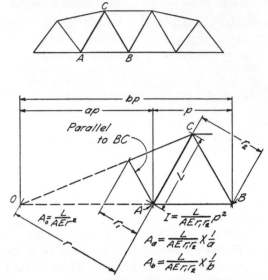

FIG. 25. DEFORMATION CONSTANTS FOR WEB MEMBERS IN A TRUSS

This expression is sometimes inconvenient for web members where chords are not parallel, because the moment center does not lie near the panel in which the section for stress is passed. If the chords are parallel, it leads to indeterminate expressions.

In these cases it is convenient to replace the distant elastic weight by two elastic weights and an elastic moment of inertia lying in the panel. Thus the true elastic area at O is $+\dfrac{L}{AEr^2}$. If the areas at A and B are to have that at O as a resultant (see Fig. 25)

$$A_a = +\frac{L}{AEr^2}\frac{bp}{p} = +\frac{L}{AEr_1r_2}\frac{1}{a}$$

$$A_b = -\frac{L}{AEr^2}\frac{ap}{p} = -\frac{L}{AEr_1r_2}\frac{1}{b}$$

since $\qquad \dfrac{r}{bp} = \dfrac{r_1}{p}$ and $\dfrac{r}{ap} = \dfrac{r_2}{p}$

For product of inertia about axes normal to the lower chord to be the same as that of A_o,

$$I_{o-o} = 0 = A_a(ap)^2 + A_b(bp)^2 + I$$

$$I = +\frac{L}{AEr_1r_2}p^2$$

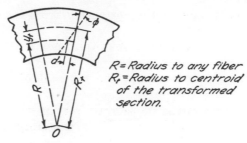

R = Radius to any fiber
R_t = Radius to centroid
    of the transformed
    section.

FIG. 26. SEGMENT OF A CURVED BEAM

Evidently no correction for the product of inertia is necessary if either axis is parallel to the lower chord.

The elastic areas A_a and A_b may be located on either chord and the moment of inertia taken along that chord provided ap and bp are computed along that chord. The positive elastic weight always lies on the side of the panel next to the moment center.

If the chords are parallel, the elastic areas become zero, the moment of inertia along the chord is still $I = + \dfrac{L}{A E r_1 r_2} p^2$, but $r_1 = r_2$.

This method of treating truss bars is sometimes advantageous for computing stresses in indeterminate structures. In most cases indeterminate trusses can be analyzed conveniently by other methods than the column analogy.

(e) Beams Sharply Curved

Beams having a radius of curvature small compared with their depth are common in machine parts; in structural design they occur in thick arched dams and at the haunched junction of beams and columns. The formula of Winkler, usually presented for the solution of such beams, leads to certain complications when used to compute deformations or for the analysis of such beams when they are statically indeterminate. For this reason, a detailed explanation of the use of the transformed section seems desirable here.

In Fig. 26 is shown a differential length of a beam having a center of curvature at O.

It has been shown that if the section is transformed by dividing each differential area by its radius of curvature R we can write

$$fR = \frac{P}{A_t} + \frac{M_t}{I_t} y_t$$

where f is the fiber stress at any distance y_t from the centroid of the transformed section

R is the radius of curvature of this fiber

P is the normal load

M_t is the moment about the centroid of the transformed section

A_t is the area of the transformed section

I_t is the moment of inertia of the transformed section about its centroid.

Also let

A = the area of the original section

R_o = the radius of curvature to the centroid of the original section

R_t = the radius of curvature to the centroid of the transformed section.

By definition $A_t = \displaystyle\int \frac{dA}{R}$

Taking moments about O

$$R_t = \frac{\displaystyle\int R \frac{dA}{R}}{\displaystyle\int \frac{dA}{R}} = \frac{A}{A_t}$$

The moment of inertia about O =

$$\int \frac{dA}{R} R^2 = \int R dA = A R_o$$

Reducing this to the centroid of the transformed section

$$I_t = A R_o - A_t R_t^2 = A R_o - A_t \frac{A}{A_t} R_t = A(R_o - R_t)$$

If, then, the area and centroid of the original section are known, it is necessary to find only the area of the transformed section in order to compute directly all quantities needed.

The angle of rotation about the centroid of the transformed section is

$$\phi = \frac{y_t}{d} = \frac{E y_t}{f} \times \text{(length of differential fiber under consideration)}$$

But $f = \dfrac{M_t y_t}{I_t R}$

$$\text{Length of any fiber} = \frac{R}{R_t}\, ds$$

Where ds is the length of the differential fiber along the axis of the centroid of the transformed section.

Hence $\phi = \dfrac{ds}{EI_t R_t}$ is the elastic area of the segment, or in general

$$A = \frac{\text{angle of arc}}{EI_t}\,.$$

If $M_t = 0$, the section moves parallel to itself and

$$\Delta = \frac{P}{E(A_t R_t)}\, ds = \frac{P}{AE}\, ds$$

Hence $\dfrac{ds}{EA}$ is the elastic centroidal moment of inertia for rib-shortening correction.

It will be seen, then, that all expressions for beams of sharp curvature take the same form as where the beams are straight if the axis of the beam is taken as the axis defined by the centroids of the transformed sections instead of by the centroids of the original sections.

(f) Compound Members—Bifurcated Members

The elastic properties of any elastic ring may be defined with reference to the termini from the principles indicated. Thus, to determine the elastic properties of the ring $ABCDA$, Fig. 27, with reference to terminals AC, apply at C a unit moment, the ring being cut at C and held at A. Now treat as a column section cut at A and uniformly loaded along ABC and compute the shear at C and the bending moment on vertical and horizontal sections through C. This gives the elastic weight and its static moments about C, from which the coördinates of the centroid may be computed.

Next apply at C a unit vertical force, the ring being cut at C and held at A. Apply the column analogy and compute the bending moments on the analogous columns on horizontal and vertical sections at C, the section being cut at A. This gives moment of inertia for vertical axis through C and product of inertia for vertical and horizontal axes through C. These may then be reduced to the centroid.

Finally apply at C a unit horizontal force, the ring being cut at C and held at A. Compute the bending moment on a horizontal section through C on the analogous column section cut at A. This is the moment of inertia for a horizontal axis through C. This may now be reduced to the centroid.

If loads occur within the ring, the elastic load on the ring may be determined from the shear (elastic load) and moments on vertical and horizontal axes through C (static moments of the elastic load about C) for the elastic column section if cut at A as above.

The elastic load and its point of application and also the elastic properties of the ring being known, the ring may be treated as is any other member.

This procedure is relatively simple but involves a good deal of computation. The problem, however, is not a very simple one. Anyone who has occasion to use the method for numerical problems will find that it leads to comparatively simple expressions.

(g) Successive Compounding

The compounding procedure just indicated may be extended indefinitely to include any number of branches. The most common and important case is that of a series of continuous arches or bents. The general procedure by this method in such a case is as follows:

(a) Apply a unit moment at the junction point of the outside bent, find the elastic area and elastic centroid.

(b) Apply a unit vertical force at the junction and find the moment of inertia about a vertical axis through this junction and the product of inertia about horizontal and vertical axes through this point. Reduce these to the centroid.

(c) Apply a unit horizontal force at the junction and find the centroidal moment of inertia of the combination for a horizontal axis through the junction. Reduce this to the centroid.

(d) Substitute these elastic properties for those of the pier in the next bent; proceed as above and continue to include any desired number of bents.

(e) In a similar way the elastic loads are to be combined for one bent after another.

(f) The reactions having been determined for the last bent of the series (which may be the center bent, combinations having been made from both ends) these can be resolved back successively through the series.

This method has enough value to justify reference to it, though, even in the case of continuous arches, other methods are more convenient.

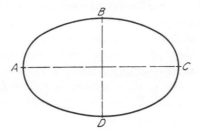

FIG. 27. CLOSED ELASTIC RING

VI. APPLICATIONS OF THEOREM

25. *Fields of Application of Theorem.*—The theorem here presented has several fields of application:

(1) In the routine analysis of symmetrical and unsymmetrical arches and bents for loads, either gravity or inclined, for temperature, for shrinkage, or for abutment displacement.

(2) In determining moments at the ends of beams fixed at ends and in determining other properties of such beams, such as the end moments corresponding to unit rotation at end, for use in connection with various methods of analysis of continuous girders or frames.[*]

(a) It is possible thus to determine constants for use in the general equations of displacements. These equations state that terminal forces and moments on a member are the sum of those due to known loads on the member or distortions in the member when the ends are fixed and to any displacements or rotations of the ends, known or to be determined. A special case of these equations, applicable where the members are straight and of uniform section, is known in American literature as the equation of slope-deflection.

Values of terminal forces in terms of the unknown terminal displacements may be substituted in the equations of static equilibrium of the joints. These equations may then be solved for the terminal displacements.

When the joint displacements have been found the terminal forces may be computed from the original equations of displacement.

(b) Constants may be determined for equations which state the existence of continuity at the joints. Of these the theorems of

---

[*]Loc. cit., page 48.

three moments and of four moments are special examples of limited application.

(c) Terminal forces may be determined for known loads or internal distortions on the assumption that the joints are not displaced and then the unbalanced terminal forces may be distributed among the connecting members in proportion to their resistance to end displacement. In a special case this is done by the method of moment distribution. The constants needed may be determined by the column analogy.

(d) In routine computations of slopes and deflections.

26. *Methods of Analysis of Continuous Frames.*—This bulletin does not deal primarily with methods of analysis of continuous frames, but only with the analysis and elastic properties of the individual members of which the frame may be made up. Some comments on methods of analysis of such frames is needed to explain applications of the column analogy indicated.

Methods of analysis of continuous frames may be divided into those involving internal work of the frame, such as the method of least work, and those involving the geometry of continuity. That all methods are really the same will at once be realized but their relations to each other will not be discussed here.

Of the geometrical methods of analysis we may distinguish those in which the displacements of the joints are treated as unknowns and those in which the terminal forces acting on the members at the joints are treated as unknowns. The former are represented in a special case by the method of slope-deflection; the latter are represented by the theorem of three moments and by the theorem of four moments.

The method in which the joint displacements are treated as unknowns might be called the Method of Joint Displacements. In this method the terminal shears and moments are written in terms of the joint displacements. The equations of statics—the forces balance at each joint—are then written for each joint. From these the terminal displacement is computed. The terminal displacement being known, the shears and moments may be found.

In the other method of analysis the terminal slopes and displacements are stated in terms of the terminal shears and moments. The equations of continuity which state that the displacement of a joint is common to the ends of all members meeting at the joint are then written for each joint. From these equations the terminal shears and moments are found directly. The equation of three moments is a familiar illustration of an equation of joint continuity. A less familiar illustration is the equation of four moments. This method might be called the Method of Continuity.

It is well to distinguish the method of slope-deflection from the equation of slope-deflection; the method, which seems to have been restricted to straight members, consists in treating joint rotations and displacements as unknowns in equations of static equilibrium for the joints. The equation of slope-deflection is merely one of many forms of the equation which relates the terminal forces to the loads and terminal displacements of a straight beam. The method of slope-deflection may be used without using the particular form of equation known as the equation of slope-deflection or the equation of slope-deflection may be used without using the method of slope-deflection.

If we write the end moments and forces in terms of loads and end displacements, we can derive from these expressions for the end rotations and displacements in terms of loads and end moments and forces. Displacements of the ends of all members at a joint are equal and angular rotation at the ends of all members meeting at a joint are equal. These displacements and rotations being in terms of end moments and forces on the beams and of the physical properties of the beams, the equations can be solved for the end moments and forces.

The Method of Terminal Force Distribution will not be discussed here. It is more closely related to the Method of Continuity than to the Method of Joint Displacements.

27. *General Equation of Displacements and Slope-Deflection.*—The general equations of end forces at any joint, A, of a structure may be written as follows, provided, as is usually true, the principal axes of the members are parallel and normal to each other:

$$M_a = \phi_a N_a - \phi_b r_a N_a + (\Delta_a - \Delta_b)\frac{d_a}{I_o} + M'_a$$

$$F_u = \frac{\Delta_a - \Delta_b}{I_o} + \frac{\phi_a d_a - \phi_b d_b}{I_o} + F'_a$$

M_a and F_a are total end moment and end force (thrust or shear) in the member

(Note that in general there will be two equations of force at any joint, one for horizontal and one for vertical forces.)

    M'_a = moment which would exist in the member if there were no rotation or displacement of the joints.

    F'_a = force which would exist in the member if there were no rotation or displacement of the joints.

    ϕ_a, Δ_a are respectively rotation and displacement at the joint considered.

ϕ_b, Δ_b are corresponding quantities at the other end, B, of each member successively.

N_a is the moment at joint A corresponding to a unit rotation of this joint, the other end being fixed.

r_a is the carry-over factor at A (the ratio of the moment at B due to a unit rotation at A to the moment at A due to such a rotation.)

I_o is the elastic moment of inertia about the centroid for any member.

d is the distance of either end from the centroidal axis of a member.

From these general forms and the equations of static equilibrium we may write the equations for every joint in a complex structure such as a continuous arch series or a Vierendeel truss. These equations may then be solved simultaneously for displacements and from these the moments, shears and thrusts may be determined.

The use of such equations, requiring a carefully selected convention of signs with resulting possibility of error from this source and involving simultaneous solution, is to be thought of as a research tool and rarely as a tool of design.

If there are no joint displacements, or if it is convenient to make separate allowance for such displacements, the process is much simplified. We then have, from $\Sigma M = 0$,

$$\phi_a = \frac{\Sigma M'_a}{\Sigma N_a} + \frac{\Sigma \phi_b r_a N_a}{\Sigma N_a}$$

the signs depending on the convention used.

This, perhaps, is more conveniently written,

$$\phi_a = \Sigma \frac{M'_a}{\Sigma N_a} + \Sigma \phi_b \frac{r_a N_a}{\Sigma N_a}$$

If connecting members are treated as prismatic,

$$N_a = 4 \frac{I}{L} \qquad r_b = -\tfrac{1}{2}$$

$$\phi_a = \tfrac{1}{2} \Sigma \frac{M'_a}{2 \Sigma \dfrac{I}{L}} - \Sigma \phi_b \frac{\dfrac{I}{L}}{2 \Sigma \dfrac{I}{L}}$$

If, further, the values M'_a are due to known rotations of the bars,

$$M'_a = \frac{6\Delta}{L \frac{L}{IE}} = 6E \frac{I}{L} \psi = 6EK\psi$$

$$\phi_a = \Sigma 3\psi \frac{K}{2\Sigma K} - \Sigma\phi_b \frac{K}{2\Sigma K}$$

which expression is convenient in finding secondary stresses in trusses. Or this may be derived from the fundamental equation above

$$\phi_a = \frac{\Sigma M'_a}{\Sigma N_a} + \frac{\Sigma\phi_a r_b N_a}{\Sigma N_a} - \frac{\Sigma(\Delta_a - \Delta_b)\frac{d}{I}}{\Sigma K_a}$$

$$M'_a = 0, \ N_a = 4\frac{I}{L}, \ r_a = -\tfrac{1}{2}, \ \frac{\Delta_a - \Delta_b}{L} = -\psi$$

$$\frac{d}{I} = 6\frac{I}{L} \cdot \frac{1}{L}$$

$$\phi_a = \frac{3\Sigma K\psi}{2\Sigma K} - \frac{\Sigma K\phi_b}{2\Sigma K}$$

These discussions include any combination of bars of any shape or form provided the axes are parallel or normal to each other, and it is not very difficult to extend the method to include skewed axes. The slope-deflection equation for prismatic beams,

$$M = \frac{2EI}{L} (2\phi_a + \phi_b - 3\psi)$$

may be derived in a number of ways and follows from the first general equation when

$$N_a = 4K, \ r_a = -\tfrac{1}{2}, \ \psi = -\frac{\Delta_a - \Delta_b}{2d}, \ \frac{d^2}{I} = \frac{\frac{L^2}{4}}{\frac{L^2}{12} \cdot \frac{L}{I}} = 3K$$

The interest in the equations at present, however, is chiefly in the utility of the column analogy in evaluating the constants M'_a, F'_a, d_a, I_o, N_a, and V_a for the members.

VII.   Conclusion

28. *Conclusion.*—The paper is restricted to geometrical relations and does not discuss applications to design.   Its thesis is simply that moments, shears, slopes, and deflections of beams due to any cause may be computed in just the same way and by the same formulas as are used in computing reactions on a short column eccentrically loaded or as would be used to compute shears and bending moments on longitudinal sections through such a column.

The column analogy is a convenient tool of mechanics, a somewhat mechanical device for a structural engineer, but one which seems to give desired results with a minimum of thought as to method of procedure or sign conventions.   In the study of continuous frames it becomes auxiliary to methods for the analysis of such frames.

The most obvious application is in the analysis of single span structures; perhaps its most important applications occur in the study of continuous bents, arches, and beams.

10

VIRTUAL WORK: A RESTATEMENT

Synopsis

The fundamental relations that determine the distortions produced in structures by internal strains may be stated in the mathematical language of the calculus and of geometry and in the engineering terminology of moment, shear, product of inertia, and moment of inertia. These theorems are, however, most readily correlated by use of the principle of virtual work. The paper restates this principle, emphasizing that the reactions to the imaginary external resistance are themselves purely imaginary and in no way necessarily related to the supports of the structure. It then illustrates in part the very broad application of the principle.

Most of the theorems developed are not new. Indeed, the writer is not sure that any of them are entirely new, nor is he here especially concerned with their lack of novelty. The paper may serve a useful purpose in bringing into logical sequence a group of geometrical principles which are essential to the study of statically indeterminate structures. If it has any such value, the omission of references to the work of many who have helped to develop or illuminate the principle of virtual work, may be pardoned.

Virtual Work—Usual Statement

Although essentially a principle of geometry, the principle of virtual work has proved the most powerful tool ever applied to the analysis of statically indeterminate structures. An examination of American textbooks leads to the belief that the broadest application of the principle has not been properly emphasized.

As usually presented, the principle may be stated somewhat as follows:† Assume any rigid body acted on by a force and reactions and let it be required to determine the deflection, $\varDelta$, in the direction, $a\,b$, of any point, a. Consider, first, the stretch—call it δ—of any differential fiber. Now considering a unit hypothetical resistance to motion at a to produce a stress, u, in the fiber, then the external work will be $1 \times \varDelta$ and the internal work will be $u \times \delta$. Then,

$$\varDelta = u\,\delta \dots\dots\dots\dots\dots\dots\dots\dots\dots(1)$$

Note.—Written discussion on this paper will be closed with the **May, 1926,** *Proceedings.* When finally closed, the paper, with discussion in full, will be published in *Transactions.*

† For the first presentation of the principle in American literature, see a paper by George F. Swain, Past-President, Am. Soc. C. E., *Journal,* Franklin Inst., February, March, and April, 1883.

Each fiber produces its independent deflection and, therefore,

$$\text{Total } \varDelta = \Sigma u \, \delta. \dots\dots\dots\dots\dots\dots\dots(2)$$

If the internal hypothetical stress resists the distortion, the internal work will be positive and the external movement opposite in direction to the hypothetical load. The same result follows from the more convenient rule, which treats lengthening and tension as positive, and indicates a positive displacement in the direction of the hypothetical resistance when the algebraic summation, $\Sigma u \, \delta$, is positive.

Reference has been made to the stretch of a differential fiber—the argument would have applied equally well to the shearing distortion of a differential cube, to the rotational distortion of a differential cylinder, to internal angular displacement, or to any other internal distortion.

Also, as Professor Swain has pointed out,* it is possible to deal with external rotation at a instead of translation. The hypothetical unit resistance is then a unit moment. Then,

$$\text{Rotation at } a = \Sigma u \, \delta,$$

in which, u is the stress in each small particle due to a unit moment at a and δ is the strain actually existing in the particle.

VIRTUAL WORK—RESTATEMENT

As the equations of virtual work just stated involve no work done by the reactions from the hypothetical unit resistance it must have been assumed that they do no work and hence that they do not move. This is commonly—although not always—stated. A more correct statement, however, is that these reactions do not have any motion which appears as a part of the described displacement, and hence the reactions to the hypothetical unit resistance are such as to fix in direction the line with reference to which the desired displacement is measured and to fix in position any assumed point on this line.

Commonly this line of reference is the line joining the supports of the structure, but it might equally well be either (1) the line joining any two points on the deflected structure or (2) any tangent to it. In the former case the unit load or moment acts on a structure simply supported at the two given points; in the latter, the structure is fixed, or cantilevered, at the point of tangency of the fixed tangent.

The general principle deduced, therefore, may be stated, as follows: To find with reference to any line of the distorted structure and with reference to any point on that line the displacement produced at any other point by given internal distortions, consider a unit resistance to such displacement applied externally at the given point, the structure being held stable by reactions fixing the point and the line of reference. Find the internal resistances produced by this imaginary external resistance. The sum of the products of the internal distortions multiplied by the imaginary internal resistances is the desired displacement.

The internal distortions may be due to any condition of stress and the strains may be either elastic or plastic, or they may be due to temperature or

---

* *Transactions*, Am. Soc. C. E., Vol. LXXXIII (1919–20), p. 622 *et seq.*

inaccurate workmanship. The external movement may be either of rotation or of translation. Rotation may be measured with reference to any line in the deflected structure. Translation may be measured in any direction with reference to any given line in the deflected structure and any given point on that line.

Virtual Work Applied to Trusses

Thus presented the broad statement of the relations of external movements to internal distortions leads directly to the usual theorems dealing with slopes and deflections. In trusses it takes the familiar form, $\sum \dfrac{s\,u\,l}{A\,E}$ (the properties of the member being s, the stress; l, the length; and A, the area; E being the modulus of elasticity), except that u should be defined with reference to the fixed or reaction points. Thus, it is possible to find the deflection of any panel point, A, with reference to a line through any other two panel points, B and C, by considering the hypothetical unit load applied at A, the truss being supported at B and C. Either B or C may be taken as fixed, the other point being, for hypothetical loads, on rollers. Similarly, the relative deflection of opposite corners of any quadrilateral of a truss may be found by taking $\Sigma\,\delta\,u$, in which, u is the stress in any bar due to a unit load at one corner in the direction of the other when the truss is supported at the other corner. This is a familiar problem in internal indetermination.

Virtual Work Applied to Beams

In the case of beams the displacements due to moment only are:

$$\Delta = \int M' \, d\,\phi \dots\dots\dots\dots\dots\dots\dots\dots\dots (3)$$

in which, Δ is the external relative movement of any point, $d\,\phi$ is the rotation (produced by the bending moments) in any differential length, and M' is the imaginary moment over this differential length produced by a unit resistance to the external movement.

If the deflection at any point from a chord of a structure, due to moments only, is to be found, the values, M', will be identical with the ordinates to an influence line for bending moment at this point on the chord. From this it follows that the deflections of any slightly curved line away from its chord equal the bending moments on the chord, treated as a beam, simply supported at its ends, due to the angle changes as loads. This is applicable in any case to a beam, a floor line, or a truss chord, if the angle changes can be computed. From it the moment-area theorems of Mohr and Greene may be shown to follow directly, or they may be taken as direct corollaries of the principle of virtual work, as will be shown.

The angle change in a differential length of the axis of a beam, if plane sections remain plane, is the strain of an outer fiber, divided by the distance of this fiber from the neutral axis. The strain of the outer fiber is $\dfrac{f}{E}\,d\,l$, in which, f is the intensity of stress in the outer fiber. Then, $d\,\phi = \dfrac{f}{E\,y}\,d\,l$, in which, y is the distance from outer fiber to neutral axis.

In all the theorems dealing with moment-areas, the term, $\dfrac{f}{y}$, may be substituted for $\dfrac{M}{I}$. Sometimes this is convenient. It also makes possible a clearer understanding of the deflection of reinforced concrete beams and, in general, gives a clearer view of the assumptions that are involved in the analysis of indeterminate structures.

If the beam formula applies, then,

$$f = \frac{M\,y}{I};\; d\,\phi = \frac{f}{E\,y}\,d\,l = \frac{M}{E\,I}\,d\,l$$

Hence,

$$\Delta = \int M'\,M\,\frac{d\,l}{E\,I}\dots\dots\dots\dots\dots(4)$$

If applied to a part of a beam containing a frictionless hinge, this expression is evidently indeterminate, since at the hinge both M and I are zero. Moment-area theorems are, therefore, indeterminate for those parts of a beam in which a hinge occurs unless the change of angle at the hinge is computed independently.

The Reciprocal Theorem

If the expressions, $\displaystyle\sum \frac{s\,u\,l}{A\,E}$ for trusses and $\displaystyle\int M'\,M\,\frac{d\,l}{E\,I}$ for beams, be used to find absolute displacements due to loads on the structure, the interchangeability of the terms, s and M, which are due to the loads, with u and M', respectively, which are due to the hypothetical external unit resistances to displacement, indicates at once the general theorem of reciprocal displacements. If "displacement" is interpreted in a general sense as either linear or angular, and "load" in a general sense as either force or moment, then in any structure the displacement at A due to a load at B has the same value as the displacement at B due to a load at A, provided that both at A and at B the force and the displacement are of the same nature, linear displacement corresponding to force along its line of action, and rotation corresponding to moment.

This theorem is useful principally in interpreting as influence ordinates those displacements of the load line of a structure which would be produced by an imaginary unit internal distortion corresponding to the internal stress for which the influence line is desired.

Greene's Theorems Derived Directly by Virtual Work

If the relative rotation at one point on a beam referred to the tangent at another point is desired, consider the beam cantilevered from one point and loaded with a unit moment at the other point. Then, $M' = \text{constant} = 1$, and,

$$\int \frac{M\,M'}{E\,I}\,d\,l = \frac{1}{E\,I} \times (\text{area under moment curve}$$

$$\text{between the points of reference})\dots\dots\dots\dots(5)$$

If, however, the deflection of the second point with reference to a tangent from the first is wanted, consider the beam to be loaded and cantilevered from the first point, with a unit load at the second. Then M' equals the distance of each section from the second point and $\int \left(\dfrac{M}{E I} d l \right)$ M' is evidently $\dfrac{1}{E I}$ times the statical moment of the area of the moment curve about the second point.

<h2 align="center">MOHR'S THEOREMS</h2>

In the case of a beam on fixed supports the change of slope at any point, A, relative to the line joining these supports may be found by applying a unit moment at the point, the beam being simply supported at the fixed points. The moment curve for M' will be found to be identical with an influence line for shear at A. Hence,

$$\int \frac{M M'}{E I} d l = \int \frac{M d l}{E I} \times \text{(shear at } A \text{ due to a unit load at each section)}$$

$$= \int \left(\text{shears at } A \text{ due to each } \frac{M d l}{E I} \right)$$

$$= \text{shear at } A \text{ on a simple beam due to the } \frac{M}{E I}\text{-curve considered as a load.} \quad (6)$$

For the deflection at A, on a simply supported beam, $D E$, apply a unit load at A. The curve for M' is then identical with an influence line for bending moment at A. Hence, the deflection of A is the bending moment at A due to the $\dfrac{M}{E I}$-curve considered as a load.

The method herein indicated of establishing the identity of the curve for M' with the influence line for some easily evaluated function, such as shear or moment, offers a general method for stating theorems of slope and deflection in the language of structural engineering. By its use may be readily determined those analogies which form the foundation for what has come to be known as the method of conjugate beams.

Evidently, any line on the beam other than $D E$ may be considered as fixed. Thus, consider a beam bent as shown in Fig. 1. The deflection of Point A with reference to the line, $B C$—Δ_a in the diagram—is the bending moment at A produced by the $\dfrac{M}{E I}$-curve between B and C on a simply supported beam, $B C$. This is sometimes a convenient theorem.

Also, the slope of the tangent at A with reference to the line, $B C$, is the shear at A on the simply supported beam, $B C$, due to the $\dfrac{M}{E \cdot I}$-curve between B and C acting as a load.

Angle Changes in Trusses

Another interesting application of the principle of virtual work is in finding the change, $\Delta\,\alpha$, of any angle, α, of a triangle (Fig. 2) due to stresses in the three sides. Apply at A and C the elements of a unit couple, causing reactions such as to hold $A\,B$ fixed in direction. Tension and increase of angle are taken as positive. Then,

$$\Delta\,\alpha = \Sigma\,\delta\,u = \Sigma\,\frac{f\,l}{E}\,u$$

or,

$$E\,\Delta\,\alpha = \Sigma\,f\,l\,u \dots\dots\dots\dots\dots\dots\dots(7)$$

in which, for any bar, f is the fiber stress, l, the length, and E the elastic modulus.

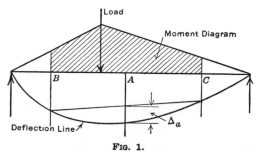

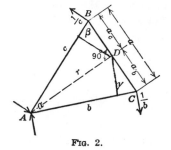

FIG. 1.   FIG. 2.

Resolving the forces at Joints B and C,

$$u_a = \frac{1}{r}\,;\quad u_b = -\,\frac{1}{b}\,\frac{a_b}{r}\,;\quad u_c = -\,\frac{1}{c}\,\frac{a_c}{r}$$

$$E\,\Delta\,\alpha = f_a\,a\,\frac{1}{r} - f_b\,b\,\frac{1}{b}\,\frac{a_b}{r} - f_c\,c\,\frac{1}{c}\,\frac{a_c}{r} = \frac{f_a\,a - (f_b\,a_b + f_c\,a_c)}{r}$$

$$= \left[f_a - \left(f_b\,\frac{a_b}{a} + f_c\,\frac{a_c}{a}\right)\right]\frac{a}{r} \dots\dots\dots\dots\dots(8)$$

in which, f_a, f_b, f_c are fiber stresses and the other terms are as shown in Fig. 2. Equation (8) is probably the most convenient formula for the angle changes. It may be modified to:

$$E\,\Delta\,\alpha = f_a\,\frac{a_b}{r} + f_a\,\frac{a_c}{r} - f_b\,\frac{a_b}{r} - f_c\,\frac{a_c}{r}$$

$$= (f_a - f_b)\,\frac{a_b}{r} + (f_a - f_c)\,\frac{a_c}{r}$$

$$= (f_a - f_b)\,\cot\gamma + (f_a - f_c)\,\cot\beta \dots\dots\dots\dots(9)$$

Equation (9) is familiar to students of secondary stresses.

Evidently, the method here presented may be readily extended to the quadrilaterals which occur in subdivided trusses and K-trusses.

Slope Deflection

The application of this method to the special case of a beam or part of a beam loaded only with moments at its two ends gives directly either the end slopes in terms of the end moments or the latter in terms of the former. In the first case given the loads on the beam, the reactions (end shears) are desired; in the second, the magnitude of the loads is to be determined for given reactions. By taking moments about B (Fig. 3), there follows,

$$\theta_a = \frac{2}{3}\, M_a\, \frac{l}{2\,E\,I} - \frac{1}{3}\, M_b\, \frac{l}{2\,E\,I} = \frac{l}{6\,E\,I}\,(2\,M_a - M_b) \ldots\ldots(10)$$

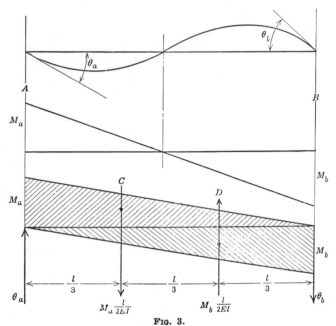

FIG. 3.

By taking moments about D,

$$\frac{M_a\, l}{2\,E\,I} = 2\,\theta_a + \theta_b$$

or,

$$M_a = \frac{2\,E\,I}{l}\,(2\,\theta_a + \theta_b) \ldots\ldots\ldots\ldots\ldots\ldots(11)$$

Both forms of equations have long been used in evaluating secondary stresses. Equation (11), combined with the device of using as unknowns the rotations of parts of the structure and evaluating them by simultaneous equations of statics, has had an elaborate development in the literature of the "slope-deflection method."

MOMENT WEIGHTS

The principle of virtual work furnishes directly a method of computing moment weights, or, as some writers call them, "elastic weights", for determining the deflected load line, or influence line, for trusses. Assume that it is desired to draw the deflected load line for a unit load as shown (Fig. 4), that is, an influence line for horizontal reaction. The angle change at a may be computed by applying a unit moment resisting this angle change. This is effected by applying loads as shown in Fig. 4 (b), acting at the points on the load line or floor as indicated by circles, and then computing $\Sigma \delta u$, in which, δ is the change in length of any bar due to the horizontal reaction, and u is the stress for the loading shown in Fig. 4 (b). These angle changes may then be treated as loads at the panel points and, when corrected for the deflection of the ends of the load line, the moment curve thus produced will have the shape of the influence line.

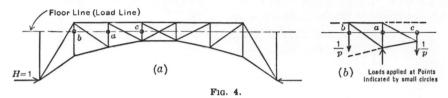

FIG. 4.

This method presents advantages in directness in some cases as where the floor-beams frame into the verticals between upper and lower panel points.

CONCLUSION

The illustrations given indicate the broad usefulness of the general principle of virtual work. The writer has thought it wise to limit them within the space which the specialized interest of the paper justifies. For the same reason, the paper is confined to the geometrical relations of distortions and does not include other relations which, in the theory of indeterminate structures, follow therefrom.*

In closing it may be well again to call attention to the purely geometrical nature of these theorems. They do not bear on the accuracy of the physical assumptions regarding the action of structures. Like all other geometrical relations, they are not open to dispute, nor are they proper subjects for experimental verification, and they are also subject to statement in an endless variety of forms or aspects of the relations involved. Familiarity with these relations is essential to facility in analyzing indeterminate structures, but neither ordinary nor extraordinary expertness in this field necessarily connotes either unusual or even common ability in designing structures or in understanding their action.

To apply these theorems to engineering structures, it is simply necessary either to show that for given values of the moments, shears, and thrusts, the strains can be predicted, or, if exact prediction is not possible, to determine by direct computation what error results from the inexactness. In analyzing indeterminate structures it is also to be noted that usually the relative and not the absolute values of these strains are in question.

Because of the definiteness of the moments, shears, and thrusts, strain measurements on statically determinate structures seem for this purpose more valuable and dependable than similar data derived from measurements on indeterminate frames. When it is established that, for any type of construction, these strains—or their relative values—can be definitely predicted, the

* For an interesting correlation of virtual work with the theorems of Castigliano, see "The Principle of Virtual Velocities and Its Application to the Theory of Elastic Structures", by Ernest Lamb. *Selected Engineering Papers No. 10*, Inst. C. E., December, 1923.

whole theory of indeterminate stress analysis follows from the relations of the distortions as a matter of geometry.   In order to be of real value in designing indeterminate structures, however, the load-strain relations must be those for conditions approaching failure and not merely those that exist at working stresses.   An understanding of these facts will make clearer the limitations of the theory of elasticity as applied in much of the literature dealing with indeterminate structures of reinforced concrete, will make possible the application of more correct theory to such structures, and will give greater confidence in the results obtained by its use.

11

ANALYSIS OF FLOW IN NETWORKS
OF CONDUITS OR CONDUCTORS

SYNOPSIS

The problem of finding the distribution of flow in networks of pipes occurs in the design of distribution systems for water. Similar problems occur in connection with distribution systems for other fluids such as steam or air and with electrical circuits. In general the analysis of such systems by formal algebraic procedures is, if the systems are complicated, very difficult. Models have been used in studying this problem, but here, as elsewhere, there are some objections to their use.

The methods here presented are methods of successive corrections. The convergence is apparently sufficiently rapid in all cases to make the methods useful in office practice. Perhaps the greatest value of the methods is in training and assisting the judgment, but this, of course, is the principal object of all analytical procedures.

Where the relation between flow and head (between current and voltage) is linear, the corrections are exact. Where this relation between flow and head is not linear, use is made of the relation between increment of flow and increment of head, which relation is linear for a given quantity of flow. If, however, the increments are fairly large, this linear relation is somewhat in error. A sufficiently exact solution is nevertheless obtained by successive correction. The method thus involves an arithmetical application of the fundamental principle of the differential calculus.

In the problems of flow discussed in detail in this bulletin it is assumed that kinetic heads and head losses at junctions are small in comparison with the lead losses due to friction, and that they may therefore be neglected.

The problems under immediate discussion deal primarily with systems carrying water and incidentally with those carrying electric currents. Additional applications of the methods here presented are suggested at the end of the paper.

Perhaps it should be added that this investigation, in a field of study which is not the major interest of the author, is a by-product of explorations in structural analysis.

The problems have been chosen to illustrate the method and not because they represent any existing layouts.

I. Introduction

1. *Type of Problem.*—As indicated later, various types of problems occur in connection with flow in networks. In what is perhaps its simplest form, the problem is usually as follows:

The quantity of fluid or of energy flowing into the system at one point is known and the point of delivery is also known. The sizes and lengths of the conductors or pipes in the system are given or assumed, and also the law controlling the relation between quantity of flow in the conductor and the loss of head or voltage in a given length.

It is usually desired to determine the total loss of head or voltage between inlet and outlet. If a single conductor connected these two points, the loss of head for given flow could be computed directly from the relation between flow and head loss. In a network, however, this loss depends on the distribution of the flow in the system. If such distribution is known, the drop of potential in each conductor can be determined directly, and the total drop found as the sum of the drops along any path connecting inlet and outlet, the total drop being of course the same whatever path is chosen.

The difficulty arises in determining the distribution of flow in the network. This is controlled by two sets of conditions, both simple and obvious:

(a) The total flow reaching any junction equals the total flow leaving it (continuity of flow)

(b) The total change in potential along any closed path is zero (continuity of potential).

These sets of conditions, together with the relation between flow and potential drop, lead to sets of equations in which either the flows in the individual conductors or the potentials at the junction points are taken as the unknowns.

If the flows are taken as the unknowns, the equations will be those for continuity of potential; if the potentials are the unknowns, the equations will be those for continuity of flow.* In either case,

---

*The two methods here presented represent general methods applicable to many engineering problems. The physical conditions controlling engineering relations often consist of two groups of laws which are quite independent of each other. In such cases either set of relations may be first expressed in terms of the other, and then a formal or an approximate solution may be obtained to satisfy the second condition. Compare the analysis of continuous frames by methods such as the theorem of three moments, where the equations to be solved represent the geometrical relations, the unknowns having been previously interrelated by statics, with the method of slope-deflection where the equations are those of statics, the unknowns having been previously related from geometrical considerations.

the order of the equations will be that of the relation between flow and loss of potential. If this relation is linear, the equations will be linear. If, however, the relation is not linear, serious difficulties arise in solving the equations.

In those cases where the relation between flow and change of head is linear, the methods to be presented may be thought of as a book-keeping procedure for solving linear equations; where the relation is not linear, the method changes the problem into that of a succession of linear relations by use of the fundamental principle of the differential calculus.

2. *Flow of Water in a Network of Pipes.*—In any network of pipes such as is shown in the problems discussed in the following pages, it is known that in each closed circuit the sum of all changes in head is zero, and that at each junction the quantity flowing into the junction equals the quantity flowing away from the junction.

It is assumed further that we know the law determining the loss of head in any length of pipe for a given flow. This law usually takes the form

$$h = CV^n$$

where h is the change in head accompanying flow in any length of pipe, C is the loss in the pipe for unit velocity of flow, and V is the velocity.

Since the quantity of water flowing in the pipe is AV, this relation may be rewritten

$$h = rQ^n$$

where r is the loss of head in the pipe for unit quantity of flow. The quantity r depends on the length and diameter of pipe and on its roughness.

The problem is to find the amount of water flowing in each pipe. When the distribution of flow is known, the losses of pressure throughout the system are readily computed.*

It is important to note that, except as noted in the footnote, only relative values of r are needed to determine distribution of flow.

II. METHODS OF ANALYSIS

3. *Methods of Analysis Proposed.*—Two methods of analysis are proposed. In one of these the flows in the pipes or conductors of

---

*In ordinary cases (on the assumption $h = rQ^n$ with n the same for all pipes) the distribution of total flow is independent of the quantity flowing. On certain assumptions as to the relation between head and flow, this will not be true. The matter does not seem of immediate practical importance, though it may be of scientific interest in some cases.

the network always satisfy the condition that the total flow into and out of each junction is zero, and these flows are successively corrected to satisfy the condition of zero total change of head around each circuit. In the other method the total change of head around each circuit always equals zero, and the flows in the pipes of the circuit are successively adjusted so that the total flow into and out of each junction finally approaches or becomes zero.

The former method is, for convenience of reference, here designated as the "Method of Balancing Heads," the latter as the "Method of Balancing Flows." The method of balancing heads is directly applicable where the quantities flowing at inlets and outlets are known. The method of balancing flows is directly applicable when the heads at inlets and outlets are known; in this case it will probably be found more convenient than that of balancing heads. In some problems it may be desirable to combine the two methods.

Both methods depend on the principle that the resistance to change in flow in any pipe equals approximately $nrQ^{(n-1)}$ where $h = rQ^n$.

III. METHOD OF BALANCING HEADS

4. *Statement of Method.*—The method of solution is as follows:

(a) Assume any distribution of flow.

(b) Compute in each pipe the loss of head $h = rQ^n$. With due attention to sign (direction of potential drop), compute the total head loss around each elementary closed circuit $\Sigma h = \Sigma rQ^n$.

(c) Compute also in each such closed circuit the sum of the quantities $R = nrQ^{(n-1)}$ without reference to sign.

(d) Set up in each circuit a counterbalancing flow to balance the head in that circuit (to make $\Sigma rQ^n = 0$) equal to

$$\Delta = \frac{\Sigma rQ^n \text{ (with due attention to direction of flow)}}{\Sigma nrQ^{(n-1)} \text{ (without reference to direction of flow)}}$$

(e) Compute the revised flows and repeat the procedure.

Continue to any desired precision.

In applying the method it is recommended that successive computations of the circuits be put on identical diagrams of the system. In office practice such diagrams will usually be white prints. Write in each elementary circuit the value ΣR, and outside the circuit write first (above) the value Σh for flow in a clockwise direction around the circuit and second (below) the value Σh for flow in a counterclockwise direction around the circuit. On the right of these figures put an arrow pointing $\searrow$ or $\nearrow$ to the larger figure. This arrow will show

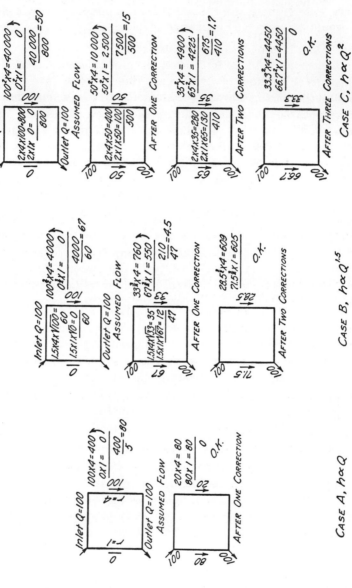

CASE A, $h \propto Q$ CASE B, $h \propto Q^{1.5}$

CASE C, $h \propto Q^2$

FIG. 1. DISTRIBUTION OF FLOW IN SINGLE CIRCUIT; METHOD OF BALANCING HEADS

correctly the direction of counterflow in the circuit. This technique is illustrated in the problems following.

5. *Proof of Method.*—If the distribution of flow assumed in the first place were correct, the change of head around any single closed circuit would be zero. This change of head is ΣrQ^n. Considering for the present a single circuit, write for each pipe

$$Q = Q_0 + \Delta$$

Then, $rQ^n = r(Q_0 + \Delta)^n = r(Q_0^n + nQ_0^{(n-1)} \Delta + \quad)$

If Δ is small compared with Q_0 the remaining terms in the expansion may be neglected.

Then, for

$$\Sigma rQ^n = 0$$
$$\Sigma rQ_0^n = -\Delta_0 \Sigma nrQ_0^{(n-1)}$$
$$\Delta = -\frac{\Sigma h}{\Sigma R} = -\frac{\Sigma rQ_0^n}{\Sigma nrQ_0^{(n-1)}}$$

Of course, if Δ is relatively large compared with Q_0 and n is greater than unity, the approximation is not very good, but this is less important than it might at first seem, because in any case we must correct for the unbalanced head produced in one circuit by corrections in the adjacent circuits, which in general requires a recomputation of all circuits. The convergence is, for practical purposes, sufficiently rapid.

6. *Illustrative Problems.*—

Problem 1.—Single Closed Circuit
(Figure 1)

This problem shows the elementary procedure for a single circuit in each of three cases: (a) where h varies as Q (streamline flow, or electrical resistance, E varies as I); (b) where h varies as $Q^{1.5}$ merely as an illustration of a fractional exponent; and (c) where h varies as Q^2, a common approximate value for water circuits.

In all of these cases it is required to distribute a flow of 100 between two pipes, one of which is four times as long as the other, but which are otherwise alike. In each case, also, to show the convergence, the first assumption is the worst possible, namely that the total flow follows the longer path.

Of course each of these cases is readily solved directly. Thus, in all cases let Q_1 be the flow in the shorter, and Q_2 that in the longer pipe. Then

(a) $\dfrac{Q_1}{Q_2} = \dfrac{4}{1}$ $\qquad$ $Q_1 = \dfrac{4}{5} \cdot 100 = 80$

(b) $\dfrac{Q_1}{Q_2} = \dfrac{(4)^{\frac{2}{3}}}{(1)^{\frac{2}{3}}}$ $\qquad$ $Q_1 = \dfrac{2.52}{3.52} \cdot 100 = 71.5$

(c) $\dfrac{Q_1}{Q_2} = \dfrac{(4)^{\frac{1}{2}}}{(1)^{\frac{1}{2}}}$ $\qquad$ $Q_1 = \dfrac{2}{3} \cdot 100 = 66.7$

The computations have in these cases been arranged in the order explained already, which has been found very convenient, namely,

(1) Write the divisor $\Sigma nrQ^{(n-1)}$ within the circuit.

(2) Write on one side of the circuit first the sum ΣrQ^n for clockwise flow, and below this the sum ΣrQ^n for counterclockwise flow. If, then, the arrow indicating the direction of flow is written on the right of these figures and pointing to the larger flow, it will correctly indicate the direction of counterflow needed to balance the circuit. In complicated problems observance of some such system is necessary.

Problem 2.—Simple Network—h Varies as Q^2
(Figure 2)

This shows a very simple network with one inlet and one outlet. It is here assumed that h varies as Q^2. All pipes are assumed to be alike. The purpose of the problem is to illustrate the method of arrangement in a case slightly more difficult than that of a single circuit.

Here, as before, a very bad first trial value was intentionally chosen to illustrate the procedure. Of course, the exact solution is at once known by inspection to be as shown, and almost any reasonable trial converges rapidly.

The arrangement of computations is that previously recommended. Note the relatively small change in $\Sigma nQ^{(n-1)}$.

Procedure

Some distribution of flow (without excesses or deficiencies at the junctions) is first assumed.

(1) Compute the unbalanced heads around each circuit. (In this case $h = Q^2$ in each pipe.) As previously noted, these are written to one side of the circuit, first (above) the heads for clockwise flow within that circuit, next (below) those for counter clock-

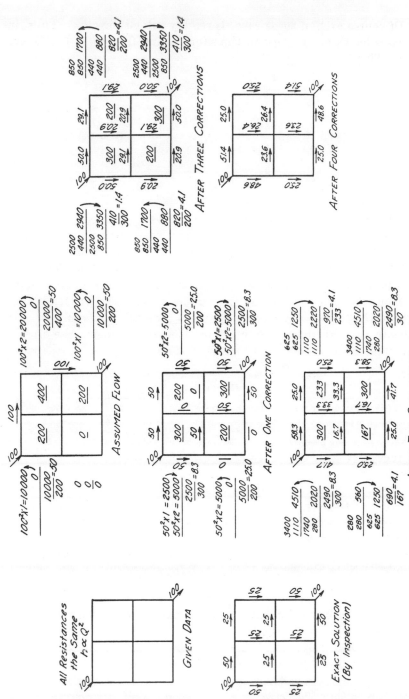

Fig. 2. Distribution of Flow in Simple Network; Method of Balancing Heads

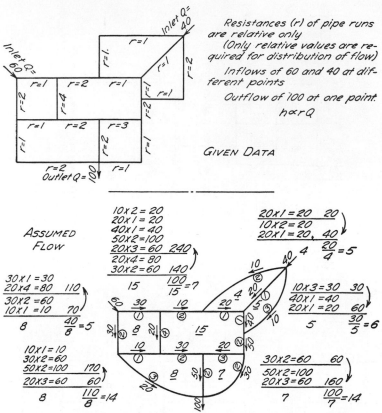

Resistances (r) of pipe runs are relative only
(Only relative values are required for distribution of flow)
Inflows of 60 and 40 at different points
Outflow of 100 at one point.
$h \propto rQ$

GIVEN DATA

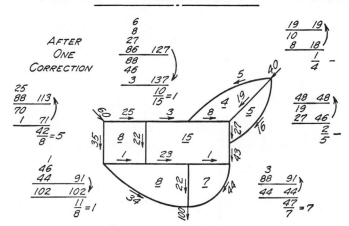

Note:-Values in circles on each pipe are resistances. Underscored values in the circuits are values $\Sigma nrQ^{n-1} = \Sigma R$

FIG. 3. DISTRIBUTION OF FLOW IN NETWORK—TWO INLETS;
METHOD OF BALANCING HEADS

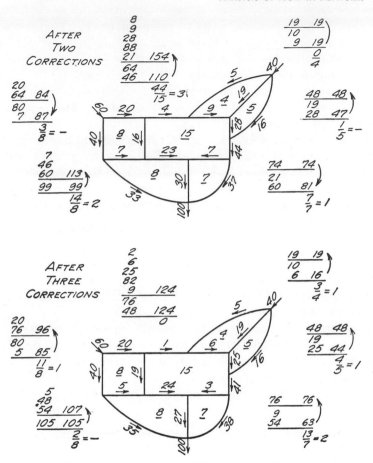

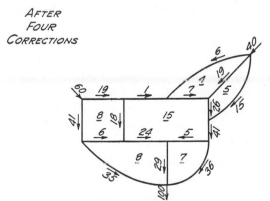

Fig. 3. Distribution of Flow in Network—Two Inlets;
Method of Balancing Heads

wise flow. The difference is the unbalanced head. The arrow, $\rangle$ or $\rangle$, written to the right of these figures, points to the larger head loss, and indicates the direction of counterflow.

(2) Compute the divisors $\Sigma nrQ^{(n-1)}$. In this case $nrQ^{(n-1)} = 2Q$ in each pipe, since $r = 1$. These are written within the circuits.

(3) Revise the flows from these counterflows, and repeat the process as often as required.

In the foregoing solution the method is intentionally applied blindly, without any judgment at all. It is at once evident that all circuits in the first trial are badly unbalanced, all flows in each circuit being in one direction. Usually the circuits which are badly unbalanced will at once be thrown more nearly into balance by guess.

Problem 3.—Complex Network—Two Inlets—h Varies as Q
(Figure 3)

This is a more complicated network, with two inlets and one outlet. The solution involves no new principles. Here it is assumed that h varies as Q. Of course, in this case the divisors for each circuit are constant throughout.

No attempt has been made to compute fractional values. It is, however, clearly possible to go to any reasonable degree of precision, but with considerable increase in the computation required if results correct to three figures are wanted.

The arrangement of computations follows that previously explained.

Problems 4 and 5.—Systems of Pipes in Different Planes Interconnected
(Figures 4 and 5)

In general, systems for distributing water in cities may, for purposes of analysis, be considered as in a single plane. In other cases, as, for example, in distributing steam or hot water to a heating system, the distribution may take place in several planes, with interconnection between the planar systems of distribution.

This type of problem presents no especially new features except that successive distribution must be made in circuits closed by the risers as well as in the circuits which lie in a plane. The pipes chosen on each floor to close the circuits containing the risers are selected arbitrarily. It will be noted that in such problems any pipe may lie in only one circuit (an outside pipe in a floor) or in two circuits, three circuits, or even in four circuits (two floor circuits and two riser circuits). The total change in flow in the pipe is the sum of the changes in all the circuits of which it is a member.

Problem 4 shows a rather impractical layout selected for simplicity of illustration. The distribution is carried through only two steps to show the procedure.

Problem 5 differs from Problem 4 only in having more risers.

Clearly the technique used in recording the flows is a matter of individual choice. Some may prefer to use isometric diagrams throughout the analysis.

It is believed that the diagrams are self-explanatory.

7. *Characteristics of Procedure.*—Certain characteristics of the procedure will be noted. When the flow is adjusted in any circuit the flow is increased in some pipes and decreased in others, so that the quantity $\Sigma R = \Sigma nrQ^{(n-1)}$ is not very much changed, and need not usually be recomputed for each change of flow.

Since the first adjustments are in a sense preliminary, it is useless to attempt precision in making them.

The answer, when finally obtained, is inevitably correct, since it satisfies the conditions that the quantities balance at each junction, and that the heads balance around each circuit. Moreover, errors in the procedure are not cumulative, and, if made, are ultimately eliminated.

IV. METHOD OF BALANCING FLOWS

8. *Statement of Method.*—In the method of analysis by balancing heads just presented, the flow at any junction is balanced throughout the analysis, but the head around any circuit is balanced by successive correction.

Another method is to keep the head balanced around any circuit throughout the analysis, in which case the flow at the junctions is balanced by successive correction.

We may, then, assume a series of heads throughout the system and compute the flow in each pipe corresponding to the differences of head. From these find the total flow to each junction except inlets and outlets. Distribute this flow to the pipes connecting at the junction in inverse proportion to their resistances. $(R = nrQ^{(n-1)})$. This, of course, causes an excess (or deficiency) of flow at the next junction, but by successive distribution the excess flow will ultimately be squeezed out at the inlets and outlets of the system.

Note, in the first place, that if the flow is distributed as in the

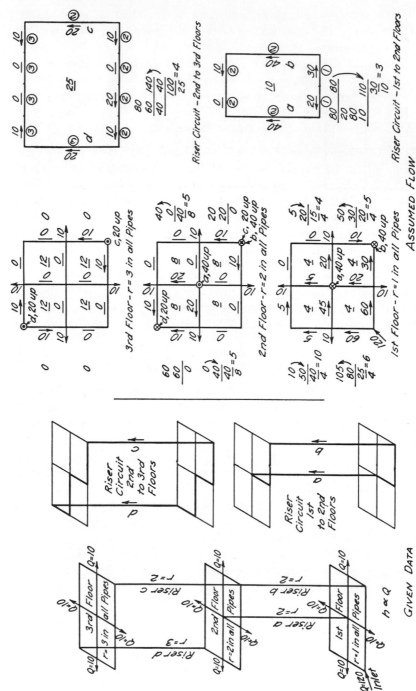

FIG. 4. DISTRIBUTION OF FLOW IN SEVERAL PLANES; METHOD OF BALANCING HEADS

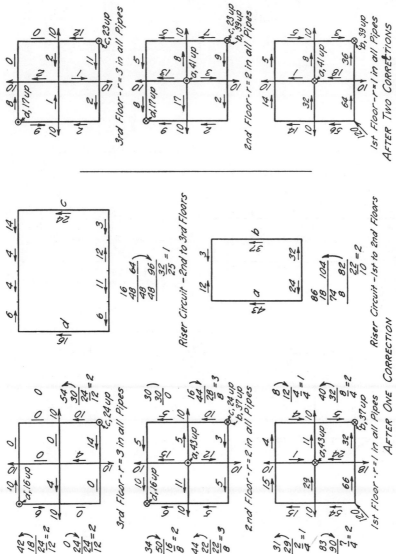

FIG. 4. DISTRIBUTION OF FLOW IN SEVERAL PLANES; METHOD OF BALANCING HEADS

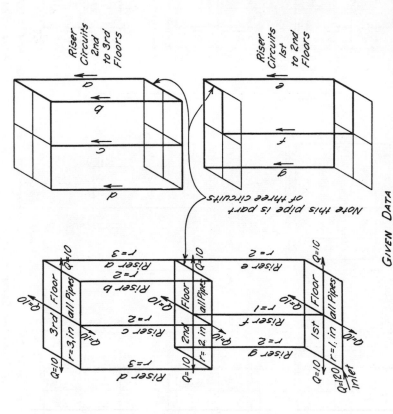

FIG. 5. DISTRIBUTION OF FLOW IN SEVERAL PLANES; METHOD OF BALANCING HEADS

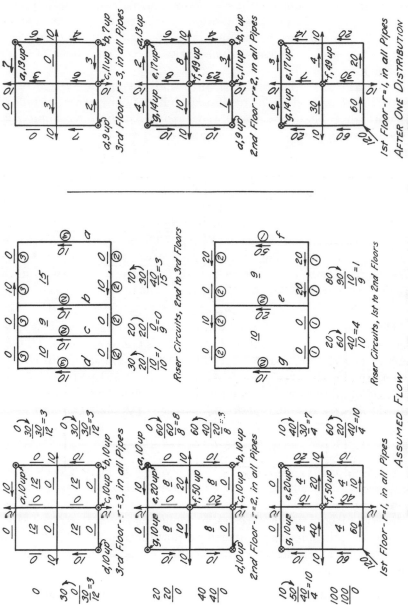

FIG. 5. DISTRIBUTION OF FLOW IN SEVERAL PLANES; METHOD OF BALANCING HEADS

foregoing the head difference between any inlet and outlet is approximately unchanged, the change of head in one direction along one part of any path connecting two openings being equal and opposite to the change of head along another part. Of course, the values $R = nrQ^{(n-1)}$ are not exact when n is greater than unity, because the values of Q are not exact. Hence revision of the values of R is necessary.

Note also that the total flow into and out of the system is in general not balanced in the beginning, but that any excess of inflow will untimately be squeezed out by successive distributions. Similarly, if there is a deficiency, we may imagine that it will inflow at the inlets and outlets.

9. *Illustrative Problems.—*

Problem 6.—Simple Network—h Varies as Q^2
(Figure 6)

The problem analyzed in Fig. 6 is the same as that previously analyzed by balancing heads in Fig. 2. The elevation at the inlet is assumed to be 100. The outflow takes place at one point as shown. It is assumed that in each pipe-run of the system the loss of head equals the square of the quantity flowing. The procedure is as follows:

Procedure

(1) Assume heads arbitrarily for inlet and outlet. In this case assume inlet at El. 100 and outlet at El. 0. Guess at heads at other junctions as closely as possible. These values are shown in circles near the junctions.

(2) Compute flow (or relative flow) in each pipe for heads assumed. In this case it is assumed that $h = rQ^2$, and therefore that

$$Q = \sqrt{\frac{h}{r}}.$$

(3) Compute excess $(+)$ or deficiency $(-)$ of flow at each junction except inlet and outlet. Write these in the squares shown for each junction.

(4) Distribute these excesses or deficiencies to the pipes connecting at each junction in inverse proportion to $R = nrQ^{(n-1)}$. In this problem all values of r are assumed equal to unity, except in the corner pipes which are twice as long, and hence have $r = 2$. Also $n = 2$. Hence the flows are distributed in proportion to $\dfrac{1}{rQ}$, where Q is the flow already computed.

(5) Carry over in the pipes connecting at each junction (except inlet and outlet) the flows distributed from adjacent junctions to

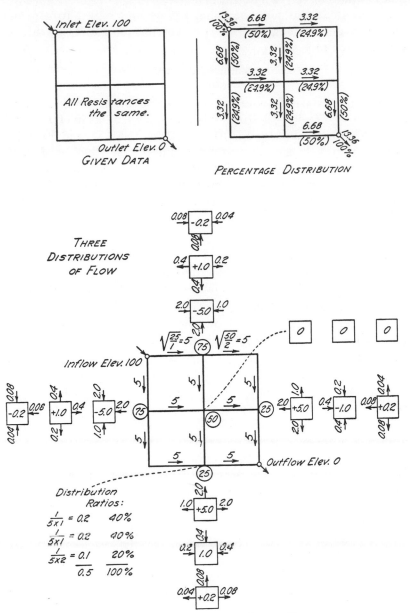

FIG. 6. DISTRIBUTION OF FLOW IN SIMPLE NETWORK;
METHOD OF BALANCING FLOWS

find new values of excesses and deficiencies.

(6) Distribute the new unbalanced flows and repeat to convergence, thus determining the relative amount of the total inflow flowing in each pipe.

Problem 7.—Multiple Inlets and Outlets
(Figure 7)

In this problem it is assumed that the elevations are known at several inlets—namely, El. 40 at inlet A, and El. 30 at inlet B—and at several outlets—namely, El. 10 at outlets B and D, and El. 0 at outlets A and C. It is desired to determine the distribution of total flow at inlets and at outlets, and, in general, the distribution of flow in the system. For simplicity of presentation it is assumed that the resistances are the same in all pipe-runs. It is also assumed that

$$h = \frac{Q^2}{1000} \text{ in any pipe.}$$

First assume heads at intermediate junctions as shown by figures in the circles at each intermediate junction.

Compute flows—or relative flows—in each pipe. Here the flow is computed as $Q = \sqrt{1000h}$.

Compute excess or deficiency of flow at each junction, and write this in the rectangle near that junction. Distribute these unbalanced flows in proportion to $\frac{1}{Q}$ at each junction. The relative values for distribution at each junction are written on the pipes at that junction.

Compute the excesses and deficiencies produced by the new flows and distribute these.

It may be assumed that in a problem of this type what is really wanted is the distribution of outflow and of inflow. Table 1 shows these flows after successive distributions in this case. The convergence here is slow and not very satisfactory, partly because the first guess as to intermediate heads is not very good. Nevertheless, the computations indicate quickly the approximate distribution of flow at inlets and outlets.

Some circuits will be found to be unbalanced as regards head. These may now be adjusted, if desired, starting with the distribution found for total flow.

10. *Remarks on Method.*—In such relatively complex problems as that just shown, it seems clear that the method of distributing flows has advantages. In general, however, it is thought to be less simple, obvious, and expeditious than that of balancing heads.

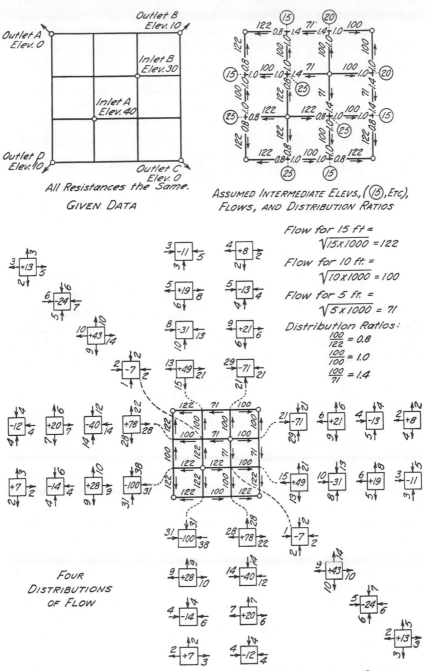

Outlet A
Elev. 0

Outlet B
Elev. 10

Inlet B
Elev. 30

Inlet A
Elev. 40

Outlet D
Elev. 10

Outlet C
Elev. 0

All Resistances the Same.

GIVEN DATA

ASSUMED INTERMEDIATE ELEVS., ((15), ETC),
FLOWS, AND DISTRIBUTION RATIOS

Flow for 15 ft =
$$\sqrt{15 \times 1000} = 122$$

Flow for 10 ft. =
$$\sqrt{10 \times 1000} = 100$$

Flow for 5 ft. =
$$\sqrt{5 \times 1000} = 71$$

Distribution Ratios:
$$\frac{100}{122} = 0.8$$
$$\frac{100}{100} = 1.0$$
$$\frac{100}{71} = 1.4$$

FOUR
DISTRIBUTIONS
OF FLOW

FIG. 7. DISTRIBUTION OF FLOW IN NETWORK—SEVERAL INLETS AND OUTLETS;
METHOD OF BALANCING FLOWS

TABLE 1
PROBLEM 7.—SUCCESSIVE VALUES OF INFLOW AND OUTFLOW

	Assumed Values	Values After One Distribution	Values After Two Distributions	Values After Three Distributions	Values After Four Distributions	Estimated True Values	
						Value	Per Cent
Inlet A................	488	552	525	543	535	537	59
Inlet B................	342	388	348	370	356	361	41
Total Inflow.........	830	940	873	913	891	898	100
Outlet A..............	244	279	259	270	263	268	30
Outlet B..............	200	158	170	162	166	166	18
Outlet C..............	244	279	259	270	263	268	30
Outlet D..............	244	182	200	192	196	196	22
Total Outflow........	932	898	888	894	888	898	100

V. TYPES OF PROBLEMS ENCOUNTERED IN NETWORKS

11. *Typical Problems.*—In systems carrying water, and in other networks of circuits, the problems may take various forms.

(a) Figure 8a. Given the inflow at one point and the point of discharge, to determine the distribution of flow and variation of head within the network. This problem represents the most elementary application of the method of balancing heads. (Problems 1, 2, 4, 5). It may also be solved by balancing flows. (Problem 6).

(b) Figure 8b. Given the distribution of inflow at several inlets and the distribution of outflow at several outlets, to determine the distribution of flow and the variation of head. (Problem 3). The problem is practically the same as that just discussed. It is more conveniently solved by balancing heads than by balancing flows.

(c) Figure 8c. Given the heads at various points of inflow or outflow, to determine the total flow and its distribution. Such a problem may occur in studying flow between reservoir systems. This may be solved directly by the method of balancing flows. (Problems 6, 7).

(d) Figure 8d. Given the heads at various points of inflow and the relation of head to flow at various points of outflow. This problem may be reduced to the problem just stated by imagining that at each outflow point an additional pipe or conductor is connected. This imaginary discharge pipe is to have such a resistance that for unit flow the loss of head would be the same as for unit flow through the outlet.

(e) Figure 8e. Given the heads at certain points of inflow or outflow and also the flow, independent of head, at other points, to

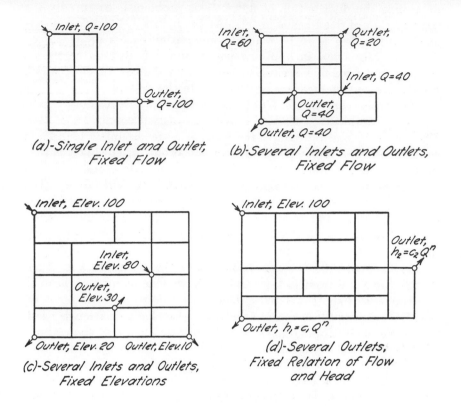

(a)-Single Inlet and Outlet,
Fixed Flow

(b)-Several Inlets and Outlets,
Fixed Flow

(c)-Several Inlets and Outlets,
Fixed Elevations

(d)-Several Outlets,
Fixed Relation of Flow
and Head

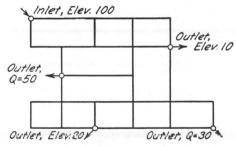

(e)-Several Outlets,
Some Heads Fixed and Some Flows Fixed

FIG. 8. TYPES OF PROBLEMS ENCOUNTERED IN DISTRIBUTING
FLOW IN NETWORKS

determine the distribution of flow. This problem is essentially the same as that of fixed heads in (c). At the points of fixed **flow** allowance for the flow is to be made in computing excess **or** deficiency of flow. Moreover, in applying the method of distributing flows, the points of fixed flow are not to be considered as openings at which water may be squeezed out or sucked into the system.

Evidently various combinations of these problems may occur.

All the problems just stated deal with constant conditions of flow. The heads in the reservoirs, for example, are assumed to remain constant in spite of the flow. A common problem, however, is that in which the flow affects the heads as the flow continues, and it is desired to study the changes in flow conditions with time. The present paper makes no direct contribution to the solution of this problem, except as it indicates methods of solution for fixed conditions. However, such problems may be conveniently studied by the method of increments, thus:

(1) Compute the flow conditions for the initial heads.

(2) Compute from inflows and outflows the changes in head in any convenient short interval of time.

(3) Compute the *changes* of flow for these changes of head. This procedure, while approximate, is quite direct.

(4) Repeat the procedure.

VI. Concluding Remarks—Other Applications of Methods

As previously stated, this monograph deals primarily with flow of water in networks of pipes. The problems are restricted to cases in which the relation between loss of head and quantity of flow is of the relatively simple form h varies as Q^n. It is sometimes proposed that the flow of liquids may be controlled by a relation of the form $h = aQ + bQ^2$. In this case we can deduce $\dfrac{\Delta h}{\Delta Q} = (a + 2bQ)$, and the counterflow required to balance the head in any circuit becomes

$$\Delta Q = - \frac{\Sigma\,(aQ + bQ^2) \text{ with due attention to direction of flow}}{\Sigma\,(a + 2bQ) \text{ without reference to direction of flow}}$$

In more general terms, if $h = f(Q)$, then $\dfrac{\Delta h}{\Delta Q} = f'(Q)$ and the counterflow

$$\Delta Q = - \frac{\Sigma f(Q) \text{ with due attention to direction of flow}}{\Sigma f'(Q) \text{ without reference to direction of flow}}$$

This suggests that such arithmetical application of the principle of the differential calculus may have application in the solution of certain problems in simultaneous equations, but no effort has been made to explore this field.

Applications of the methods in the study of electrical circuits are evident.

This paper deals directly only with networks of definite conductors. Clearly, however, the methods may also be applied to study distribution of flow in those cases where no pipes really exist, but where the flow is diffused, as in cases of percolation through earthen dams or through soil strata where the operation of wells is to be investigated. In such cases flow in a series of imaginary pipes is substituted for the diffused flow. This leads, of course to the "flow net" picture. The principal value of the method in this connection is in checking and revising an assumed flow net, the pipes being assumed to be elements of the flow net and of uniform resistance per unit of length.

This suggests extension of the method to a general method of studying flow nets in moving water.

The methods apparently have important applications in the study of any field of potential.

Clearly many variations of technique are possible in applying the methods. Thus, a circuit is unbalanced only by counterflow in adjacent circuits, and so it is possible to merely "carry over" a certain fraction of such counterflows. Also it is possible to use the results from balancing other circuits in computing each successive circuit. Considerable experimenting with various procedures leads the writer to believe that the technique recommended will be found most satisfactory because of its simplicity.

It will bear repetition that the first approximations need not be made very formally. With some experience it is possible to nearly adjust a network at once by a little judicious guessing.